Residential
Wiring

Second Edition

 AMERICAN TECHNICAL PUBLISHERS, INC.
HOMEWOOD, ILLINOIS 60430

Gary S. Rockis
Suzanne M. Rockis
Thomas E. Proctor

Residential Wiring contains procedures commonly practiced in industry and the trade. Specific procedures vary with each task and must be performed by a qualified person. For maximum safety, always refer to specific manufacturer recommendations, insurance regulations, specific job site and plant procedures, applicable federal, state, and local regulations, and any authority having jurisdiction. The material contained is intended to be an educational resource for the user. American Technical Publishers, Inc. assumes no responsibility or liability in connection with this material or its use by any individual or organization.

American Technical Publishers, Inc., Editorial Staff

Editor in Chief:
    Jonathan F. Gosse
Production Manager:
    Peter A. Zurlis
Art Manager:
    James M. Clarke
Technical Editor:
    Russell G. Burris
Copy Editor:
    Richard S. Stein
Cover Design:
    Ellen E. Pinneo
Illustration/Layout:
    Mark S. Maxwell
    William J. Sinclair
    Thomas E. Zabinski
    Gianna C. Butterfield

National Electric Code and NEC are registered trademarks of the National Fire Protection Association. Underwriters Laboratories Inc. is a registered trademark of Underwriters Laboratories Inc.

2 3 4 5 6 7 8 9 – 06 – 9 8 7 6 5 4 3 2 1

Printed in the United States of America

ISBN 0-8269-1654-6

Residential Wiring

Acknowledgements

The author and publisher are grateful to the following companies and organizations for providing technical information and assistance:

Advantage Drills Inc.
AEMC® Instruments
American Beauty Soldering Tools
Amprobe/Advanced Test Products
Ansul/Tyco Safety Products
Baldor Electric Company
BernzOmatic Corp.
Bowers, Division of Norris Industries
Broan-NuTone LLC
Bussman Mfg., a McGraw-Edison Co. Division
Carrier Corporation
Cooper Wiring Devices
Crouse Hinds Co.-Arrow Hart
Fluke Corporation
General Electric Co.
Grand Pointe Homes
Greenlee Textron Inc.
Harvey Hubbell, Inc.
ITT Holub Industries
Kennedy Mfg. Co.
Kidde
Klein Tools, Inc.

Ideal Industries, Inc.
Leviton Manufacturing Co., Inc.
Lew Electric Fittings Co.
Milwaukee Electric Tool Corporation
M & W electric Manufacturing Co., Inc.
NuTone, Division of Scovill
Panduit Corp.
Raco Inc.
Republic Steel Corp.
Rund Lighting, Inc.
Siemens
Square D Company
Square D/Schneider Electric
The Stanley Works
The Wiremold Co.
TRW Crescent Wire and Cable
Vaco Products, Inc.
Wadsworth Electric Mfg. Co., Inc.
Wen Products
Wilden Enterprises, Inc.
Zircon Corporation

Residential Wiring

Contents

Residential Wiring

Introduction

Residential Wiring has been extensively revised to provide an overview of typical residential wiring systems, electrical device and component installation, and basic troubleshooting procedures. Large, detailed illustrations are used to supplement concise text. Test instrument procedures are detailed with sequenced steps. Factoids, Technical Tips, and Safety Tips complement the content presented. An extensive Glossary and comprehensive Appendix offer additional reference material.

Residential Wiring, 2nd Edition begins with an introduction to electricity, residential electrical system principles, tools, and safety. The operation and installation of common electrical devices (switches, receptacles, and boxes) and components (light fixtures, fans, and appliances) are covered in detail. Wiring procedures are presented with references to personal protective equipment based on requirements specified in National Fire Protection Association standard *NFPA 70E, Standard for Electrical Safety in the Workplace* emphasized throughout the book. Chapter 12 – Structured Wiring Systems covers the latest technology in voice-data-video, security, and fire alarm systems.

Residential Wiring is one of many high-quality training products available from American Technical Publishers, Inc. To obtain information about related training products, visit the American Tech web site at www.go2atp.com.

The Publisher

Residential Wiring

Features

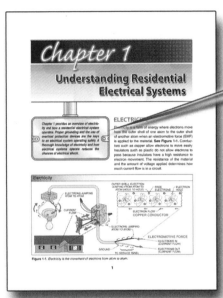

Chapter Introductions provide an overview of key content in the chapter

Safety Information is included throughout the book

Large, detailed wiring layouts show common component connections

Illustrated step-by-step procedures depict common test instrument procedures

Chapter 1

Understanding Residential Electrical Systems

Chapter 1 provides an overview of electricity and how a residential electrical system operates. Proper grounding and the use of overload protection devices are the keys to an electrical system operating safely. A thorough knowledge of electricity and how electrical systems operate reduces the chances of electrical shock.

ELECTRICITY

Electricity is a form of energy where electrons move from the outer shell of one atom to the outer shell of another atom when an electromotive force (EMF) *VOLTAGE* is applied to the material. **See Figure 1-1.** Conductors such as copper allow electrons to move easily. Insulators such as plastic do not allow electrons to pass because insulators have a high resistance to electron movement. The resistance of the material and the amount of voltage applied determines how much current flow is in a circuit.

Figure 1-1. *Electricity is the movement of electrons from atom to atom.*

Ohm's law is the relationship between voltage, current, and resistance properties in an electrical circuit. The relationship between voltage, current, and resistance is typically visualized by using Ohm's law in pie chart form. **See Figure 1-2. See Appendix.**

Figure 1-2. *Any missing value in Ohm's law can be found when the other two values are known.*

Generated Electricity

Generated electricity is the alternating current (AC) created by power plant generators. Power plant generators create three-phase alternating current electricity. Generators produce electricity when magnetic lines of force are cut by a rotating wire coil (armature). **See Figure 1-3.** The stronger the magnetic field and/or the faster the rotation, the higher the voltage produced.

The voltage output of commercial generators is several thousand volts (typically 22,000 V). The AC electrical output of commercial (power plant) generators travels to transformers for voltage and current control prior to distribution. A *transformer* is an electric device that uses electromagnetism to change (step-up or step-down) AC voltage from one level to another. **See Figure 1-4.** Electricity is used in circuits specifically designed to carry voltage and current through controlled paths (conductors) to operate specific loads.

Electricity Distribution

The transformers at a power plant step-up the voltage from the generators (22,000 V) to approximately 240,000 V. **See Figure 1-5.** The high- voltage electricity is distributed across high-voltage power lines to step-down transformer substations. The substations step-down the electrical voltage from 240,000 V to 12,000 V for local distribution. The local voltage distribution level of 12,000 V is step-downed further by transformers to voltages of 600 V, 480 V, 240 V, or 120 V for consumer use.

Figure 1-3. *An excess electron buildup produces an arc during electrostatic discharge (ESD).*

Residential Use

Local underground vaults and pole transformers step-down electricity to 120V/240V to service apartments, condominiums, townhomes, and homes. **See Figure 1-6.** Service entrances (overhead or underground) provide the connection for the distributed power to the power company meter of the residence. Electric meters record the amount of electricity used for billing.

Transformers

Figure 1-4. *Voltage and current change from the primary to secondary sides (windings) of transformers.*

Service Panels

A *service panel* is an electrical device containing fuses or circuit breakers for protecting the individual circuits of a residence and is a means of disconnecting the entire residence from the distribution system. **See Figure 1-7.** Service panels are wall-mounted in basements, utility rooms, and attached garages. Wherever a service panel is mounted, the panel must be easily accessible to the occupants of the residence.

RESIDENTIAL ELECTRICAL CIRCUITS

Residential electrical circuits include lighting circuits, general-purpose receptacle (small appliance) circuits, special-purpose receptacle (ranges, ovens, and GFCIs) circuits, and special hard-wired loads such as

Electricity Distribution

Siemens

Figure 1-5. *Typical power company steam turbine generators have three armatures as part of the rotor to create 3ϕ power.*

Service Entrances

Figure 1-6. *Clearance requirements protect service-drop conductors from physical damage and protect personnel from contact with the conductors.*

room heaters, water heaters, and air conditioner circuits. A *circuit* is a complete path (when ON) for current to take that includes electrical control devices, circuit protection, conductors, and load(s).

See Figure 1-8. A *complete path* is a grouping of electrical devices and wires that create a path for current to take from the power source (service panel), through controls (switches), to the load (light fixtures and receptacles), and back to the power source. The service panel also provides circuit protection by fuses or circuit breakers.

GROUNDING

Grounding is an integral part of any properly operating electrical system. In residences, grounding protects the occupants by providing a safe pathway for unwanted electricity that might otherwise create a hazard. Electricity always takes the easiest flow path to ground.

Grounding is typically established at two levels: system grounding and equipment grounding. A *system ground* is a special circuit designed to protect the entire distribution system of a residence. An *equipment ground* is a circuit designed to protect individual components connected to an electrical system.

Service Panels

Figure 1-7. *Service panels provide the disconnect from the utility company, system ground, circuit breakers for hot conductors, and neutral bus bars for returning common conductors.*

Residential Electrical Systems

Figure 1-8. *Residential electrical systems are comprised of a number of individual circuits that, when a control (switch) is closed, create a complete path and keep the load ON.*

System Grounding

The primary function of system grounding is to protect the service entrance wiring and connections from lightning and high voltage surges. A system ground provides protection by safely routing lightning and high voltage surges away from the service entrance through the use of a highly conductive pathway to Earth. The two methods of grounding an electrical system are metal water pipe grounding and alternative electrode grounding. **See Figure 1-9.**

Water Pipe Grounding. A *water pipe ground* is a continuous underground metallic pipe that supplies a residence with water and is typically the best electrical ground for a residential electrical system. Water pipes work well as grounds because a large surface area of the pipe is in contact with the earth. The large

surface area reduces resistance and allows any unwanted electricity to easily pass through the pipe to the earth.

When a water pipe is used for grounding, the water pipe run must never be interrupted by a plastic fitting or have an open section of plumbing. Water meters are a source of open circuits when removed. To provide protection when a water meter is removed, a shunt, or meter bonding wire, must be permanently installed. A *shunt* is a permanent conductor placed across a water meter to provide a continuous flow path for ground current. **See Figure 1-10.**

A water pipe grounding electrode conductor connection must be made within 5′ of a building's point of entry.

Electrical System Grounding Methods

Figure 1-9. *Water pipe grounding and electrode grounding are the two main types of grounding for residences.*

Electrical Shunts

Figure 1-10. *Electrical shunts provide a continuous electrical flow path (ground) when a valve or meter is removed or when nonconducting materials are used, such as plastic ferules or rubber gaskets.*

Electrode Grounding. An *electrode* is a long metal rod used to make contact with the earth for grounding purposes. When no satisfactory grounding electrode is readily available, the common practice is to drive one or more metal rods (connected in parallel) into the ground. **See Figure 1-11.** The electrode and circuit must provide a flow path to earth with less than 25 Ω of resistance. When local soils are extremely salty, acidic, or alkaline, the local building inspector or the NEC® should be consulted to determine the correct type of electrode to use.

Equipment Grounding

The primary function of equipment grounding is to protect individual electrical devices. *Equipment grounding* safely grounds any devices attached to a system or plugged into receptacles inside a home. **See Figure 1-12.** When an appliance has not been properly grounded, electrical current caused by a short will seek the easiest path to earth. Unfortunately, the human body is an electrical conductor and allows current to reach earth by traveling through the body (electric shock). Properly grounded devices protect the body by harmlessly conducting unwanted electricity to ground.

Electrode Grounding

Grounding Electrode System	Minimum Size	Notes
Metal underground water pipe	10′ length	Requires supplemental electrode
Metal frame in building		Where effectively grounded
Concrete-encased electrode	2″ of concrete encasement 10′ of ½″ steel bars or 20′ of #4 Cu	
Ground ring	20′ of #2 Cu	Minimum depth 2½′

Alternative Electrodes	Minimum Size	Burial Requirements
Pipe or conduit (iron or steel shall be galvanized or metal coated)	¾″D × 8′ length	
Rods of iron and steel	⅝″D × 8′ length	
Rods of stainless steel and nonferrous rods (shall be listed if less than ⅝″D)	½″D × 8′ length	
Plate of iron or steel	¼″D × 2 sq ft	
Plate of nonferrous metal	.06″D × 2 sq ft	

Figure 1-11. *Grounding electrode systems or alternative electrodes are used for grounding residential electrical systems.*

Equipment Grounding

IMPROPER OR NO GROUND   PROPER GROUND

Figure 1-12. *When an electrical component is not grounded or is grounded improperly, any faults within the component can create a potentially hazardous situation. Touching the component can cause current to flow through the body resulting in electric shock or electrocution.*

Grounding Small Appliances. Small appliances are easily incorporated into a grounded system. Most small electrical appliances are designed with three-prong grounded plugs that match a standard three-prong grounded receptacle. **See Figure 1-13.**

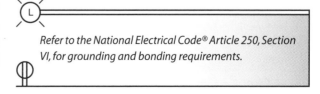

Refer to the National Electrical Code® Article 250, Section VI, for grounding and bonding requirements.

Small Appliance Grounding

Figure 1-13. *A three-prong plug provides a fault current flow path from the small appliance to earth through the grounding system.*

The U-shaped blade of the plug and the U-shaped hole in the receptacle are the ground connections. The U-shaped blade of a plug is longer than the current-carrying blades. The added length insures a strong ground connection while the plug is being inserted or removed from a receptacle. **See Figure 1-14.**

Manufacturers of electrical equipment such as appliances, tools, wires, and fuses manufacture products that must meet minimum required codes and standards to ensure products are built for safe operation. Exceeding minimum requirements helps establish the reputation of a company for producing reliable quality products, and also reducing product liability issues that may arise from electrical shocks, fire, and injuries.

Three-Prong Plugs

Cooper Wiring Devices

Figure 1-14. *Three-prong grounded plugs have a grounding blade that is longer than the current-carrying blades to ensure a grounded connection when the plug is being connected or disconnected.*

FUSES

A *fuse* is an electrical device used to limit the rate of current flow in a circuit. Fuses typically contain a piece of soft metal that melts, opening the circuit when the fuse is overloaded.

The three broad categories of fuses are plug, cartridge, and blade. **See Figure 1-15.** The typical homeowner generally requires 15 A or 20 A plug fuses and 30 A or 40 A cartridge fuses. Occasionally a service panel blade fuse may need to be replaced. Blade fuses typically have a 60 A or 100 A rating and are found in the main disconnect of the service panel.

For each category of fuse, several specific types of fuses can be found for specific applications. **See Figure 1-16.** Time-delay fuses are one specific type of fuse that is quite popular.

Plug fuses are no longer used, except for replacement of existing fuses in older buildings.

Tech Tip: Overload Protection

Fuse Types

Figure 1-15. *Each type of fuse has a typical application in a residential service panel.*

Fuse Categories

FUSETRON
DUAL-ELEMENT
PLUG FUSE

FUSTAT FUSE

CIRCUIT BREAKER FUSE

PLUG FUSES

GLASS TUBE

STANDARD CARTRIDGE

RENEWABLE FUSE

CARTRIDGE FUSES

CONDUCTOR STRIP

ORDINARY ONE-TIME FUSE
(CUTAWAY VIEW)

FUSETRON DUAL-ELEMENT FUSE
(CUTAWAY VIEW)

BLADE FUSES

Bussman Mfg., a McGraw-Edison Co. Division

Figure 1-16. *Each type of fuse can be further divided into specific applications.*

Standard Plug Fuses

A *standard plug fuse* is a screw-in type electrical safety device that contains a metal conducting element designed to melt when the current through the fuse exceeds the rated value. **See Figure 1-17.** During a serious overload condition, the melting of the conductor strip is almost instantaneous.

General specifications that apply to fuses include mountings, materials of construction, fuse types, and features. Mounting choices include solderable or surface mount, solderable with leads, and replaceable with holder or clips. Common materials of construction include glass, ceramic, and sand. Fuse types can be miniature, subminiature or micro, midget, automotive, blade type, PC board, and protective.

Standard Plug Fuses

STEP 1

STEP 2

STEP 3

STEP 4

**BLOWN FUSE DURING
SMALL OUTAGE**

STANDARD PLUG

SEQUENCE
OF EVENTS

**FUSE REACTION TO
SEVERE OVERLOAD**

Bussman Mfg., a McGraw-Edison Co. Division

Figure 1-17. *Plug fuses react differently depending on the amount of overload.*

Time-Delay Plug Fuses

A *time-delay plug fuse* is a screw-in type electrical safety device with a dual element. The first element provides the protection of a standard plug fuse for short circuits, and the second element protects against heating due to light overloads (the second element does not instantaneously melt). **See Figure 1-18.** The second element is useful in preventing nuisance tripping caused by motor-driven appliances such as refrigerators and air conditioners starting up. Manufacturers of time-delay plug fuses have created plugs with various responses to shorts and overloads.

Figure 1-18. *Time-delay plug fuses respond differently to shorts and overloads than standard plug fuses.*

Type S Plug Fuse

A *Type S plug fuse* is a screw-in type electrical safety device that has all the operating characteristics of a time-delay plug fuse plus the added advantage of being non-tamperable. A Type S fuse is considered non-tamperable because the fuse cannot be installed into a base unless the fuse matches the size of the base. **See Figure 1-19.** Each Type S base adapter is sized for a particular size fuse. Due to the non-tamperable design, a 20 A Type S fuse will not fit into a 15 A Type S base.

Figure 1-19. *Type S plug fuses have a distinctive base size, and once screwed into a panel, only Type S plug fuses of a specific amperage can be used.*

Fuse holders are devices for containing, protecting, and mounting fuses. Fuse holder designs include open or fully closed. Open fuse holder designs are fuse clips, fuse blocks, socket, and plug-on cap varieties. Fully enclosed designs use a fuse carrier inserted into a holder.

Cartridge Fuses

A *cartridge fuse* is a snap-in type electrical safety device that operates on the same basic heating principle as a plug fuse. However, instead of a screw base, cartridge fuses are secured by clips. Many cartridge fuses have dual elements that absorb temporary overloads (such as with motor startup) without blowing, while protecting against dangerous overloads and short circuits. **See Figure 1-20.** Cartridge fuses should be removed and installed using fuse pullers.

Figure 1-20. *Cartridge fuses are found with a number of different amperage ratings.*

Cartridge fuses can be purchased as one-time-use fuses or as renewable element fuses. Renewable element cartridge fuses have replaceable elements and are typically used for industrial applications.

Blade Cartridge Fuses

A *blade cartridge fuse* is another snap-in type electrical safety device that also operates on the heating effect of the element. Blade cartridge fuses are typically used for high amperage rated applications found in industry. Blade fuses are secured by clips and may be one-time use or renewable. **See Figure 1-21.**

Cooper Wiring Devices

Figure 1-21. *Blade cartridge fuses, like all fuse types, are found as one-time use fuses and as time-delay fuses.*

A fuse puller is used to safely remove blade fuses and cartridge fuses from electrical boxes and cabinets.

To help prevent electrical shock, proper personal protective equipment (PPE) must be worn at all times when performing tasks on energized circuits.

Circuit Breaker Fuses

A *circuit breaker fuse* is a screw-in type electrical safety device that has the operating characteristics of a circuit breaker. The advantage of a circuit breaker fuse is that the fuse can be reset after an overload and used again and again. **See Figure 1-22.**

Figure 1-22. *Circuit breaker fuses are similar to circuit breakers in that a circuit breaker fuse can be reset after an overload and used again and again.*

CIRCUIT BREAKERS

Circuit breakers are similar to fuses in function. A *circuit breaker* is a fixed electrical safety device designed to protect electrical devices and individuals from overcurrents. Unlike most fuses, circuit breakers can be reset. They are the most popular overcurrent safety device. **See Figure 1-23.** The trip lever handle of a circuit breaker represents the position of the contacts when the circuit breaker is ON and when the breaker is tripped OFF. A circuit breaker may be reset by moving the trip lever handle to the full OFF position and then returning the handle to the ON position. Individuals must ensure the source of an overload is repaired before attempting to reset a breaker. The three types of circuit breakers are thermal, magnetic, and thermal-magnetic.

Figure 1-23. *Circuit breakers have standard voltage ratings with varying amperages, similar to fuses, but can be reset after encountering an overload.*

Thermal Circuit Breakers

A *thermal circuit breaker* is an electrical safety device that operates with a bimetallic strip that warps when overheated. The bimetallic strip is two pieces of metal made up of dissimilar materials that are permanently joined together. Because metals expand and contract at different rates, heating the bimetallic strip causes the strip to warp or curve. The warping effect of the bimetallic strip is utilized as the tripping mechanism for the thermal breaker. **See Figure 1-24.**

Figure 1-24. *Thermal circuit breakers have a bimetallic strip that warps with an increase in heat caused by excessive current flow.*

Typical household wattages include a hair dryer at 1400 W, a vacuum cleaner at 1000 W, a television at 150 W, and a stereo music system at 30 W.

Once a thermal breaker has tripped, the bimetallic strip cools allowing the strip to reshape and allowing the breaker to be reset. Individuals must reset the trip lever handle to reactivate the circuit breaker and restore power to the de-energized circuit. As with all circuit breakers, the source of an overload must be removed before attempting to reset the breaker.

Magnetic Circuit Breakers

A *magnetic circuit breaker* is an electrical safety device that operates with miniature electromagnets. Electromagnets are created by passing current through a coil of wire. The greater the current, the stronger the magnetic field created by the coil. When the current through the coil exceeds the rated value of the breaker, the magnetic attraction becomes strong enough to activate the trip bar and open the circuit. **See Figure 1-25.** Once the overload is removed, the trip bar can be reset to the original position reactivating the circuit.

Figure 1-25. *Excessive current creates a magnetic field strong enough to move the trip bar forward, causing the breaker to open.*

Circuit breakers are typically housed in circuit breaker panels, although enclosures for individual circuit breakers are available.

Thermal-Magnetic Circuit Breakers

A *thermal-magnetic circuit breaker* is an electrical safety device that combines the heating effect of a bimetallic strip with the pulling strength of a magnet to move the trip bar. **See Figure 1-26.** The magnetic portion consists of a permanent magnet or electromagnet in series with the bimetallic strip. Thermal-magnetic breakers have the fastest response times to serious overloads of any type of circuit breaker.

No matter which type of internal mechanism a circuit breaker uses, externally, most circuit breakers look the same. Circuit breakers are available in a variety of amperages, but the voltage is typically rated as 115 V for single pole residential breakers or 230 V for double pole residential breakers. To gain access to the circuit breaker connections in a service panel, the cover of the panel must be removed.

GROUND FAULT CIRCUIT INTERRUPTERS

A *ground fault circuit interrupter (GFCI)* is a fast-acting electrical device that detects low levels of leakage current to ground and opens the circuit in response to the ground fault. **See Figure 1-27.** GFCIs limit electric shock by opening circuits before an individual receives a serious injury. GFCIs do not protect against line-to-line contact.

Thermal-Magnetic Circuit Breakers

Figure 1-26. *The action of the bimetallic strip is aided by the presence of a magnet.*

Ground Fault Circuit Interrupter (GFCI)

Cooper Wiring Devices

Figure 1-27. *GFCIs are used for outdoor receptacle applications and anywhere where extra protection is required.*

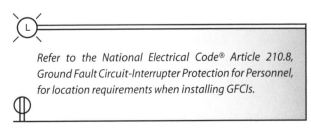

Refer to the National Electrical Code® Article 210.8, Ground Fault Circuit-Interrupter Protection for Personnel, for location requirements when installing GFCIs.

Necessity of GFCIs

Ground fault circuit interrupters were created because of the limitations of commonly used circuit breakers. Individuals have been electrocuted by equipment in electrical systems where the fault current was not great enough to trip a standard circuit breaker. The situation exists because standard circuit breakers are designed to trip only when large currents are present (short or overload). Currents present from deteriorating insulation and minor equipment damage do not produce enough current flow to open a standard circuit breaker. As an alternative, GFCIs are specifically designed with leakage currents in mind. A GFCI can react to a current as small as $\frac{5}{1000}$ (.005) of an amp in a fraction of a second.

GFCI Operation

A sequence of events takes place when a fault current is detected by a GFCI. Typically, the load (electric shaver, drill, or garden tool) has the same amount of current flowing to the load (black or red wire) as flowing away from the load (white wire). However, in the event of a ground fault, some of the current, which normally returns to the power source through the white wire (neutral), is diverted to ground. **See Figure 1-28.**

Because a current imbalance exists between the hot and neutral wires, the sensing device detects the current difference and signals an amplifier. When the amplified signal is large enough, the amplifier activates the interrupting device. Once the interrupting device is activated, the circuit is opened and current to the load is shut off. After the ground fault has been discovered and repaired, the GFCI is reset and the process begins again. GFCIs have a test circuit built into the unit so that the GFCI can be tested on a monthly basis without a ground fault condition.

Per the NEC®, all receptacles installed in kitchen countertop areas require GFCI protection.

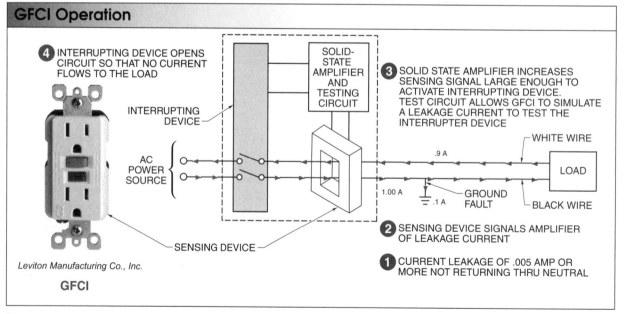

Figure 1-28. *Most GFCIs trip in 25 ms but can take several seconds.*

GFCI Required Locations

The National Electrical Code (NEC®) requires ground fault circuit interrupters for protection in the following areas:

1. Residential. **See Figure 1-29.**
   - Outdoor receptacles
   - Bathrooms
   - Residential garages
   - Kitchens (countertop areas)
   - Unfinished basements and crawl spaces
2. Construction Sites
3. Mobile Homes and Mobile Home Parks
   - Outdoor receptacles
   - Bathrooms
4. Swimming Pools and Fountains
   - Receptacles near pools
   - Lighting fixtures and lighting outlets near pools
   - Underwater lighting fixtures over 15 V
   - Electrical equipment used with storable pools
   - Fountain equipment operating at over 15 V
   - Cord-connected and plug-connected equipment for fountains

Figure 1-29. *GFCIs are installed indoors and outdoors of residences.*

Installing GFCIs

GFCIs are installed in standard receptacle boxes indoors and in weatherproof boxes outdoors. GFCI receptacles are typically installed individually. **See Figure 1-30.** GFCIs can also be installed to protect several standard receptacles in one circuit. GFCIs are considered easy to install and most manufacturers supply an installation kit to aid in installation. In addition to receptacle types, GFCIs are available as circuit breakers to protect entire circuits. Kits are also available to match GFCIs to existing circuit breaker panels.

Figure 1-30. *A GFCI can be wired to protect a single receptacle, multiple receptacles when wired in parallel, and entire circuits when installed as a circuit breaker in the service panel.*

Chapter 1

Test

Name _____   Date _____

Residential Electrical Systems

_____   1. The flow of electricity through a residential electrical system is from ___
                                      to ___. A POWER SOURCE, TO A LOAD, BACK TO A POWER SOURCE

__B (5)_____   2. Using Ohm's law, current flow (A) through a circuit is ___ A when the
                                      circuit is supplied with 120 V and has 24 Ω of resistance?
                                      A. 0.2   **B.** 5
                                      C. 120   **D.** 2880

__D (22,000)_____   3. The voltage output of commercial generators is typically ___V.
                                      A. 230   **B.** 1200
                                      C. 460   **D.** 22,000

A COMPLETE PATH   4. A(n) ___ is a grouping of electrical devices and wires that create a path
   CIRCUIT   for current to take from the power source (service panel), through con-
                                      trols (switches), to the load (light fixtures and receptacles), and back to
                                      the power source.

SYSTEM GROUNDING   5. ___ grounding is designed to protect the entire electrical network.

EQUIPMENT GROUNDING   6. ___ grounding is designed to protect individual electrical components.

METAL UNDERGROUND   7. A(n) ___ is considered the best ground for a residential electrical sys-
WATER PIPE GROUNDING   tem. (COPPER PREFFERED)

    T   Ⓕ   8. An alternative electrode must be at least 10′ in length.

    Ⓣ   F   9. An iron plate may be used as a made electrode.

    Ⓣ   F   10. A metal underground water pipe requires a supplemental electrode.

    T   Ⓕ   11. The minimum conduit diameter for a made electrode is 5/8″.

_____#2_____   12. A 20′ length of # ___ Cu may be used as a ground ring.

_____2½″_____   13. The minimum burial depth of a ground ring is ___′.

19

BIMETALLIC STRIP   **14.** A(n) ___ strip trips a thermal circuit breaker.

(T)   F   **15.** The NEC® requires GFCI protection on construction sites.

(T)   F   **16.** Circuit breakers have standard voltage ratings but vary in amperage ratings.

CIRCUIT BREAKER   **17.** ___ fuses can be reset.

BLADE   **18.** ___ cartridge fuses are typically used for high-amperage-rated applications.

CURRENT   **19.** Electromagnets are created by passing ___ through a coil of wire.

$\frac{5}{1000}$, (.005) AMP   **20.** A GFCI can react to current as little as ___ A in less than a fraction of a second.

METAL STRIP   **21.** Standard plug fuses have a(n) ___ strip that melts when current exceeds the rated value of the fuse.

B (2")   **22.** A concrete-encased electrode shall be encased in ___" of concrete.
- **A.** 1½
- **B.** 2
- **C.** 2½
- **D.** 4

C (20')   **23.** A ground ring of #2 Cu shall be a minimum of ___' in length.
- **A.** 10
- **B.** 15
- **C.** 20
- **D.** 40

(T)   F   **24.** A made electrode may be a nonferrous metal plate .06" thick × 2 sq ft.

(T)   F   **25.** Pipe or conduit made electrodes shall be galvanized or metal-coated.

GROUND CONNECTION   **26.** The U-shaped blade of a three-prong grounded plug is the ___ connection.

FLOW PATH   **27.** Electricity always seeks the easiest ___ to ground.

SHUNT   **28.** A meter ___ provides a continuous electrical path when a water meter is removed.

T   (F)   **29.** Fuses limit the rate of current flow in a circuit.

(T)   F   **30.** Main service panel cartridge fuses are commonly of the blade type.

(T)   F   **31.** A circuit breaker is reset by moving the handle to the full OFF position and then to the ON position.

T   (F)   **32.** GFCIs protect receptacles and plugs only.

PULLERS   **33.** Fuse ___ should be used when removing fuses.

Grounding Electrodes

___8'___   **1.** The minimum length of A is ___'.

___45°___   **2.** The maximum angle of B is ___°.

___2½'___   **3.** The minimum depth of C is ___'.

___¾"___   **4.** The minimum diameter of D is ___".

___½"___   **5.** The minimum diameter of E is ___".

___10'___   **6.** The minimum length of F is ___'.

___2 sq ft___   **7.** The minimum size of G is ___ sq ft.

___¼"___   **8.** The minimum thickness of G is ___" for steel.

___.06"___   **9.** The minimum thickness of G is ___" for nonferrous metal.

(A)

(B)

(C)

(D)

(E)

(F)

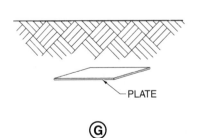

(G)

Electrical Service

_____C_____ 1. Circuit breakers

_____G_____ 2. Meter socket

_____A_____ 3. Panel disconnect

_____D_____ 4. Ground bus bar

_____H_____ 5. Meter

_____B_____ 6. Phase 2 neutral bus bar

_____I_____ 7. Service mask

_____F_____ 8. MBJ

_____E_____ 9. GEC

_____J_____ 10. Phase 1 neutral bus bar

Grounding Systems

<u>H</u>   **1.** Grounding prong

<u>C</u>   **2.** Grounding rod (electrode)

<u>E</u>   **3.** Ground conductor

<u>J</u>   **4.** Load

<u>D</u>   **5.** Service panel grounding bar

<u>I</u>   **6.** Receptacle

<u>B</u>   **7.** GEC wire

<u>F</u>   **8.** Green hex grounding screw

<u>A</u>   **9.** Neutral conductor

<u>G</u>   **10.** Grounding slots

Fuses

_____ 1. Glass tube fuse

_____ 2. Renewable cartridge fuse

_____ 3. Circuit breaker plug fuse

_____ 4. One-time blade fuse

_____ 5. Fusetron dual-element plug fuse

_____ 6. Fusetron dual-element blade fuse

_____ 7. Fustat plug fuse

_____ 8. Standard cartridge fuse

A   B   C

D   E   F

G   H

Chapter 2
Electrical Tools and Safety

Chapter 2 discusses the quality of tools and how to organize and use tools safely. Chapter 2 explains general electrical safety rules and safety on the construction site. Individuals must follow all OSHA and NFPA 70E safety rules and conform to all codes and rules when performing electrical work.

QUALITY TOOLS

"Get the right tool for the job" has been said over and over again. It was discovered long ago that, to do a job correctly, quality tools and instruments are required. Electrical work especially requires quality tools. Experience has shown that individuals are more productive when they use quality tools and instruments. **See Figure 2-1.** Quality tools last longer and more consistently provide quality results. By comparison, inferior tools result in lost time and money due to breakage and unnecessary mistakes.

Electricians are not required to buy every electrical tool immediately on entering an apprenticeship, because quality tools are expensive. Typically, an apprentice or journeyman electrician purchases a few basic quality tools at first and then adds other tools as needed. By acquiring quality tools over time, elec-tricians create a selection of quality tools that are useful in the work the electrician performs. Taking time to create a tool inventory allows individuals to pick and choose the best types and manufacturers of tools for the type of work performed.

Ideal Industries

Quality tools make a job easier by being reliable, whenver and wherever needed.

Electrical Tools and Instruments

Fluke Corporation

DIGITAL MULTIMETER

Measures electrical properties such as voltage, current, and resistance

Amprobe/Advanced Test Products

RECEPTACLE TESTER

Instrument used to determine if a receptacle is properly wired, energized, and grounded

Ideal Industries, Inc.

SOLENOID VOLTAGE TESTER

Measures the approximate voltage amount and type of voltage (AC or DC)

Klein Tools, Inc.

TEST LIGHT (NEON TESTER)

Illuminates when a voltage or specific voltage is present.

Figure 2-1. *Individuals should use quality tools and instruments because inferior tools result in lost time and money due to breakage and unnecessary mistakes.*

ORGANIZED TOOL SYSTEMS

Because electrical tools are expensive to replace, individuals must protect their investment. To be effective, electrical tools must be available when needed, and protected from damage caused by the environment and daily use. An organized tool system must provide both a central location for retrieval of electrical tools and a means of protecting the tools during storage.

Electrical tools are organized in several ways depending upon where and how frequently the tools are used. When tools are used at a repair bench or at home for hobbies, a pegboard may be appropriate. When electrical tools are used at a construction site, a leather pouch is typically used to carry the most commonly used tools. When tools are to be transported to another job site or home, a toolbox is typically used.

Pegboards

Pegboard is a thin constructed board typically available in 4′ x 8′ sheets that is perforated with equally spaced holes for accepting hooks. **See Figure 2-2.** Pegboard is constructed of heavy-duty tempered material that is best suited for the weight of tools. When pegboard is mounted, outlines of tools can be made at the hooks for inventory purposes. Tool outlines can be painted onto the pegboard or cut out of self-adhesive shelf paper.

Electrical Tool Pouches

An *electrical tool pouch* is a small, open tool container (pouch) for storing a few commonly used electrical tools. An electrical tool pouch is typically made of heavy-duty leather, and is designed to be used with a belt that holds the pouch in place. **See Figure 2-3.**

Tool pouches can be simple in design and hold only a few tools, or they can be relatively large and designed to hold a wide selection of tools. The type of pouch chosen depends on the type of work an individual is planning to perform.

A typical electrician's tool pouch includes assorted cutting pliers, adjustable pliers, an adjustable wrench, nutdrivers, a torpedo level, regular and Phillips screwdrivers, a measuring tape, and a wire stripper/crimper.

Organizing Tool Storage

Figure 2-2. *When pegboards are used to store tools, outlines of the tools painted on the pegboard make it easy to check that all tools are put away.*

Toolboxes made from composite material are the strongest. Steel boxes are 55% as strong and aluminum boxes, 40%.

Electrical Tool Pouches

Klein Tools, Inc.

SMALL ELECTRICIAN TOOL SET

Figure 2-3. *Tool pouches can be simple in design or relatively large, depending on the type of work an individual is planning to perform.*

Toolboxes

Most individuals prefer to store tools in a quality toolbox. **See Figure 2-4.** A well-designed toolbox can be locked and will keep tools clean and dry. In addition, toolboxes, whether fixed or portable, provide a place where all tools can be collected. To ensure a complete inventory of tools at the end of the day or after a job, a list of all tools owned can be kept in the toolbox as a checklist.

Toolboxes

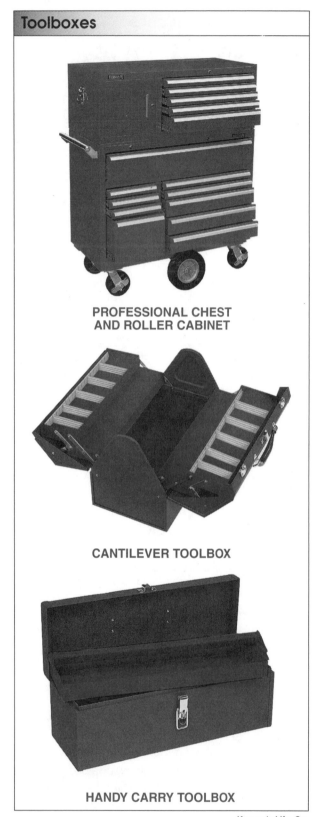

**PROFESSIONAL CHEST
AND ROLLER CABINET**

CANTILEVER TOOLBOX

HANDY CARRY TOOLBOX

Kennedy Mfg. Co.

Figure 2-4. *Tools can be collected in a toolbox. Toolboxes keep tools clean and dry, and can be locked for security.*

Whichever system an individual chooses, organization is a must. An organized tool system ensures that tools are kept clean, dry, and at the fingertips of the individual when needed.

TOOL SAFETY

All tools can be dangerous when left in the wrong place, such as on a ladder. Many accidents are caused by tools falling off ladders, shelves, and scaffolds that are being used or moved.

Every tool should have a designated place in a toolbox. Do not carry tools in clothes pockets unless the pocket is designed for the tool. Keep pencils in a pocket designed for pencils; do not place pencils behind an ear or under a hardhat or cap.

Keep tools with sharp points away from the edges of benches or work areas, because individuals brushing against a tool can cause the tool to fall and injure a leg or foot. When carrying edged and sharply pointed tools, carry the tool with the cutting edge or the point down and outward from the body. An individual setting a tool down should place the tool back in a toolbox, or at least in a safe location. Electrical tools are divided into three categories: hand, power, and testing.

Hand Tools

Tool safety requires tool knowledge. Tool safety not only requires that the proper type of hand tool be chosen, but also that the correct size of tool be chosen. Individuals should use quality hand tools, and use the tools only in the manner in which they were designed to be used. **See Figure 2-5.**

Proper Hand Tool Use. Individuals must understand how to correctly use each tool owned. Tools must not be forced into a use beyond normal function. Questions must be asked when the proper and safe operation of a tool is not understood. Individuals are often tempted to use a screwdriver for a chisel or pliers as a wrench, but the correct tool will perform the task faster and safer. **See Figure 2-6.** The cost of a tool and the time taken to purchase a tool will prove far less costly than a serious accident caused by using a tool incorrectly.

Hand Tools

Ideal Industries, Inc.

FUSE PULLER

Safely removes cartridge-type fuses

Greenlee Textron Inc.

WIRE STRIPPER

Removes insulation from small-diameter wire

The Stanley Works

HACKSAW

Cuts heavy cable, pipe, and conduit

Klein Tools, Inc.

ADJUSTABLE WRENCH

Tightens thick items such as hex head bolts and nuts, conduit couplings, and lag bolts

Klein Tools, Inc.

UTILITY KNIFE

Cuts and scores drywall for drywall operations

Klein Tools, Inc.

FISH TAPE

Used to pull wire through conduit and wires around obstructions in walls

Klein Tools, Inc.

CRIMPING PLIERS

Used to crimp die marked insulated and noninsulated solderless terminals

NEEDLE⌐ *Klein Tools, Inc.*

LONG-NOSE PLIERS

Useful for bending wire and positioning small components

The Stanley Works.

SIDE-CUTTING PLIERS

Used to cut cable, remove knockouts, twist wire, and debur conduit

Klein Tools, inc.

TONGUE-AND-GROOVE PLIERS

Used to tighten box connectors, locknuts, and conduit couplings

Klein Tools, Inc.

ELECTRICIAN'S KNIFE

Removes insulation from nonmetallic cable and service conductors

The Stanley Works

DIAGONAL CUTTING PLIERS

Useful for cutting wire and cables that are difficult to reach

The Stanley Works

HAMMER

Used to mount electrical boxes with nails, and determine height of receptacle boxes

Klein Tools, Inc.

POCKET LEVEL

Useful in leveling thermostats and conduit bends

The Stanley Works.

FLATHEAD SCREWDRIVER

Used to install and remove threaded fasteners

Figure 2-5. *Understanding how to choose the correct type and size of hand tool for a task is important.*

Safe Use of Hand Tools

SELECT A SCREWDRIVER OF LENGTH AND TIP FITTED TO THE WORK. SCREWDRIVERS ARE SPECIFIED BY THE LENGTH OF THE BLADE. THE TIP SHOULD BE STRAIGHT AND NEARLY PARALLEL SIDED. IT SHOULD ALSO FIT THE SCREW SLOT AND BE NO WIDER THAN THE SCREW HEAD.

IF THE TIP IS TOO WIDE IT WILL SCAR THE MATERIAL AROUND THE SCREW HEAD. IF THE SCREWDRIVER IS NOT HELD IN LINE WITH THE SCREW IT WILL SLIP OUT OF THE SLOT AND MAR BOTH THE SCREW AND THE WORK.

IF THE TIP IS ROUNDED OR BEVELED IT WILL RAISE OUT OF THE SLOT, SPOILING THE SCREW HEAD. REGRIND OR FILL THE TIP TO MAKE IT AS SHOWN AT TOP. THE TWO COMMON SCREWDRIVER HEADS ARE PHILLIPS AND FLAT HEAD.

TO CUT HORIZONTALLY ACROSS THE GRAIN WITH THE WORK HELD IN THE VISE, PRESS THE FOREFINGER AND THUMB TOGETHER ON THE CHISEL TO ACT AS A BRAKE. TO AVOID SPLINTERING THE CORNERS, CUT HALFWAY FROM EACH EDGE TOWARD THE CENTER. REMOVE THE CENTER STOCK LAST.

WOOD CHISEL

NOTE: NEVER STRIKE A HAMMER WITH A HAMMER.

WOOD HAMMER

FORCE MUST ALWAYS BE AGAINST FIXED JAW

SCREWDRIVER   **ADJUSTABLE WRENCH**   **COMPASS SAW**

Figure 2-6. *A screwdriver sometimes is used as a chisel, or pliers as a wrench, but the correct tool will perform the task faster and safer.*

Maintaining Hand Tools in Proper Operation. Periodic checks of hand tools will aid in keeping tools in good condition. Always inspect a tool before using the tool. Do not use a tool that is in poor or faulty condition. Tool handles must be free of cracks and splinters and be fastened securely to the working part of the tool. Damaged tools are not only dangerous to the user but are also less productive than tools in good working condition. When inspection indicates a dangerous condition, repair or replace the tool immediately.

Cutting tools must be sharp and clean, because dull tools are dangerous. The extra force exerted when using dull tools often results in losing control of the tool. Dirt or oil on a tool can cause the tool to slip on the work and cause injury.

Power Tools

Do not use any power tools without knowing the operation, methods of use, and safety precautions of the power tool. **See Figure 2-7.** Authorization from a supervisor can be required before using a power tool.

Power Tools

ELECTRIC POWER DRILL
Used with drill bits to drill medium-size and large holes

Milwaukee Electric Tool Corp.

BATTERY POWERED DRILL
Used with drill bits to drill holes and with assorted bits for working fasteners

Milwaukee Electric Tool Corp.

ELECTRIC DIE GRINDER
Used to cut wood, drywall, and metal

Milwaukee Electric Tool Corp.

CARBIDE TIPPED BIT
Used to drill into masonry
Milwaukee Electric Tool Corp.

TWIST DRILL BIT
Used for drilling small holes
Milwaukee Electric Tool Corp.

STEP DRILL BIT
Used to drill multiple size holes in wood, metal, and plastic
Milwaukee Electric Tool Corp.

SPADE BIT
Used to drill medium-size holes

SHIP AUGER BIT
Used to rough bore holes
Advantage Drills Inc.

HOLESAW
Used to drill large holes
Milwaukee Electric Tool Corp.

IMPACT DRIVER AND SOCKET BITS
Used to install and remove fasteners quickly
Klein Tools, Inc.

GRINDING WHEELS AND BITS
Used to grind wood, plastic, and metal
Advantage Drills Inc.

Figure 2-7. *Power tools must only be used with a proper understanding of tool operation and the safety precautions associated with the tool.*

Grounding. All power tools are grounded except for power tools that are approved double-insulated. Non-double insulated power tools must have a three-conductor cord. A three-prong plug connects to a grounded receptacle (outlet). **See Figure 2-8.** OSHA and local codes must be consulted for the proper grounding specifications of power tools. A proper ground ensures that a faulty power tool causing an electrical short will trip a circuit breaker or blow a fuse in the circuit.

Non-current-carrying metal parts that are connected to ground include all metal boxes, raceways, enclosures, and equipment. Unwanted current exists because of insulation failure or because a current-carrying conductor makes contact with a non-current-carrying part of the system. In a properly grounded system, the unwanted current flow trips fuses or circuit breakers. Once the fuse or circuit breaker is tripped, the circuit is open and no additional current flows.

Grounding

Figure 2-8. *A proper ground ensures that a faulty power tool causing an electrical short will trip a circuit breaker or blow a fuse in the circuit.*

Double-insulated tools have two prongs and will have a notation on the specification plate that the tool is double-insulated. Double-insulated tools are relatively safe but grounded tools are typically used on job sites. Electrical parts in the motor of a double-insulated tool are surrounded by extra insulation to help prevent shock; therefore, the tool does not have to be grounded. Both the interior and exterior of double-insulated tools must be kept clean of grease, dirt, and water that might conduct electricity.

Safety Rules for Power Tools

When handling power tools, the following safety rules must be followed:

- Power tools must be inspected and serviced by qualified repair personnel at regular intervals as specified by the manufacturer or OSHA.
- Know and understand all the safety recommendations of the manufacturer.
- Inspect electrical cords to verify that the cords are in good condition.
- Verify that all safety guards are in place and in proper working order. Do not remove, displace, or jam guards or any other safety devices. **See Figure 2-9.**
- Make all adjustments, blade changes, and inspections with the power OFF (cord disconnected).
- Before connecting a tool to a power source, ensure that the on/off switch is in the OFF position.
- Wear safety goggles and a dust mask when using power tools. **See Figure 2-10.**
- Ensure that the material to be worked is free of obstructions and securely clamped.
- Be attentive (focused on the work) at all times.
- A change in the sound of a power tool during operation normally indicates trouble. Investigate any change in sound immediately.
- When work is completed, shut the power OFF. Wait until a portable tool stops before leaving or laying down the tool.
- When a power tool is defective, remove the tool from service. Alert other personnel to the situation.
- Avoid operating power tools in locations where sparks could ignite flammable materials.
- Unplug power tools by pulling on the plugs; never pull on the cord.

Tool Guards

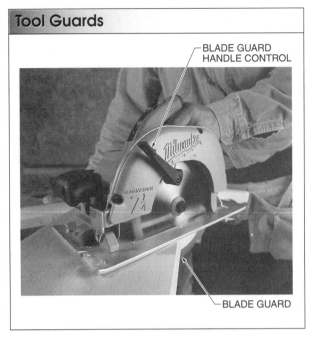

Figure 2-9. *Do not remove, displace, or jam guards or any other safety devices on a power tool.*

Power Tool Dust

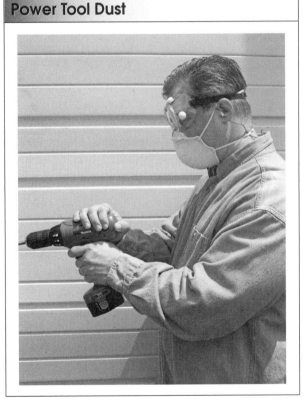

Figure 2-10. *When using power tools for tasks that may result in potentially hazardous dust or other air contaminants, wear safety goggles and a dusk mask.*

TEST INSTRUMENTS

Proper equipment and procedures are required when taking measurements with test instruments. To take a measurement, the test instrument must be set to the correct measuring position and properly connected into the circuit to be tested; the displayed measurement is then read and interpreted. There is always the possibility that the test instrument will be set to the incorrect function or incorrect range, and/or will be misread. Test instruments not properly connected to a circuit increase the likelihood of an improper measurement and may create an unsafe condition.

Voltage Indicators

A *voltage indicator* is a test instrument that indicates the presence of voltage when the test tip touches, or is near, an energized hot conductor or energized metal part. The tip glows and/or the device creates a sound when voltage is present at the test point. Voltage indicators are used to test receptacles, fuses, circuit breakers, cables, and other devices in which the presence of voltage must be detected. **See Figure 2-11.** The hot side (short slot or black wire) of a standard receptacle is typically used to test a voltage indicator for proper operation.

Voltage indicators are available in various voltage ranges (a few volts to hundreds of volts) and in the different voltage types (AC, DC, AC/DC) for testing various types of circuits.

Voltage Indicator Advantages/Disadvantages. The advantages of voltage indicators are that voltage indicators are inexpensive, are small enough to carry in a pocket, are easy to use, are nonconductive, and indicate a voltage without touching any live parts of a circuit, even through conductor insulation. One disadvantage of voltage indicators is that voltage indicators indicate only that voltage is present, not the actual amount of voltage. Another disadvantage of voltage indicators is that voltage indicators may not provide an indication that voltage is present, even when voltage is present. Voltage indicators can be fooled by wires or cables that are shielded.

Voltage Indicators

Figure 2-11. *A voltage indicator is a test instrument that indicates the presence of voltage when the test tip touches, or is near, an energized hot conductor or energized metal part.*

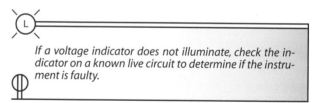

If a voltage indicator does not illuminate, check the indicator on a known live circuit to determine if the instrument is faulty.

Voltage Indicator Applications. Voltage indicators are used for many applications such as finding a break in an extension cord or wire, or determining when a receptacle is hot (energized). One important application of a voltage indicator is in making a preliminary test to determine if any metal parts or wires are hot before beginning service on a circuit or component. A fault occurs when any hot (energized) conductor touches a metal part that is not grounded. Faults occur because of a nick in conductor insulation, or when an exposed metal terminal screw contacts another metal part when a switch or receptacle is loose or not connected properly.

Voltage Indicator Measurement Procedures

Before taking any measurements using a voltage indicator, ensure the indicator is designed to take measurements on the circuit being tested. Refer to the operating manual of the test instrument for all measuring precautions, limitations, and procedures. Always wear required personal protective equipment and follow all safety rules when taking a measurement. **See Figure 2-12.** To test for voltage using a voltage indicator, apply the following procedures:

Voltage Indicator Measurement Procedure

① VERIFY VOLTAGE INDICATOR VOLTAGE RATING

AIR COMPRESSOR

③ REMOVE VOLTAGE INDICATOR FROM CIRCUIT

② PLACE TEST TIP ON OR NEAR WIRE

④ ALWAYS TAKE SECOND MEASUREMENT WITH OTHER INSTRUMENT

Figure 2-12. *Always verify that a voltage indicator or any test instrument has a voltage rating higher than the highest potential voltage in the circuit being tested.*

SAFETY PROCEDURES

- Follow all electrical safety practices and procedures.
- Check and wear personal protective equipment (PPE) for the procedure being performed.
- Perform only authorized procedures.
- Follow all manufacturer recommendations and procedures.

1. Verify that the voltage indicator has a voltage rating higher than the highest potential voltage in the circuit being tested. Residential circuits are typically 115 V. When circuit voltage is unknown, slowly bring the voltage indicator near the conductor or slot being tested. The voltage indicator will glow and/or sound when voltage is present. The brighter a voltage indicator glows, the higher the voltage or the closer the voltage indicator is to the voltage source.
2. Place the tip of the voltage indicator on or near the wire or device being tested. When testing an extension cord for a break, test several points along the wire. Expect the voltage tester to turn on and off when moved along a cord that has twisted wire conductors, because the hot wire will change position along the cord.
3. Remove the voltage indicator from the test area.
4. When the voltage indicator does not indicate the presence of voltage by glowing or making a sound, do not assume that there is no voltage and start working on exposed components of a circuit. Always take a second test instrument (voltmeter or multimeter) and measure for the presence of voltage before working around or on exposed wires and electrical components.

Test Lights

Electrical circuits can be tested safely and inexpensively with a test light. **See Figure 2-13.** Most hardware stores have test lights at a low cost. A *test light (neon tester)* is a test instrument that is designed to illuminate in the presence of 115 V and 230 V circuits. A soft glow indicates a 115 V circuit; a brighter glow indicates a 230 V circuit. Many residential electrical problems can be solved by determining if voltage is present at a location in the circuit.

Test Lights (Neon Testers)

TEST LEAD TIPS

VOLTAGE TEST LEAD

COMMON TEST LEAD

FINGER GUARD

FINGER GUARD

NEON BULB

Figure 2-13. *A test light (neon tester) is a test instrument that is designed to illuminate in the presence of 115 V and 230 V circuits.*

Test Light Advantages/Disadvantages. The advantages of using test lights are that test lights are inexpensive, small enough to carry in a pocket, and easy to use. The disadvantages of test lights are that test lights have a limited voltage range and cannot determine the actual voltage of a circuit, only that voltage is present in a circuit. Test lights that have a wider voltage range are better than test lights that have only one voltage rating. For example, a neon test light rated for 90 VAC to 600 VAC is better than a test light rated for only 120 VAC. Neon test lights have a very high resistance so the neon bulb draws very little current when taking measurements. The small current draw allows neon bulbs to have a longer life expectancy than other test lights. Another disadvantage of neon test lights is that neon test lights must not be used to test ground fault circuit interrupters (GFCIs).

Test Light Applications

Test lights are primarily used to determine when voltage is present in a circuit (the circuit is energized), such as when testing receptacles. When testing a receptacle, the test light bulb illuminates when the receptacle is properly wired and energized.

When a receptacle is properly wired, a test light bulb will illuminate when the test light leads are connected between the neutral slot and the hot slot. A test light bulb will also illuminate when the leads are connected between the ground slot and the hot slot. If the test light illuminates when the leads are connected from the neutral slot to the ground slot, the hot (black) and neutral (white) wires are reverse wired. The situation of having the hot and neutral wires reversed (nonpolarized) is a safety hazard and must be corrected.

If a test light illuminates when the test leads are connected to the neutral slot and hot slot but does not light when connected to the ground slot and hot slot, the receptacle is not grounded. When a test light illuminates, but is dimmer than when connected between the neutral slot and hot slot, the receptacle has an improper ground (having high resistance). Improper grounds are also a safety hazard and must be corrected.

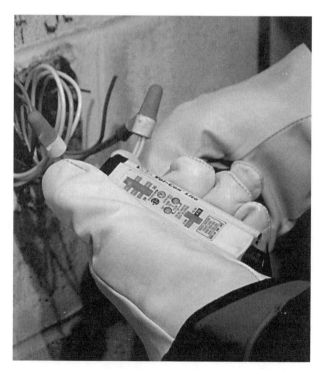

For additional protection from electric shock when testing energized circuits with a test instrument, rubber insulating gloves and leather protective gloves should be worn.

Test Light Measurement Procedures

Before using a test light, always check the test light on a known energized circuit that is within the test light's rating to ensure that the test light is operating correctly.

Before taking any measurements using a test light, ensure the test light is designed to take measurements on the circuit being tested. Refer to the operating manual of the test instrument for all measuring procedures, limitations, and precautions. **See Figure 2-14.**

To test for voltage using a test light, apply the following procedures:

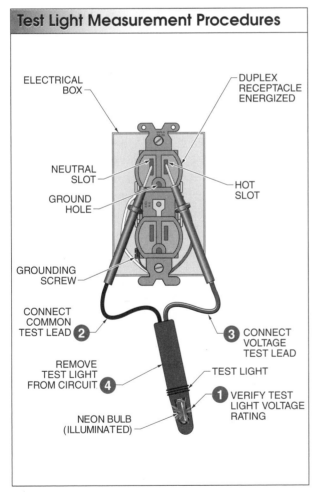

Figure 2-14. *Care must be taken to ensure that the exposed metal tips of the test light leads or any test instrument do not touch fingers or any metal parts not being tested.*

1. Verify that the test light has a voltage rating higher than the highest potential voltage in the circuit. Care must be taken to guarantee that the exposed metal tips of the test light leads do not touch fingers or any metal parts not being tested.
2. Connect one test lead of the test light to the neutral side of the circuit or ground. When testing a circuit that has a neutral or ground, connect to the neutral or ground side of the circuit first.
3. Connect the other test lead of the test light to the other side (hot side) of the circuit. Voltage is present when the test light bulb illuminates. Voltage is less than the rating of the test light when the test light is dimly lit, and is higher than the rating of the test light when the test light glows brighter than normal. Voltage is not present in a circuit or present at a very low level when a test light does not illuminate.
4. Remove the test light from the circuit.

Continuity Testers

A *continuity tester* is a test instrument that is used to test a circuit for a complete path for current to flow. A closed switch that is operating correctly has continuity while an open switch does not have continuity. **See Figure 2-15.** A continuity tester or test instrument with continuity test mode indicates when an electrical device or circuit has a complete path by emitting an audible sound (beep). Indication of a complete path is used to determine the condition of a device, such as a switch, as open or closed.

Continuity Tester Advantages and Disadvantages. The main advantage of using a continuity tester or continuity test mode of a test instrument is the audible response (beep). An audible response allows an individual to concentrate on the testing procedures without looking at the test instrument.

Continuity Testers

OHM MEASUREMENT
(Ω, kΩ, MΩ) AND
CONTINUITY BUZZER

(1KΩ)

Ω

AC A

AC / DC V
Automatic
Selection

OFF

Figure 2-15. *A continuity tester is a test instrument that is used to test a circuit for a complete path for current flow.*

The main disadvantage of using a continuity tester is that a continuity tester only emits a sound when continuity is detected. Continuity testers only operate on circuits that have very low resistance (40 Ω or less) and will not indicate the actual resistance of a circuit or device.

Continuity Tester Applications

Continuity testers are used to test for a complete flow path (open, broken, or closed) in any de-energized low-resistance device. A continuity tester is a common test tool to use when testing single-pole, 3-way, and 4-way switches. For example, a 3-way switch has one terminal that is the "common" terminal. Depending upon the manufacturer, the common terminal can be located in any position on a 3-way switch. The common terminal is often identified on a 3-way switch by a different color. On specialty switches, such as automobile switches, the common terminal is not identified. Continuity testers are used to determine the common terminal and proper switch operation.

Continuity Tester Measurement Procedures

Continuity is tested with a test instrument set to the continuity test mode. Before taking any continuity measurements using a continuity tester, ensure the meter is designed to take measurements on the circuit being tested. Refer to the operating manual of the test instrument for all measuring procedures, limitations, and precautions. Always wear required personal protective equipment and follow all safety rules when taking the measurement. **See Figure 2-16.** To take continuity measurements with a continuity tester, apply the following procedures:

SAFETY PROCEDURES

- Follow all electrical safety practices and procedures.
- Check and wear personal protective equipment (PPE) for the procedure being performed.
- Perform only authorized procedures.
- Follow all manufacturer recommendations and procedures.

1. Set the continuity tester function switch to continuity test mode as required. Most test instruments have the continuity test mode and resistance mode sharing the same function switch position.
2. With the circuit de-energized, connect the test leads across the component being tested. The position of the test leads is arbitrary.
3. When there is a complete path (continuity), the continuity tester beeps. When there is no continuity (open circuit), the continuity tester does not beep.
4. After completing all continuity tests, remove the continuity tester from the circuit or component being tested and turn the instrument OFF to prevent battery drain.

A continuity tester must only be used on de-energized circuits or components. Any voltage applied to a continuity tester causes damage to the test instrument and/or harm to the individual. Always test a circuit for voltage before taking a continuity test.

Continuity Tester Measurement Procedures

INSTRUMENT BEEPING

CONTINUITY–BEEP NO CONTINUITY– NO BEEP ③

SET FUNCTION SWITCH TO CONTINUITY TEST MODE ①

REMOVE CONTINUITY TESTER FROM DEVICE AND TURN OFF ④

THREE-WAY SWITCH

0.0Ω

0L

SWITCH UP

0L

0.0Ω

SWITCH DOWN   INSTRUMENT BEEPING

② **CONNECT TEST LEADS**

Figure 2-16. *When checking the continuity of a circuit, the circuit must be de-energized.*

Voltage Testers

A *voltage tester* is an electrical test instrument that indicates the approximate amount of voltage and the type of voltage (AC or DC) in a circuit by the movement of a pointer (and vibration, on some models). When a voltage tester includes a solenoid, the solenoid vibrates when the tester is connected to AC voltage. Some voltage testers include a colored plunger or other indicator such as a light that indicates the polarity of the test leads as positive or negative when measuring a DC circuit. **See Figure 2-17.**

Voltage Tester Advantages/Disadvantages. The main advantage of voltage testers is that individuals can concentrate on placing the test leads of the instrument instead of reading the instrument. A disadvantage of solenoid voltage testers is that solenoid voltage testers affect electronic equipment measurements. Solenoid voltage testers and multimeters cannot be used to test GFCIs because the solenoid causes the tester to have high resistance to current flowing. Nonsolenoid voltage testers are low impedance (low resistance) and can be used to test GFCIs. GFCIs are designed to trip at approximately 6 mA (0.006 A).

Voltage Testers

NEON BULB

COLORED PLUNGER

AC VOLTAGE TESTER

DC/AC VOLTAGE TESTER

Figure 2-17. *A voltage tester is an electrical test instrument that indicates the approximate amount of voltage and the type of voltage (AC or DC) in a circuit by the movement of a pointer (and vibration on some models).*

Voltage Tester Applications. Voltage testers are used to take measurements any time the voltage of the circuit being tested is within the rating of the tester and an exact voltage measurement is not required. Exact voltage measurements such as 118.7 V are not required to determine when a receptacle is hot, a system is grounded, fuses or circuit breakers are good or bad, or when a circuit is 115 V, 230 V, or 460 V.

Voltage Tester Measurement Procedures

Before using a voltage tester or any voltage measuring instrument, always check the voltage tester on a known energized circuit that is within the voltage rating of the voltage tester to verify proper operation.

Before taking any voltage measurements using a voltage tester, ensure the tester is designed to take measurements on the circuit being tested. Refer to the operating manual of the test instrument for all measuring procedures, limitations, and precautions. Always wear required personal protective equipment and follow all safety rules when taking the measurement. **See Figure 2-18.** To take a voltage measurement with a voltage tester, apply the following procedures:

SAFETY PROCEDURES

- Follow all electrical safety practices and procedures.
- Check and wear personal protective equipment (PPE) for the procedure being performed.
- Perform only authorized procedures.
- Follow all manufacturer recommendations and procedures.

1. Verify that the voltage tester has a voltage rating higher than the highest potential voltage in the circuit being tested.

2. Connect the common test lead to the point of testing (neutral or ground).

3. Connect the voltage test lead to the point of testing (ungrounded conductor). The pointer of the voltage tester indicates a voltage reading and vibrates when the current in the circuit is AC. The indicator shows a voltage reading and does not vibrate when the current in the circuit is DC.

4. Observe the voltage measurement displayed.

5. Remove the voltage tester from the circuit.

Figure 2-18. *The pointer of a voltage tester indicates the voltage reading and vibrates when the current in a circuit is AC.*

Digital Multimeters

A *digital multimeter* is an electrical test instrument that can measure two or more electrical properties and display the measured properties as numerical values. Basic digital multimeters measure resistance (continuity) and AC or DC voltage and current. Advanced digital multimeters include special functions such as measuring frequency, capacitance, and temperature. **See Figure 2-19.**

Figure 2-19. *A digital multimeter is an electrical test instrument that that can measure two or more electrical properties and display the measured properties as numerical values.*

Digital Multimeter Advantages/Disadvantages. The main advantage of digital multimeters compared to analog multimeters is the ability of a digital multimeter to record measurements in addition to making it easy to read measured displayed values.

Digital Multimeter Applications. Digital multimeters are used to take measurements any time the voltage, current, or resistance of the circuit being tested is within the rating of the meter and an exact measurement is expected. Exact voltage measurements are required to determine the amount of

power consumed by a circuit, if a brownout is occurring, if fuses or circuit breakers are good or bad, or if a circuit is 12 V, 24 V, 115 V, 230 V, 460 V, or any voltage.

Digital Multimeter Measurement Procedures

Before using a digital multimeter or any measuring instrument, always check the digital multimeter on a known energized circuit that is within the voltage rating of the meter to verify proper operation.

Before taking any voltage measurements using a digital multimeter, ensure the meter is designed to take measurements on the circuit being tested. Refer to the operating manual of the test instrument for all measuring procedures, limitations, and precautions. Always wear required personal protective equipment and follow all safety rules when taking the measurement. **See Figure 2-20.** To take a voltage measurement with a digital multimeter, apply the following procedures:

SAFETY PROCEDURES

- Follow all electrical safety practices and procedures.
- Check and wear personal protective equipment (PPE) for the procedure being performed.
- Perform only authorized procedures.
- Follow all manufacturer recommendations and procedures.

1. Set the function switch of the voltmeter to AC voltage.
2. Plug the black test lead into the common jack (marked COM).
3. Plug the red test lead into the voltage jack (marked V).
4. Measure the voltage into the transformer. Connect the voltmeter between the common and hot terminals on the primary side of the transformer. The problem is located upstream from the transformer when there is no voltage present or the voltage is not at the correct level. The problem may be a blown fuse or open circuit. Voltage must be reestablished to the transformer before the transformer can be tested.

5. Measure the voltage out of the transformer. Connect the voltmeter between the common and hot terminals on the secondary side of the transformer. Voltage must be present at the secondary side terminals when voltage is supplied to the primary side of the transformer. The transformer is open and must be replaced when there is no voltage reading on the secondary side terminals.
6. Remove the voltmeter from the circuit.

Safety Rules for Test Instruments

Proper equipment and procedures are required when taking measurements with test instruments. To take a measurement, the test instrument must be set to the correct measuring position and properly connected into the circuit to be tested; the displayed measurement is then read and interpreted. There is always the possibility that the test instrument will be set to the incorrect function or incorrect range, and/or will be misread. Test instruments not properly connected to a circuit increase the likelihood of an improper measurement and may create an unsafe condition.

Figure 2-20. *Depending on the electrical property being tested, the test leads of a multimeter may have to be connected to a circuit in a specific manner.*

When handling test instruments, the following safety rules must be followed:

- Choose the correct test instrument for an application. Any test instrument is designed for taking measurements on some type of application, but not for all applications.

- Test instruments that are damaged (cracked or with missing parts or worn insulation) must not be used.

- Inspect the test leads of a test instrument on a regular basis (each time used).

- The battery door of test instruments must be kept closed during instrument operation.

- Test the fuses of a test instrument on a regular basis. **See Figure 2-21.**

Figure 2-21. *The fuses of a test instrument must be checked on a regular basis to ensure they are in good condition.*

To clean a test instrument, periodically wipe the case of the instrument with a damp cloth and mild detergent. Do not use abrasives or solvents.

- When taking a measurement, keep fingers behind the finger guards on the test leads.

- Test instruments must not be used in hazardous environments (explosive gas, vapor, or dust) unless specifically designed for hazardous environments.

- Before use, verify that the test leads of a test instrument are in the proper jacks—the jacks that correspond to the setting of the function switch—before taking any measurements. **See Figure 2-22.**

- Before use, verify the operation of the test instrument by measuring a known voltage.

- Before taking a measurement, verify that the function switch of a test instrument matches the desired measurement and the conections of the test leads to the circuit.

- To take a measurement, connect the common (negative) test lead of a test instrument before connecting the voltage (positive) test lead. To disconnect, disconnect the positive test lead first.

ELECTRICAL SAFETY

The safety of an individual working with electricity is far more advanced today than 20 years ago. State and local safety laws, NFPA 70E, and OSHA safety rules are in place to create a safe working environment. **See Figure 2-23.** Individuals using common sense, safeguards, proper equipment, and safety practices are safe when working on electrical equipment.

An individual must understand electricity and be able to apply the principles of safety to all tasks performed. When an individual performs tasks without regard to safety, the individual is disregarding the safety of fellow workers. Electricity must be respected, but respect for electricity comes from understanding electricity. Whenever an individual has a doubt about electricity, the individual must ask for assistance from an electrician. All unsafe conditions, equipment, tools, or work practices must be reported to appropriate persons as soon as possible.

Function Switch Settings

1 15.0 VAC

6 READ VOLTAGE DISPLAYED

2 PLUG BLACK TEST LEAD INTO COMMON JACK

3 PLUG RED TEST LEAD INTO VOLTAGE JACK

SET FUNCTION SWITCH TO AC VOLTAGE (ṽ) 1

CONNECT COMMON TEST LEAD TO CIRCUIT 4

5 CONNECT VOLTAGE TEST LEAD TO CIRCUIT

L1   LIGHT   N

115 VAC

CORRECT VOLTAGE MEASUREMENT CONNECTION

FUNCTION SWITCH INCORRECTLY SET TO VOLTAGE POSITION

L1   FUSE   LIGHT SWITCH   LIGHT   N

INCORRECT METER CONNECTION

1 DETERMINE IF AMMETER RANGE IS HIGH ENOUGH

2 SET FUNCTION SWITCH TO AC VOLTAGE (ṽ)

READ CURRENT DISPLAYED 4

1.2 AC V

POSITION ONE CONDUCTOR IN JAWS 3

L1   FUSE   LIGHT SWITCH   LIGHT   N

115 VAC

CORRECT CURRENT MEASUREMENT CONNECTION

⚠ **WARNING**

INCORRECT SETTINGS MAY CAUSE INJURY AND/OR EQUIPMENT DAMAGE

Figure 2-22. *Before taking any measurements using a test instrument that has a function switch, verify that the test leads of the test instrument are in the proper jacks that correspond to the setting of the function switch.*

Electrical Safety Organizations

NFPA 70E	29 CFR 1926 OSHA	
Standard for Electrical Safety in the Workplace - 90 - Electrical Safety in the Workplace -100 - Safety-Related Work Practices -200 - Safety-Related Maintenance Requirements -300 - Safety Requirements for Special Equipment -400 - Installation Safety Requirements	**U.S. Department of Labor** Occupational Safety & Health Administration **Construction Industry** Safety and Health Regulations for Construction 1926 Subpart K - Electrical	-1926.400 - Introduction -1926.402 - Applicability -1926.403 - General Requirements -1926.404 - Wiring Design & Protection -1926.405 - Wiring Methods & Equipment for general use -1926.406 - Specific Purpose Installations -1926.407 - Hazardous -1926.416 - General Requirements -1926.417 - Lockout and Tagging of Circuits

Figure 2-23. *State and local safety laws, NFPA 70E, and OSHA safety rules are in place to create a safe working environment.*

Electric Shock

Electric shock is the condition that occurs when an individual comes in contact with two conductors of a circuit or when the body of an individual becomes part of an electrical circuit. In either case, a severe shock can cause the heart and the lungs to stop functioning. Also, due to the heat produced by current flow, severe burns can occur where the electricity (current) enters and exits the body. **See Figure 2-24.**

Individuals using portable power tools must ensure that the power tool is safe and in proper operating condition. Portable power tools that are not double insulated must have a third wire on the plug for grounding in case a short occurs. Theoretically, when electric power tools are grounded, fault current flows through the third wire to ground instead of through the body to ground.

Out of Service Protection

Before any repair is performed on a piece of electrical equipment, an individual must be absolutely certain the source of electricity is locked out and tagged out (out of service) by a lockout/tagout device. **See Figure 2-25.** Whenever an individual leaves a job for any reason, upon returning to the job the individual must ensure that the source of electricity is still locked out and tagged out. **See Figure 2-26.**

Electrical Shock Effects

CURRENT INCREASES AS RESISTANCE DECREASES

CURRENT FLOW PATH

115 V CIRCUIT

APPROXIMATE CURRENT*	EFFECT ON BODY†
over 20	Causes severe muscular contractions, paralysis of breathing, heart convulsions
15-20	Painful shock May be frozen or locked to point electrical contact until circuit is de-energized
8-15	Painful shock Removal from contact point by natural reflexes
8 or less	Sensation of shock but probably not painful

CURRENT
1000 mA — CURRENT IN 100 W LAMP CAN ELECTROCUTE 20 ADULTS
50 mA — HEART CONVULSIONS, USUALLY FATAL
15 mA - 20 mA — PAINFUL SHOCK. INABILITY TO LET GO
0 mA - 5 mA — SAFE VALUES
1 mA
0 mA — NO SENSATION

* in mA
† effects vary depending on time, path, amount of exposure, and condition of body

Figure 2-24. *Possible effects of electrical shock include the heart and lungs ceasing to function, and/or severe burns where the electricity (current) enters and exits the body.*

Lockout/Tagout Kits

Ideal Industries, Inc.

HASPS FOR MULTIPLE LOCKOUTS

REUSABLE DANGER TAG

TAG TIES

LOCKS

DANGER
DO NOT OPERATE
This lock/tag may only be removed by:
Name
Dept.
Expected Completion

LOCKOUT/TAGOUT KIT

Figure 2-25. *Lockout/tagout devices are available for locking out and tagging out any type of electrical equipment.*

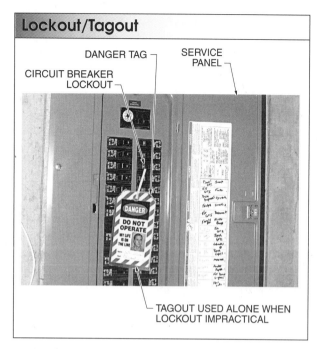

Figure 2-26. *Whenever an individual leaves a job for any reason, upon returning to the job the individual must ensure that the source of electricity is still locked out and tagged out.*

Safety Color Codes and Safety Labels

Federal law (OSHA) has established specific colors to designate cautions and dangers that are encountered when performing electrical tasks. **See Figure 2-27.** Individuals must understand the sigificance of colors, signal words, and symbols as related to electrical hazards.

ELECTRICAL CODES

The *National Electrical Code® (NEC®)* is a book of electrical standards that indicate how electrical systems must be installed and how work must be performed. The NEC® is a 775-page book that states the standards for all residential, commercial, and industrial electrical work. The NEC® is amended every three years to stay current with new safety issues, electrical products, and procedures.

In most areas the NEC® and local code requirements are the same, but the NEC® sets only minimum requirements. Local codes, particularly in large cities, may be stricter than those of the NEC®. In the case of stricter local codes, the local code must be followed.

Notes explaining some of the NEC® requirements for general lighting and appliance circuits can be shown on electrical plans. Numbers and notes on electrical plans refer to specific articles and tables in the NEC® code. **See Figure 2-28.** When more specific requirements (codes) are established by local city councils, the local codes are obtained from the local building inspector.

PERSONAL PROTECTIVE EQUIPMENT

Personal protective equipment (PPE) is clothing and/or equipment worn by individuals to reduce the possibility of injury in the work area. The use of personal protective equipment is required whenever work occurs on or near energized exposed electrical circuits. The National Fire Protection Association standard NFPA 70E, *Standard for Electrical Safety in the Workplace*, addresses electrical safety requirements for employee workplaces that are necessary for safeguarding employees in pursuit of gainful employment.

NFPA 70E

For maximum safety, personal protective equipment and safety requirements for test instrument procedures must be followed as specified in NFPA 70E, OSHA Standard Part 1910 Subpart 1– *Personal Equipment* (1910.132 through 1910.138), and other applicable safety mandates. Personal protective equipment includes protective clothing, head protection, eye protection, ear protection, hand and foot protection, back protection, knee protection, and rubber insulated matting. **See Figure 2-29.**

⚠	CAUTION

Use extreme caution when working with electrical conductors and power lines. According to U.S. government statistics, electrical injuries are not the most common type of accidental injury but have the highest fatality rate when they do occur. The biggest electrical hazard is a live power line, and the injury rates are highest in construction, manufacturing, and services industries. These industries account for only 7% of the workforce but 44% of electrical injuries.

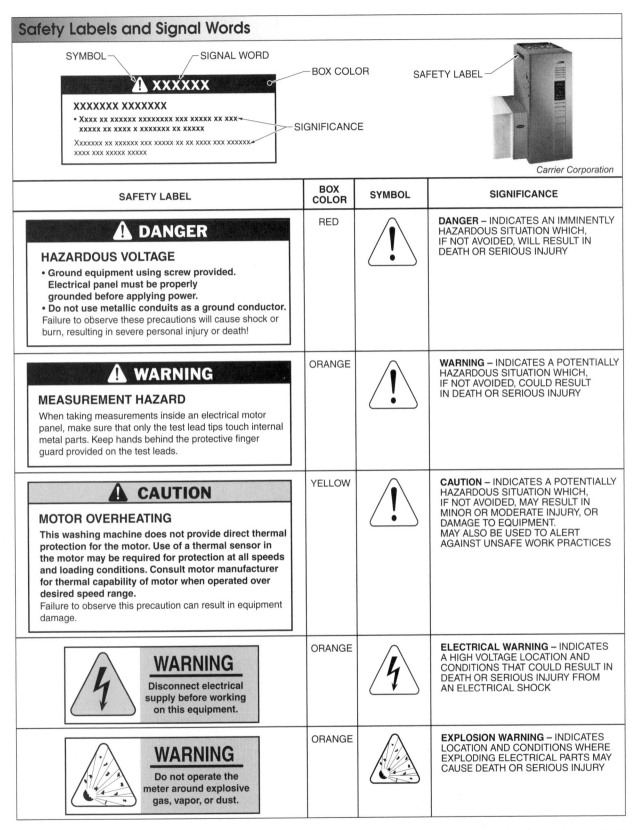

Safety Labels and Signal Words

SAFETY LABEL	BOX COLOR	SYMBOL	SIGNIFICANCE
⚠ **DANGER** — **HAZARDOUS VOLTAGE** • Ground equipment using screw provided. Electrical panel must be properly grounded before applying power. • Do not use metallic conduits as a ground conductor. Failure to observe these precautions will cause shock or burn, resulting in severe personal injury or death!	RED	⚠	**DANGER** – INDICATES AN IMMINENTLY HAZARDOUS SITUATION WHICH, IF NOT AVOIDED, WILL RESULT IN DEATH OR SERIOUS INJURY
⚠ **WARNING** — **MEASUREMENT HAZARD** When taking measurements inside an electrical motor panel, make sure that only the test lead tips touch internal metal parts. Keep hands behind the protective finger guard provided on the test leads.	ORANGE	⚠	**WARNING** – INDICATES A POTENTIALLY HAZARDOUS SITUATION WHICH, IF NOT AVOIDED, COULD RESULT IN DEATH OR SERIOUS INJURY
⚠ **CAUTION** — **MOTOR OVERHEATING** This washing machine does not provide direct thermal protection for the motor. Use of a thermal sensor in the motor may be required for protection at all speeds and loading conditions. Consult motor manufacturer for thermal capability of motor when operated over desired speed range. Failure to observe this precaution can result in equipment damage.	YELLOW	⚠	**CAUTION** – INDICATES A POTENTIALLY HAZARDOUS SITUATION WHICH, IF NOT AVOIDED, MAY RESULT IN MINOR OR MODERATE INJURY, OR DAMAGE TO EQUIPMENT. MAY ALSO BE USED TO ALERT AGAINST UNSAFE WORK PRACTICES
WARNING Disconnect electrical supply before working on this equipment.	ORANGE	⚡	**ELECTRICAL WARNING** – INDICATES A HIGH VOLTAGE LOCATION AND CONDITIONS THAT COULD RESULT IN DEATH OR SERIOUS INJURY FROM AN ELECTRICAL SHOCK
WARNING Do not operate the meter around explosive gas, vapor, or dust.	ORANGE		**EXPLOSION WARNING** – INDICATES LOCATION AND CONDITIONS WHERE EXPLODING ELECTRICAL PARTS MAY CAUSE DEATH OR SERIOUS INJURY

Carrier Corporation

Figure 2-27. *Federal law (OSHA) has established specific colors to designate cautions and dangers that individuals must understand.*

NEC® Code Book		
Chapter	Articles	Description
	1	Introduction
1	2	Definitions
2	10	Wiring and Protection
3	43	Wiring Methods and Materials
4	21	Equipment for General Use
5	27	Special Occupancies
6	23	Special Equipment
7	10	Special Conditions
8	4	Communication Systems
9	-	Tables

Figure 2-28. *The National Electrical Code® (NEC®) is a book of electrical standards that indicate how electrical systems must be installed and how work must be performed.*

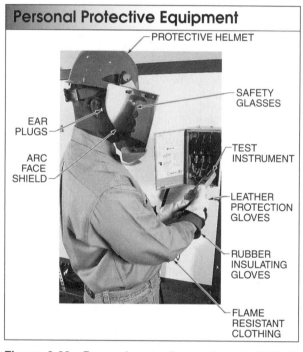

Figure 2-29. *Personal protective equipment (PPE) is clothing and/or equipment worn by individuals to reduce the possibility of injury in the work area and is specified by the National Fire Protection Association Standard NFPA 70E, Standard for Electrical Safety in the Workplace.*

Personal Protective Equipment Safety Rules

The following personal protective equipment safety rules must be followed when performing tasks on electrical systems:

- Wear protective clothing for the task being performed.
- Wear safety glasses, goggles, or an arc face shield, depending on the task being performed. **See Figure 2-30.**

Figure 2-30. *Always wear safety glasses, goggles, or an arc face shield, depending on the electrical task being performed.*

- Wear thick-soled rubber work shoes for protection against sharp objects and insulation against electrocution. Wear work shoes with safety toes when required for the task. **See Figure 2-31.**
- Wear rubber boots in damp locations.
- Wear an approved safety helmet (hard hat). Confine long hair and be careful to avoid having long hair near powered tools.

Electrical Work Shoes

Figure 2-31. *Wear thick-soled rubber work shoes for protection against sharp objects and insulation against electrocution. Certain tasks require work shoes with steel toes.*

- Wear electrical gloves and cover gloves when taking measurements on energized circuits. Electrical gloves provide protection against electrocution and cover gloves protect electrical gloves from damage. **See Figure 2-32.**

FIRE SAFETY

The chance of fire is greatly reduced by good housekeeping. Keep debris in designated containers and away from buildings.

If a fire should occur, the first thing an individual must do is provide an alarm. The fire department must be called and all personnel on the job must be alerted. During the time before the fire department arrives, a reasonable effort should be made to contain the fire. In the case of a small fire, portable fire extinguishers (available around the site) are used to extinguish the fire. The stream from fire extinguishers must be directed to the base of fires. Each type of fire is designated by a class letter. **See Figure 2-33.**

There are five common classes of fires that fire extinguishers are typically purchased to fight.

Class A Fires

Class A fires occur in wood, clothing, paper, rubbish, and other such items. Class A fires are typically controlled with water. (Symbol: green triangle.) **See Figure 2-34.**

Hand Protection from Electrocution

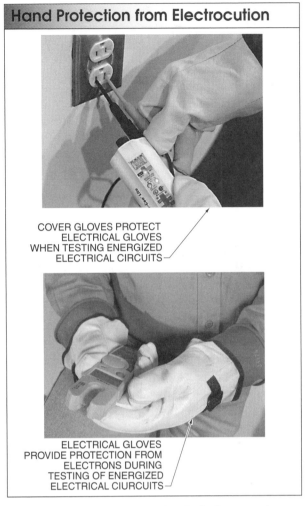

Figure 2-32. *Always wear electrical gloves and cover gloves when taking measurements on energized circuits.*

Class B Fires

Class B fires occur in flammable liquids such as gasoline, fuel oil, lube oil, grease, thinner, and paints. The agents required for extinguishing Class B fires dilute or eliminate the air to the fire by blanketing the surface of the fire. Chemicals such as foam, CO_2, dry chemical, and Halon are used on Class B fires. (Symbol: red square.)

Class C Fires

Class C fires occur in facilities near or in electrical equipment. The extinguishing agent for Class C fires must be a nonconductor of electricity and provide a smothering effect. CO_2, dry chemical, and Halon extinguishers are typically used. (Symbol: blue circle.)

Classes of Fire

TRASH • WOOD • PAPER

BOXES

ORDINARY COMBUSTIBLES

LIQUID • GREASE

SOLVENT CEMENT

FLAMMABLE LIQUIDS

MOTORS • TRANSFORMERS

MOTOR

ELECTRICAL EQUIPMENT

ZIRCONIUM • TITANIUM

D

METAL

COMBUSTIBLE METALS

GREASE

DEEP FAT FRYER

COMMERCIAL COOKING GREASE

Figure 2-33. *There are five common classes of fires that fire extinguishers are typically purchased to fight: Class A, Class B, Class C, Class D, and Class K.*

Class D Fires

Class D fires occur in combustible metals such as magnesium, potassium, powdered aluminum, zinc, sodium, titanium, zirconium, and lithium. The extinguishing agent for Class D fires is a dry powdered compound. The powdered compound creates a smothering effect that is somewhat effective. (Symbol: yellow star.)

Class K Fires

Class K fires occur in kitchens with grease. The extinguishing agent for Class K fires is a wet chemical (potassium acetate).

Fire class symbols appear on each fire extinguisher. A red sign typically points to the location of a fire extinguisher. Because not all fire extinguishers can be used on all types of fires, individuals must be aware of how to identify which fire extinguisher to use on what type of fire.

When firefighters are called, be prepared to direct the firefighters to the location of the fire. Also, inform the firefighters of any special problems or conditions that exist, such as downed electrical wires or chemical leaks from electrical equipment.

Fire Extinguishers

FIRE EXTINGUISHERS ARE LABELED WITH OPERATING INSTRUCTIONS

INSTRUCTIONS

1. PULL PIN. HOLD UNIT UPRIGHT.

2. FREE HOSE. STAND BACK 6 FEET AIM AT BASE OF FIRE.

3. SQUEEZE LEVER AND SWEEP SIDE TO SIDE.

ABC KIDDE DRY CHEMICAL ABC

FIRE EXTINGUISHER CAN BE USED ON CLASS A, B, AND C FIRES

Kidde

Figure 2-34. *Most fires are fought with fire extinguishers containing water, CO_2, dry chemicals, Halon®, or wet chemicals.*

Chapter 2

Test

Name_____ Date _____

Electrical Tools and Safety

LONG (NEEDLE) NOSE PLIER **1.** ___ are appropriate for bending wire and positioning small components.

WIRE STRIPPERS **2.** ___ are for removing insulation from small-diameter wire.

SIDE-CUTTING PLIERS **3.** ___ are appropriate for cutting cable, removing knockouts, twisting wire, and deburring conduit.

(T)   F   **4.** Neon testers are used to determine the presence of 115 V–230 V in circuits.

(T)   F   **5.** All power tools must be grounded unless the power tool is double-insulated.

SAFETY TOES **6.** Appropriate electrical protective clothing includes items such as safety glasses, insulating gloves, a hard hat, and work shoes with ___ toes.

T   (F)   **7.** A continuity tester indicates the condition of a circuit with lights.

C (A & B) **8.** A fish tape may be used to ___ .
     A. pull wire through conduit   **C.** both A and B
     B. route wire through wall cavities   **D.** none of the above

TONGUE-N-GROOVE PLIERS. **9.** ___ are used to tighten box connectors, locknuts, and small conduit couplings.

FUSE PULLER **10.** A(n) ___ is used to safely remove cartridge fuses.

HAMMER **11.** Because of their length, most ___ can be used to determine vertical wall placement of receptacle boxes.

(T)   F   **12.** A keyhole saw can be used in drywall to cut openings for outlet boxes.

(T)   F   **13.** Cable strippers are often used to strip nonmetallic sheathed cable.

LEATHER **14.** An electrician's pouch is usually made of heavy-duty ___.

BLADE/TIP WIDTH **15.** Screwdrivers are specified by ___ width.

ADJUSTABLE WRENCH   **16.** When using a(n) ___ wrench, force should always be applied against the fixed jaw.

C (A & B)   **17.** A continuity tester ___.

      A. has a self-contained battery   **C.** both A and B
      B. tests for unbroken circuits   **D.** none of the above

SH   **18.** ___ are bits are commonly used with electric drills for rough boring holes.

_____   **19.** ___ are used to tighten box connectors, lockouts, and conduit couplings.

_____   **20.** OSHA has designated the color ___ to indicate portable containers that are dangerous because they contain flammable liquids.

T   F   **21.** Electrical shock occurs when an individual comes in contact with two conductors of a circuit or when the body of an individual becomes part of a circuit.

T   F   **22.** Unsafe conditions must be reported to a supervisor.

T   F   **23.** A utility knife is often used to cut small pipe and conduit.

_____   **24.** All adjustments to power tools must be made with the tool ___.

_____   **25.** Many accidents are caused by ___ falling off ladders, shelves, and scaffolding that are being moved.

_____   **26.** Double-insulated tools have ___ prong(s).

      A. one   **C.** three
      B. two   **D.** four

_____   **27.** The first thing to do when a fire occurs is to give a(n) ___.

_____   **28.** The two most common screwdriver heads are Phillips and ___.

T   F   **29.** Generally, double-insulated tools must not be used in wet working conditions.

T   F   **30.** Power tools must be inspected by an OSHA representative every six months.

Fire Classification

_____   1. Class A fire

_____   2. Class B fire

_____   3. Class C fire

_____   4. Class D fire

WOOD (A)   MOTOR (B)   PAINT (C)   METAL (D)

Color Codes

OHSA COLOR CODES   GREEN - SAFETY ZONE

YELLOW - CAUTION

RED - DANGER / FLAMABLE
EMERGENCY STOP BUTTON

ORANGE - MOVING MACHINE PARTS.

PURPLE - RADIATION

_____ 1. Warning labels

_____ 2. Caution labels

_____ 3. Electrical warning labels

_____ 4. Danger labels

_____ 5. Explosion warning labels

Fire Safety

_____ 1. A water extinguisher can be used with a Class ___ fire.

T   F   2. Multipurpose dry chemical extinguishers can be used with all classes of fires.

T   F   3. Pump tank extinguishers with plain water should be used for Class B fires.

T   F   4. Carbon dioxide extinguishers should be used for Class A fires.

_____ 5. The stream from extinguishers should be directed at the ___ of flames.

_____ 6. Carbon dioxide extinguishers may be used for Class B and Class ___ fires.

_____ 7. Dry powdered compound extinguishers are used on Class ___ fires.

_____ 8. When a fire occurs, the first thing an individual must do is ___.

T   F   9. The extinguishing agent for a Class D fire must be a dry powdered compound.

T   F   10. Water should not be used on Class C fires.

Tool Safety

T   F   1. Cutting tools should be sharp and clean.

T   F   2. Tools should not be carried in a pocket unless the pocket is designed for that tool.

T   F   3. Pencils should be carried behind an ear.

T   F   4. When carrying sharply pointed tools, carry the point away from the body.

T   F   **5.** Tools should be used only for the tasks for which they are designed.

T   F   **6.** Power tools should be inspected and serviced regularly.

T   F   **7.** Power tool guards may be used to facilitate work.

T   F   **8.** A hammer should never be struck against another hammer.

T   F   **9.** Always shut off power to an electrical tool when the work is completed.

T   F   **10.** All adjustments, blade changes, etc., to power tools should be made when the power is OFF and the cord is disconnected.

T   F   **11.** A change in sound during tool operation can indicate trouble with a power tool.

T   F   **12.** Material on which work is to be done should always be checked to see that it is free of obstructions.

T   F   **13.** Safety goggles must always be worn when performing work.

T   F   **14.** Before using a power tool, check the electrical cord to verify condition.

T   F   **15.** The safety recommendations of the manufacturer must always be read before using a new power tool.

Chapter 3

Electrical Plans

Chapter 3 provides an understanding of electrical symbols, abbreviations, and diagrams that are used when working in the residential electrical industry. The ability to identify commonly used electrical symbols, recognize electrical abbreviations, and read electrical circuit diagrams is required for efficient understanding of residential electrical circuits, as well as wiring and troubleshooting circuits.

LANGUAGE OF ELECTRICAL PRINTS

All trades have a specific language that must be understood in order to transfer information efficiently within the trade. Trade languages include symbols, drawings or diagrams, schematics, words, phrases, and abbreviations. To perform electrical work, individuals must understand the electrical language, have an understanding of how electrical components function, and have an understanding of the relationships among components and devices in a circuit. With an understanding of the electrical language, an individual is able to read drawings and diagrams, understand circuit operation, and troubleshoot various problems. Electrical prints that are used to convey electrical information include pictorial drawings, electrical layouts, schematic diagrams, and line diagrams.

Pictorial Drawings

A *pictorial drawing* is a drawing that shows the length, height, and depth of an object in one view. Pictorial drawings indicate physical details such as holes and shoulders of an object as seen by the eye. **See Figure 3-1.**

Pictorial Drawings

Figure 3-1. *Pictorial drawings show the physical details of electrical components as seen by the eye.*

Electrical Abbreviations and Symbols

A *symbol* is a graphic element that represents a component, device, or quantity. Symbols are used to represent electrical components and devices on electrical and electronic diagrams. An *abbreviation* is a letter or combination of letters that represents a word. **See Figure 3-2.**

Figure 3-2. *Common electrical symbols are used on residential wiring drawings.*

Electrical Layouts

An *electrical layout* is a drawing that indicates the connections of all devices and components in a residential electrical system. Electrical layouts represent as closely as possible the actual location of each part of an electrical circuit. Electrical layouts often include details of the type of wire and the kind of hardware used to fasten wires and cables to terminals and boxes. **See Figure 3-3.**

An electrical layout typically indicates the devices and components of a system with rectangles or circles. The location or layout of all system devices and components is accurate on the electrical diagram for the particular dwelling. All connecting wires are shown connected from one part to another. Individuals should use electrical layouts when constructing a dwelling and when performing maintenance.

Schematic Diagrams

A *schematic diagram* is a drawing that indicates the electrical connections and functions of a specific circuit arrangement using graphic symbols. Schematic dia-grams do not indicate the physical size or appearance of any component or device found in a circuit. Typically, schematic diagrams are associated with electronic circuits and not with residential electrical systems.

Schematic diagrams are used to show the wiring required for the proper operation of a component (light or motor). **See Figure 3-4.** Schematic diagrams are essential when troubleshooting because schematic diagrams enable an individual to trace a circuit and all functions without regard to the actual size, shape, or location of the component, device, or part.

The CSI MasterFormat™ is a master list of numbers and titles for organizing information about construction requirements, products, and activities into a standard sequence. The CSI MasterFormat™ is broken up into divisions that define the broad area of construction. An estimator must be able to read and interpret architectural and shop drawings such as wiring diagrams and schematic diagrams. Familiarity with various lines, drawing scales, symbols, and abbreviations is required to develop an accurate bid.

Electrical Layouts

Figure 3-3. *Electrical layouts show as accurately as possible the actual location of each component of an electrical circuit.*

Schematic Diagrams

Figure 3-4. *Schematic diagrams show the components of an electrical system laid out so that the circuit is easy to read instead of showing the actual position of the components.*

ELECTRICAL CIRCUITS

An *electrical circuit* is an assembly of conductors (wires), electrical devices (switches and receptacles), and components (lights and motors) through which current flows. An electrical circuit is complete (a closed circuit) when current flows from the power source (service panel) to the load (lights and motors), and back to the power source. A circuit is not complete (an open circuit) when current does not flow. A broken wire, a loose connection, or a switch in the OFF position stops current from flowing in an electrical circuit. **See Figure 3-5.**

Residential Electrical Circuit Devices and Components

All industrial and residential electrical circuits include five basic parts. The five parts include a component (load) that converts electrical energy into some other usable form of energy such as light, heat, or motion; a source of electricity; conductors to connect the individual devices and components; a method of controlling the flow of electricity (switch); and protection devices (fuses or circuit breakers) to ensure that the circuit operates safely within electrical limits.

Electrical Circuits

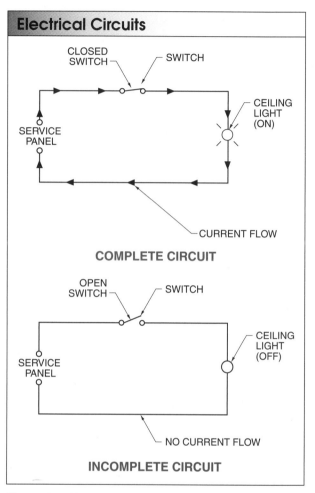

Figure 3-5. *When an electrical circuit is complete (closed circuit), current flows to the load (load is ON) and back to the power source (service panel). When a circuit is not complete (open circuit), current does not flow through the load (load is OFF).*

Electrical circuit devices and components can be shown using line diagrams, wiring diagrams, and/or schematic diagrams. For example, an automobile interior lighting circuit includes the five components of a typical electrical circuit. **See Figure 3-6.** The source of electricity is the battery, conductors can be either chassis wires or the car frame, the control device is a plunger-type door switch, the load is the interior light, and a fuse is the protection device.

Standard practices for drawing electrical and electronic diagrams are detailed in Electrical and Electronic Diagrams, *ANSI Y14.15.*

Electrical Circuit Components

WIRING DIAGRAM

SCHEMATIC DIAGRAM

Figure 3-6. *All electrical circuits include a power source, conductors, a load, a control device, and overload protection.*

Tech Tip: Circuit Application

SCHEMATIC DIAGRAM

PICTORIAL DIAGRAM

Residential electrical circuit wiring diagrams can become quite complicated. **See Figure 3-7.** All residential circuits use the service panel as the power source for the dwelling. Conductors are the wires pulled through conduit or metallic and nonmetallic cables. The most common control device for a residence is a single-pole switch. Control devices can be single-pole switches, three-way switches, motion detectors, timers, or thermostats. Loads found in residential circuits include lamps, motors, televisions, radios, and appliances. The typical overcurrent device used to protect a residential electrical circuit is a circuit breaker.

Rund Lighting, Inc.

Photoelectric and timer switches increase the security and convenience of landscape lighting.

Residential Electrical Circuit Components

POWER WIRES FROM METER

MAIN DISCONNECT

SERVICE PANEL IS POWER SOURCE

OVERCURRENT PROTECTION IS PROVIDED BY CIRCUIT BREAKER

CONDUIT (EMT) USED AS GROUND

BLACK WIRE

CONDUIT (EMT) FITTING

WHITE WIRE

TO GROUND SYSTEM

SINGLE-POLE SWITCH USED TO CONTROL LIGHT

GROUNDED METAL CONDUIT

WHITE WIRE

METAL BOX

RED WIRE

RED WIRE

WHITE WIRE

BLACK WIRE

LOAD (LIGHT BULB)

SINGLE-POLE SWITCH

Figure 3-7. *Residential electrical circuits include a power source (service panel), conductors (wiring), a load (such as a light), control devices (switches), and overload protection (fuses or circuit breakers).*

Manually and Automatically Controlled Circuits

A *manually controlled circuit* is any circuit that requires a person to initiate an action for the circuit to operate. **See Figure 3-8.** Line diagrams can be used to illustrate manually controlled circuits that have a single-pole switch (S) controlling a light bulb in a fixture. The voltage level of the circuit is typically indicated at the top of a line diagram. Circuit voltages in a residence are typically 115 VAC, but can be 12 VAC, 18 VAC, 24 VAC, or 230 VAC.

Dark nodes are used on line diagrams or schematics to indicate an electrical connection. When a node is not present, the wires only cross each other and are not electrically connected. Line diagrams are read from left (L1) to right (L2).

Flipping a single-pole switch (S1) to the ON position allows current to pass from the hot conductor (L1), through the closed contacts of the wall switch (S1), through the lamp (L), and on through the common conductor (L2), forming a complete path (circuit) for current to flow and allow the light to illuminate.

Manually Controlled Circuits

COMPLETE CIRCUIT LINE DIAGRAM

MANUAL CIRCUIT ACTIVATION

OPEN CIRCUIT LINE DIAGRAM

Figure 3-8. *Manually controlled circuits require a person to initiate an action for the circuit to operate.*

Flipping the switch to the OFF position opens the contacts of the switch, stopping the flow of current to the lamp and turning the light OFF.

Automatically controlled devices have replaced many functions that were once performed manually. As a part of modern technology, automated control circuits are designed to replace manual devices. Any manually controlled circuit can be converted to automatic operation. For example, an electric motor on a sump pump can be turned ON and OFF automatically by adding an automatic control device such as a float or pressure switch. **See Figure 3-9.** Float and pressure switch control circuits are used to turn sump pumps OFF and ON to prevent flooding automatically. An automatic control circuit turns on a pump when water reaches a predetermined level, which removes the water. The float or pressure switch senses the change in water level and automatically stops the pump.

Automatically Controlled Circuits

COMPLETE CIRCUIT LINE DIAGRAM

AUTOMATIC CIRCUIT ACTIVATION

Figure 3-9. *Automatically controlled circuits do not require the interaction of a person to control a function, such as turning a pump ON.*

When a sump pump uses an automatic float switch circuit, float switch contacts FS1 determine when current passes through the circuit to start the motor. Current passes through float switch contacts FS1 and the motor to L2 when float switch contacts FS1 are closed. To start the pump motor, current must flow from the power source, through the load, and back to the power source, making a complete circuit. The pump moves water until the water level drops enough to open the float switch contacts FS1 and shut the pump motor OFF. A power failure or the manual opening of the contacts prevents the pump from automatically moving water even after the water reaches the predetermined level.

Another example of automatic control is a photocell controller. **See Figure 3-10.** Photocell controllers automatically detect the absence of light and respond by sending commands to loads (lights). A photocell controller responds to the absence of light by turning lights inside or outside a dwelling ON.

Photocell controllers can also transmit OFF commands in response to approaching daylight. A photocell controller responds to light by turning connected lighting loads inside or outside the dwelling OFF. Photocell controllers are mounted to standard octagon electrical boxes or directly to controlled lighting.

ELECTRICAL PLANS

An *electrical plan* is a drawing and list that indicates what devices are to be used, where the electrical devices are to be placed, and how the devices are to be wired. **See Figure 3-11.** Electrical plan drawings indicate the use of switches, lights, and receptacles with symbols. Symbols always represent real-world devices. Because electrical symbols are easy to draw, symbols are used in place of actual pictorial drawings of electrical devices. Electrical plans are easier to draw and understand when the plans are drawn using symbols. Electrical plans drawn with detailed pictorial drawings of each device and component are difficult to understand.

Photocell Controllers

FLOODLIGHT

PHOTOCELL CONTROLLER

POOL

FLOODLIGHT DISCONNECT

Figure 3-10. *Photocell controllers respond to the absence of light by turning connected lighting loads inside or outside a dwelling ON, and respond to light by turning lights OFF.*

Electrical Plans

ELECTRICAL LAYOUT

PICTORIAL DIAGRAM

Figure 3-11. *Basic electrical plans provide information about what type of device is used where in a room. Pictorial diagrams can be used to show the room after wiring and drywalling.*

Understanding electrical device symbols is the key to understanding electrical plans. **See Figure 3-12.** Architects always use symbols when creating electrical plans. Electrical device symbols and the operation of the devices must be understood to properly wire circuits from electrical plans. When interpreting electrical plans, unfamiliar symbols must be identified before any work is started. **See Figure 3-13.**

The more time spent analyzing electrical plans, the easier it becomes to understand electrical symbols and the functions of a specific circuit. **See Figure 3-14.** Most electrical plans used in constructing new homes today are drawn to provide the same types of information from one home to another.

Electrical Plan Information

Electrical plans are important because electrical plans indicate what tasks an individual must perform. Electrical plans provide information similar to a good road map. Road maps indicate the location of roads, towns, and points of interest. A good electrical plan indicates the location of all major electrical devices and connections. Electrical plans are also used to determine the number of openings in walls and ceilings and to estimate the amount of wire and conduit that is required for the job. Electrical plans must provide enough information to indicate the best and shortest way to complete a job.

Division 26 of the CSI MasterFormat™ specification system includes descriptions of electrical site work, conduit, panelboards, lighting, telecommunication systems, and HVAC systems.

Trus Joist, A Weyerhaeuser Business

When wood I-joists are installed, conductors are routed through prefabricated knockouts.

Electrical Devices and Symbols

Cooper Wiring Devices
SINGLE-POLE SWITCH

S

Cooper Wiring Devices
DIMMER SWITCH

S$_D$

Cooper Wiring Devices
THREE-WAY SWITCH

S$_3$

Cooper Wiring Devices
SWITCH AND CONVENIENCE OUTLET

Cooper Wiring Devices
DUPLEX CONVENIENCE RECEPTACLE

Cooper Wiring Devices
WEATHERPROOF CONVENIENCE RECEPTACLE

W.P.

Cooper Wiring Devices
RANGE OUTLET

R

Cooper Wiring Devices
LAMP HOLDER

L   L$_{PS}$

Broan-NuTone LLC
VENTILATING FAN

F   F

Figure 3-12. *Understanding electrical device symbols is the key to understanding electrical plans.*

Residential Electrical Symbols

GENERAL OUTLETS		AUXILIARY SYSTEMS	
Symbol	**Description**	**Symbol**	**Description**
◯ or Ⓛ	Lighting (wall)	▪	Pushbutton
or ◻	Lighting (ceiling)		Buzzer
▢◯	Ceiling lighting outlet for recessed fixture (Outline shows shape of fixture.)		Bell
◻—	Continuous wireway for fluorescent lighting on ceiling, in coves, cornices, etc. (Extend rectangle to show length of installation.)		Combination bell-buzzer
Ⓛ	Lighting outlet with lamp holder	CH	Chime
ⓁPS	Lighting outlet with lamp holder and pull switch	◇	Annunciator
Ⓕ	Fan outlet	D	Electric door opener
Ⓙ	Junction box	M	Maid's signal plug
Ⓓ	Drop-cord equipped outlet	◻	Interconnection box
—Ⓒ	Clock outlet	Ⓣ	Thermostat
		▶	Outside telephone
		▷	Telephone
		R	Radio outlet
To indicate wall installation of above outlets, place circle near wall and connect with line as shown for clock outlet.		TV	Television outlet

CONVENIENCE OUTLETS		MISCELLANEOUS	
Symbol	**Description**	**Symbol**	**Description**
⊖	Duplex convenience receptacle	◣	Heating panel
⊖3	Triplex convenience outlet (Substitue other numbers for other variations in number of plug positions.)	▨	Service panel
⊖	Duplex convenience outlet — split wired	▬	Distribution panel
⊖GR	Duplex convenince outlet for grounding-type plugs	- - - -	Switch leg indication. (Connects outlets with control points.)
⊖WP	Weatherproof convenience outlet	Ⓜ	Motor
⊖X"	Multioutlet assembly (Extend arrows to limits of installation. Use appropriate symbol to indicate type of outlet. Also indicate spacing of outlets as X inches.)	⏚	Ground connection
⊖S	Combination switch and convenience outlet	—‖—	2-conductor cable
⊖R	Combination radio and convenience outlet	—⧻—	3-conductor cable
⊙	Floor outlet	—⧼—	4-conductor cable
⊖R	Range outlet	◀—	Cable returning to service panel
⊛DW	Special-purpose outlet. (Use subscript letters to indicate function. DW–dishwasher, CD–clothes dryer, etc.)	⌇	Fuse
		—o o—	Circuit breaker

SWITCH OUTLETS			
Symbol	**Description**	**Symbol**	**Description**
S–S₁	Single-pole switch	S_D	Dimmer switch
S₂	Double-pole switch	S_P	Switch and pilot light
S₃	Three-way switch		Weatherproof switch
S₄	Four-way switch	S_WP	

MISCELLANEOUS (cont.)	
⊖a, b ⊖a, b ⊛a, b ◻a, b	Special outlets. (Any standard symbol given above may be used with the addition of subscript letters to designate some special variation of standard equipment for a particular architectural plan. When so used, the variation should be explained in the key to symbols and, if necessary, in the specifications.)
⊖ GFCI	Ground-fault circuit interrupter
⊖ WP	Weatherproof

Figure 3-13. *When interpreting electrical plans, unfamiliar symbols must be identified before any work is started.*

Residential Electrical Plans

ELECTRICAL PLAN — NEC©

A   210.7(A). All receptacles installed on 15 A and 20 A circuits shall be located in accordance with type of room and use.
B   210.8(A). All 125 V, 1φ receptacles shall have GFCI protection when installed in: (1) bathrooms, (2) garages, (3) outdoors where there is direct grade access, (4) crawl spaces below grade level and unfinished basements, (5) kitchen countertops, (6) boathouses.
C   210.23. Individual branch circuits can supply any load for which they are rated.
D   210.52(A). General provicions for installing receptacle outlets in dwelling units.
   210.52(B). For small appliance load, including refrigeration equipment, in kitchen, pantry, and breakfast room, two or more 20 A appliance circuits shall be provided. Such circuits shall have no other outlets. Countertop outlets shall be supplied at each wall counter that is 12″ or wider.
E   210.52(E). All receptacles installed outdoors must be of GFCI type.
F   210.52(H). Hallways 10′ in length or more shall have a receptacle provided.
G   220.12. Unit lighting load for dwelling occupancies shall not be less than 3 VA per sq ft. See Table 220.12 in determining load on "VA per sq ft" basis, outside dimensions of the building shall be used, excluding open porches, garages, unused spaces, unless adaptable for future use.
H   210.11(C)(2). At least one 20 A circuit shall be provided for a laundry receptacle.
I   220.4(D). For general illumination one 15 A branch circuit is required for every 600 sq ft area.

$$(3 \text{ VA} \times 600 \text{ sq ft} = 1800 \text{ VA} \tfrac{1800}{120} = 15 \text{ A})$$

J   220.52(A). Feeder load for two small appliances circuits to be 3000 VA (1500 VA for each two-wire circuit).
   220.52(B). Each laundry circuit feeder load calculation to be at least 1500 VA.

K   230.42(A). Service entrance conductors per 220 and 310.15.
L   410.8. Fixtures in Clothes Closets.
M   422.11(E). Branch circuit to a single non-motor appliance not to exceed OCPD rating. If an appliance is rated at 13.3 A or less, the next standard OCPD is required, not to exceed 150% of the appliance rating.
N   725. Remote control, signaling, and Power Limited circuits.

ELECTRICAL KEY PLAN

Letter	NEC©	Subject
A	210.7(A)	Receptacle Location
B	210.8(B)	GFCI Location
C	210.23	Receptacles
D	210.52(A)(B)	Circuits (Load Rating)
E	210.52(E)	GFCI Location (Outdoors)
F	210.52(H)	Receptacle Location (Hallways)
G	220.12	Lighting Load
H	210.11(C)(2)	Laundry Circuit
I	220.4(D)	Circuits (General Purpose)
J	220.16	Circuits (Small Appliance)
K	230.42	Service Entrance
L	410.8	Fixtures (Clothes Closet)
M	422.28	Circuits (Branch)
N	725	Signaling and Power Limited Circuits

ELECTRICAL PLAN FOR ONE-FAMILY DWELLING

Figure 3-14. *Residential electrical plans must follow NEC® standards and local electrical codes.*

DEVELOPING ELECTRICAL PLANS

A complete electrical plan or set of plans is developed in two main parts: component plan(s) and wiring plan(s).

Component Plans

A *component plan* is a group of schedules that state the required locations for receptacles, lights, and switches according to the NEC® and local codes. To be effective, a component plan must include devices that satisfy all the electrical requirements for light, heat, and power to a given area.

To aid in the determination of which electrical devices are required for a system, electrical component lists are created with the component plan for each area of a residence such as the living room, kitchen, bedrooms, and bathrooms. A *component list* is a list of electrical equipment indicating manufacturer, specifications, and how many of each electrical component are required for a room or area. A partial component list is a component schedule. **See Figure 3-15. See Appendix.** Careful study of an electrical component list or schedule will aid in developing a checklist for work to be performed. Additional ideas can be obtained from component plans that were not initially recognized as being required from the electrical plan. Sample component plans and component lists are available in home planning books and magazines. Public and school libraries and the internet are sources for finding home component plans, lists, and schedules.

Component Plan Schedules

Area	Convenience Receptacles	Special-Purpose Outlets	General Lighting	Major Appliances	General Switching for All Areas
Bedrooms	No space along a wall should be more than 6′ from a receptacle outlet. Any wall space 2′ or larger should have a minimum of 1 receptacle. NEC® 210.52 (A).	TV outlet, intercom, speakers (music), and telephone jack	Ceiling, wall or valence light, lamp switched at receptacle	Room air conditioner, electric baseboard heat	Switches are typically placed opposite the hinged side of door. When there are two or more entrances to a room, multiple switching should be used.

Door switch can be used for closet light so that the switch turns the light ON and OFF as the door opens and closes.

Switches with pilot lights should be used on lights, fans, and other electrical devices which are in locations not readily observable. |
Living Room	No space along a wall should be more than 6′ from a receptacle outlet. Any wall space 2′ or larger should have a minimum of 1 receptacle. NEC® 210.52 (A).	TV outlet, intercom, speakers (music)	Ceiling fixture, recessed lighting, valence light, lamp switched at receptacle, possible dimmer	Room air conditioner, built-in stereo system, electric baseboard heating	
Family Room	No space along a wall should be more than 6′ from a receptacle outlet. Any wall space 2′ or larger should have a minimum of 1 receptacle. NEC® 210.52 (A).	TV outlet, intercom, speakers (music), bar area (ice maker, blenders, small refrigerator, hot plate), telephone jack, thermostat	Ceiling fixture, recessed lighting, valence lights, studio spot lights, lamp switched at receptacle, fluorescent light, possible dimmer	Room air conditioner, built-in stereo system, electric baseboard heating	
Dining Room	No space along a wall should be more than 6′ from a receptacle outlet. Any wall space 2′ or larger should have a minimum of 1 receptacle. NEC® 210.52 (A).	Elevated receptacles (48″) for buffet tables, speakers (music)	Ceiling chandelier, recessed lighting, valence lighting for china hutch	Room air conditioner, electric baseboard heating	

Figure 3-15. *Component lists and schedules are created for each area of a residence such as the living room, kitchen, bedrooms, and bathrooms.*

To develop a component plan, apply the following procedures:

• Use as many resources as possible for ideas.

• Keep the electrical plan as simple and straightforward as possible, so the plan can be easily understood.

Wiring Plans

Once the locations of receptacles, lights, and switches have been determined and indicated on a component plan, a wiring plan can be drawn. **See Figure 3-16.** A wiring plan is a floor plan drawing that indicates the placement of all electrical devices and components and the wiring required to connect all the equipment into circuits. Wiring plans are the basis for all electrical work performed at a residence. The purpose of a wiring plan is to group individual electrical devices into specific circuits. A wiring plan is essential when determining the number of components per circuit (load) and the best route for wiring to take. Time spent studying a wiring plan aids in anticipating problems and reducing the amount of materials required. Slash marks indicate the number of conducting wires in cables or conduit and an arrow symbolizes the circuit connection to the service panel.

Pictorial drawings (construction layouts) illustrate how wiring will look after all circuit wiring is installed. **See Figure 3-17.**

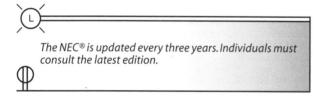

The NEC® is updated every three years. Individuals must consult the latest edition.

Manufacturer Specifications

When an individual installs an electrical appliance such as washing machine, dryer, or electric oven, the individual must follow the directions or specifications provided by the manufacturer. Manufacturer specifications indicate the size of wire that must be used and the amount of overload protection that must be provided. The specifications set by manufacturers must agree with or surpass the standards of the NEC®.

Electrical Plans

ARROW INDICATES WIRE RUN TO PANEL BOX

SLASH MARKS INDICATE NUMBER OF CONDUCTORS

Figure 3-16. *A wiring plan provides a detailed layout of cable or wire (in conduit), routes, and number of conductors.*

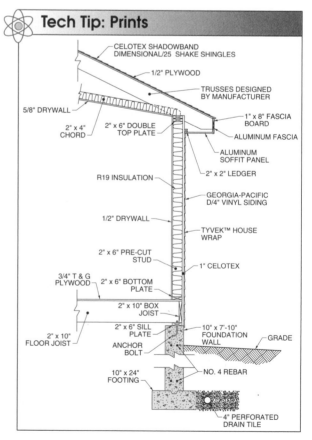

Tech Tip: Prints

CELOTEX SHADOWBAND DIMENSIONAL/25 SHAKE SHINGLES
1/2" PLYWOOD
TRUSSES DESIGNED BY MANUFACTURER
5/8" DRYWALL
2" x 4" CHORD
2" x 6" DOUBLE TOP PLATE
1" x 8" FASCIA BOARD
ALUMINUM FASCIA
ALUMINUM SOFFIT PANEL
2" x 2" LEDGER
R19 INSULATION
GEORGIA-PACIFIC D/4" VINYL SIDING
1/2" DRYWALL
TYVEK™ HOUSE WRAP
2" x 6" PRE-CUT STUD
1" CELOTEX
3/4" T & G PLYWOOD
2" x 6" BOTTOM PLATE
2" x 10" BOX JOIST
2" x 6" SILL PLATE
10" x 7'-10" FOUNDATION WALL
GRADE
2" x 10" FLOOR JOIST
ANCHOR BOLT
NO. 4 REBAR
10" x 24" FOOTING
4" PERFORATED DRAIN TILE

Pictorial Drawings (Construction Layouts)

Figure 3-17. *Pictorial drawings (construction layouts) indicate how a circuit will appear when wiring is completed.*

Name_____ **Date** _____

Electrical Plans

_____ **1.** An electrical ____ is a drawing that shows where electrical devices are to be placed.

_____ **2.** The ____ plan provides a detailed layout of the cable routes and the number of conductors.

_____ **3.** Residential electrical system installations must comply with ____.

     A. the NEC®   **C.** electrician's union requirements

     B. local building codes   **D.** both A and B

_____ **4.** ____ are used to represent switches, lights, and receptacles on electrical plans.

     A. Pictorial drawings   **C.** Symbols

     B. Orthographic drawings   **D.** none of the above

_____ **5.** The NEC® sets ____ requirements for residential electrical installations.

     A. minimum   **C.** cost

     B. maximum   **D.** none of the above

   T   F   **6.** The overload protection required for an electrical appliance is provided by manufacturer specifications.

   T   F   **7.** A component plan may be used to determine the best required location for switches, lights, and receptacles.

   T   F   **8.** Electrical plans show all necessary framing details of the structure.

_____ **9.** Switches are typically placed opposite the ____ side of a door.

_____ **10.** All 115 V, 1ϕ receptacles installed in bathrooms shall have ____ protection.

_____ **11.** At least one ____ A circuit shall be provided for a laundry circuit.

   T   F   **12.** In general, service entrance conductors shall have an ampacity of not less than the sum of non continuous plus 125% of continuous loads.

T F **13.** Ruled lines extending from a receptacle symbol indicate a wall receptacle.

T F **14.** Subscript letters can be added to a standard symbol to designate a variation of a standard piece of equipment.

_____ **15.** Hallways over ___ shall have a receptacle provided.
    A. 4' wide   **C.** 10' long
    B. 8' high   **D.** none of the above

_____ **16.** Switch outlets are represented on plans by ___.
    A. circles with letters   **C.** letters with or without
                  subscripts
    B. circles without letters **D.** none of the above

T F **17** Individual branch circuits can supply any load for which the branch circuit is rated.

T F **18.** A cable returning to a service panel is represented by a dashed line on plans.

_____ **19.** The branch circuit load used during calculations for laundry circuits is to be ___.

_____ **20.** The symbol for a thermostat is a T inside a(n) ___.

Electrical Symbols

_____ **1.** Lighting outlet   _____ **7.** Interconnecting telephone

_____ **2.** Fuse   _____ **8.** Range outlet

_____ **3.** Clock outlet   _____ **9.** Motor

_____ **4.** Switch leg   _____ **10.** Ground connection

_____ **5.** Fan outlet

_____ **6.** Service panel

(A)   (B)   (C)   (D)   (E)

(F)   (G)   (H)   (I)   (J)

Porch Entrance

Draw the appropriate electrical symbols as indicated.

1. GFCI weatherproof duplex convenience outlet

2. Recessed ceiling outlet

3. Single-pole switch controlling the recessed ceiling outlet

4. Chime

5. Closed-circuit television camera

PORCH ENTRANCE

One-Family Dwelling

_____ **1.** Symbols at ___ represent duplex convenience outlets.

_____ **2.** ___ duplex convenience outlets are located on either side of the kitchen sink.

_____ **3.** BR 2 contains one switched ___ in the ceiling.

_____ **4.** A(n) ___ W heater is located in the laundry.

_____ **5.** Lighting outlets in the hallway ceiling are controlled by ___ switches.

_____ 6. The one-family dwelling contains approximately ___ sq ft (disregarding the entry).

_____ 7. The service panel is located in the ___.

_____ 8. A switch to the right of the bathroom door controls a ___-mounted lighting outlet.

_____ 9. A(n) ___ outlet is shown at H in the diagram.

_____ 10. The electrical service to the dwelling is brought in ___.

_____ 11. The two duplex convenience outlets on the switch leg in the living room are __-wired.

_____ 12. Pushbuttons at the front and back doors control a(n) ___ and a bell in the kitchen.

_____ 13. Each bedroom has a total of ___ duplex convenience outlets.

_____ 14. ___ GFCI convenience outlets are located at E in the diagram.

_____ 15. The hallway has a total of ___ duplex convenience outlet(s).

Partial Floor Plan

Draw the appropriate electrical symbols as indicated.

1. Six duplex convenience outlets

2. Two three-way switches controlling an overhead light

3. Ceiling lighting outlet with lampholder

4. Lighting outlet with lampholder and pull switch

5. Television outlet

6. Thermostat

7. Interconnecting telephone

8. Ceiling fan

Symbols

_____ 1. ◯

_____ 2. ⊡

_____ 3. ─o⌒o─

_____ 4. ▶┤

_____ 5. ☐

_____ 6. ⊙

_____ 7. o☐

_____ 8. ☐D

_____ 9. ▬▬

_____ 10. Ⓜ

Chapter 4

Making Electrical Connections

Chapter 4 provides an overview of how to make electrical connections that are mechanically and electrically secure. Splices and connections are identified and procedures are provided on how to avoid the troublesome points of splices and connections. Common splices and connections (soldered and solderless) are shown with procedures and proper tool usage.

ELECTRICAL SUPPLIES

Typical electrical supplies required to wire a residence are hand tools, solder, soldering tools, tape, solderless connectors, crimping tools, and wire markers.

Solder

The solder that is typically used in electrical work is an alloy of 60% tin and 40% lead. The amount of tin determines the strength of the solder and the amount of lead determines the melting point of the solder. The 60/40 mixture provides dependable strength at a reasonable melting temperature. Flux is added to solder to clean metal surfaces and ensure the solder adheres to the metal surface. Flux removes oxides and other small impurities from metal surfaces to improve the connection.

Solder is purchased in many forms. The two most common types of solder are rosin core and acid core. Rosin core solder is preferred on small electrical applications because the flux is contained within the solder. **See Figure 4-1.** Acid core solder must never be used on electrical connections because acid core solder corrodes electrical connections. When using solid core solder, the solder must be used with a brushed-on flux because solid core solder contains no flux.

American Beauty Soldering Tools

When soldering an electrical connection, heat sinks such as alligator clips are used to protect the electrical device or component from the heat of soldering.

Solder

Solder Wire Diameters*		
.015	.032	.093
.020	.040	.125
.025	.062	

* in inches

1 LB SPOOL

Figure 4-1. *Solder is available as rosin core (wire) and acid core (wire) and in various sizes.*

Tape

Although many types of tape can be used as insulation on electrical wiring, plastic tape, which insulates against voltages up to 600 V per wrap, is typically used for residential wiring. **See Figure 4-2.**

Wire Nuts

Wire nuts are designed to hold several electrical wires firmly together and to provide an insulating cover for the connection. Wire nuts are available in several sizes. **See Figure 4-3.** The size of a wire nut is determined by the number and size of wires (conductors) to be connected. Manufacturers of wire nuts use color coding to indicate the maximum number of conductors allowed per connection, but the color coding scheme can vary by manufacturer.

Tape Types

PLASTIC (PVC)

RUBBER

FRICTION

Figure 4-2. *Plastic tape is used almost universally on residential wiring.*

A wire nut is a solderless plastic connector that uses a tapered metal coil spring to twist wires together. Wire nuts are typically used to connect wire sizes AWG No. 22 through No. 8. All wire nuts have a listing of the size and number of wires they can safely connect. This listing is normally found on the wire nut box.

Wire Nuts

Ideal Industries, Inc.

Color	Wire Combinations
Gray	300 V Rating (#22 AWG to #16 AWG) MIN: Two #22 wires MAX: Two #16 wires
Blue	300 V Rating (#22 AWG to #14 AWG) MIN: Two #22 wires MAX: Three #16 wires
Orange	600 V Rating (#22 AWG to #14 AWG) MIN: One #18 wire with one #20 wire MAX: Four #16 wires with one #20 wire
Yellow	600 V Rating (#18 AWG to #12 AWG) MIN: Two #18 wires MAX: Four #14 wires with one #18 wire
Red	600 V Rating (#18 AWG to #10 AWG) MIN: Two #14 wires MAX: Two #14 wires with two #12 wires

Figure 4-3. *Wire nuts are used extensively for splices in outlet and junction boxes.*

Wire Markers

A *wire marker* is a preprinted peel-off sticker designed to adhere to insulation when wrapped around a conductor. Wire markers resist moisture, dirt, and oil and are used to identify conductors that have the same color but different uses. For example, the two hot black conductors (L1 and L2) of a home can each be marked with a different lettered and numbered wire marker. **See Figure 4-4.** Wire markers are still used even when different-colored conductors are used. Using wire markers in addition to color coding further clarifies the uses of all conductors.

Wire Markers

Figure 4-4. *Wire markers are used to further clarify the meaning of a conductor in addition to color coding.*

SPLICES

A *splice* is the joining of two or more electrical conductors by mechanically twisting the conductors together or by using a special splicing device. Individuals must be careful when making splices because splices can cause electrical problems. Splices must be able to withstand any reasonable mechanical strain that might be placed on the connection. Electrical splices must also allow electricity to pass through the connection as if the connection were one wire.

Wire amperage is a measurement of how much current a wire can carry safely. Ampacity varies according to the size of the wire. When wiring a circuit, wiring that has amperage ratings that exceed circuit demands must be installed. For dedicated appliance circuits, the wattage rating of the appliance should be checked to ensure the appliance does not exceed the maximum wattage rating of the circuit. **See Figure 4-5.**

Conductor Amperage and Wattage Ratings

	Gauge	Amperage	Maximum Watt Load
For Branch Circuits			
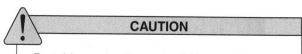 8	8	40	7680 W (240 V)
10	10	30	2880 W (120 V) 5760 W (240 V)
12	12	25	1920 W (120 V) 3840 W (240 V)
14	14	20	1440 W (120 V)
For Bells, Thermostats, and Cords			
16	16	11	---
18	18	8	---
20	20	6	---

Figure 4-5. *The amperage and wattage ratings of conductors vary with the AWG size of the wire.*

Types of Splices

Many types of wire splicing can be found in a residence. Typical residential wire splices are pigtail, Western Union, T-tap, portable cord, and cable.

Pigtail Splices. Because a pigtail splice is simple to make, it is the most commonly used electrical splice. **See Figure 4-6.** *Note:* There are two ways to end pigtail splices: bent over and cut off.

When a pigtail splice is taped, the ends must be bent over so the sharp wire points do not penetrate the tape. When wire nuts are used instead of tape, the ends of the conductors are cut off.

When more than two wires are joined by a pigtail splice, all wires must be twisted together securely before the wire nut is installed. **See Figure 4-7.** Twisting the wires together insures that all the wires are properly fastened before installing a wire nut.

Western Union Splices. A *Western Union splice* is a type of splice that is used when the connection

must be strong enough to support long lengths of heavy wire. **See Figure 4-8.** When a splice is to be taped, care must be taken to eliminate any sharp edges from the wire ends. In the 1800s, Western Union splices were used to repair telegraph wires.

T-Tap Splices. A T-tap splice is a type of splice that allows a connection to be made without cutting the main wire. **See Figure 4-9.** A T-tap splice is one of the most difficult splices to perform correctly. A certain amount of practice is required to make a T-tap connection look neat. Good technique must be used to ensure proper T-tap splicing.

Portable Cord Splices. Portable cord splices are a weak type of splice because there is no connector to hold the conductors together. **See Figure 4-10.**

> ⚠️ **CAUTION**
>
> *Portable cord splices should be used for emergency purposes only.*

COMBINATION WIRE STRIPPER/ CRIMPER/CUTTER

WIRE STRIPPER

Greenlee Textron Inc.

Wire strippers and stripper/crimper/cutter tools are used to remove insulation from electrical wires, crimp terminals, and shear small-diameter bolts.

Pigtail Splices

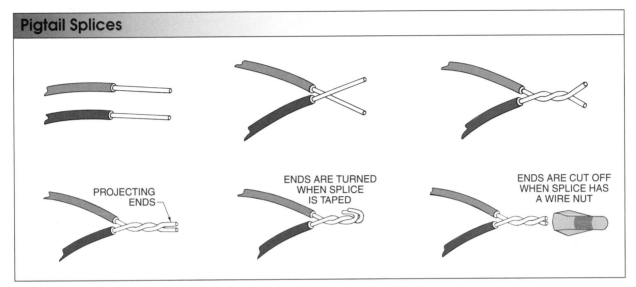

PROJECTING ENDS

ENDS ARE TURNED WHEN SPLICE IS TAPED

ENDS ARE CUT OFF WHEN SPLICE HAS A WIRE NUT

Figure 4-6. *Pigtail splices are the most common splices used in residential wiring.*

Multiple-Wire Pigtail Splices

THREE CONDUCTOR SPLICE

TWIST CONDUCTORS TOGETHER

CONDUCTORS PROPERLY FASTENED

ITT Holub Industries

WIRE NUT INSTALLED

Figure 4-7. *Multiple-wire pigtail splices require that the wires be twisted together prior to the wire nut being installed.*

Western Union Splices

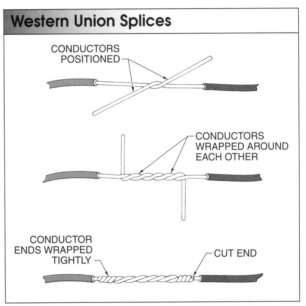

CONDUCTORS POSITIONED

CONDUCTORS WRAPPED AROUND EACH OTHER

CONDUCTOR ENDS WRAPPED TIGHTLY

CUT END

Figure 4-8. *Western Union splices are used where considerable strain is placed on the connection.*

Prior to splicing or connecting conductors together, refer to National Electrical Code® (NEC®), Requirements for Electrical Installations. *Several different methods are listed, including brazing, soldering, welding with a fusible metal alloy, and connecting with a device identified for electrical use such as a wire nut. The NEC® also covers terminal types, temperature limitations, equipment provisions, and separate connector provisions for electrical splices.*

T-Tap Splices

Figure 4-9. *T-tap splices are used to splice a conductor to a through wire.*

Portable Cord Splices

Figure 4-10. *Staggering the splices of a large sized portable cord reduces the bump created.*

Portable cords with stranded wires or solid wires can be spliced if the conductors are 14 AWG or larger. Electrified tape cannot be used so the splice must retain the insulation and outer covering properties of the portable cord.

Cable Splices. Large stranded cables are not often used in residential wiring. However, cable splices are used in other applications such as for battery jumper cables and welding cables. **See Figure 4-11.** When jumper cables or welding cables are broken, the cables can be temporarily repaired by using cable splicing.

Taping Splices

Taping is required to protect splices from oxidation (formation of rust) and to insulate individuals against electrical shock. Taping must provide at least as much insulative and mechanical protection for the splice as the original insulation. Although one wrap of tape (plastic or vinyl) provides insulative protection up to 600 V, several wraps are required to provide a strong mechanical protection. **See Figure 4-12.** When plastic tape is used, the tape is stretched as it is applied. Stretching secures the tape more firmly.

Cable Splices

Figure 4-11. *Large stranded cables must be carefully spliced and firmly secured using cable splicing procedures.*

Taping Splices

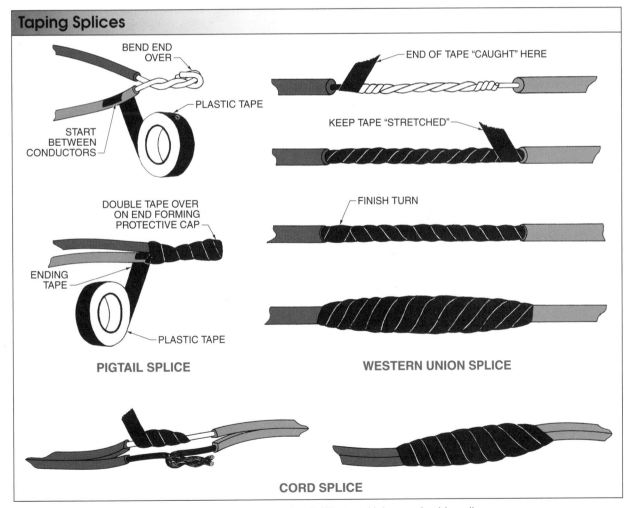

PIGTAIL SPLICE

WESTERN UNION SPLICE

CORD SPLICE

Figure 4-12. *Individual techniques are used to tape pigtail, Western Union, and cable splices.*

Soldering Splices

Once the decision to solder an electrical splice has been made and the insulation has been stripped off the wire, the splice should be soldered as soon as possible. The longer a metal conductor is exposed to dirt and air, the greater the oxidation present on the wire, and the less chance an individual has of achieving a properly soldered connection. Clean metal surfaces are required to allow molten solder to flow freely around the connection.

The metal surfaces of the conductors are cleaned with light sandpaper, emery cloth, or by applying flux to the surfaces. Solder typically is in wire form and is melted with heat from a soldering device such as a soldering iron, soldering gun, or propane torch. **See Figure 4-13.**

Figure 4-13. *Heat for soldering splices is provided by soldering irons, soldering guns, or propane torches.*

Electric soldering irons and soldering guns are used when electricity is available. A propane torch is used to solder large wires or when there is no electricity at the job site. Whatever heating method

is used, individuals must apply solder to the splice on the side opposite the point where heat is being applied. **See Figure 4-14.** Melting solder flows toward the source of heat. Thus, if the top of the wire is hot enough to melt the solder, the bottom of the wire closest to the heat source will draw the solder down through all the wires. The splice must be allowed to cool naturally without movement. Once cooled, the splice is cleaned of any excess flux with a damp rag and taped.

CAUTION

Do not blow on or dip the soldered connection in water to cool. Rapid cooling reduces the strength of solder connections.

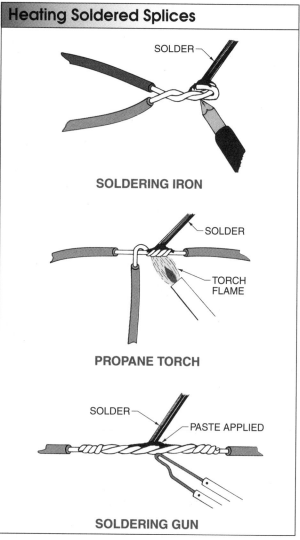

Figure 4-14. *Heat is applied from beneath a splice while solder is applied from above.*

Because solderless connectors save time and are easy to use, an individual is no longer required to solder each and every splice. Solderless connections not only take less time to make connections, but also require less skill. However, individuals should understand how to solder. No matter what type of splice is being used, all splices must be accessible and made in an approved junction box.

SOLDERLESS CONNECTORS

A *solderless connector* is a device used to join wires firmly without the help of solder. Because solderless connectors are convenient and save time, several types have been developed. Some of the most commonly used solderless connectors approved by Underwriters Laboratories® are split-bolt connections, screw terminals, back-wired connectors, wire nuts, and crimps.

Split-Bolt Connectors

A *split-bolt connector* is a type of solderless mechanical connection used for joining large cables such as in service entrances. A split bolt is slipped over the wires to be connected so that a nut can be attached. Split-bolt connectors must be made of the same material as conductors to prevent corrosion. **See Figure 4-15.**

Figure 4-15. *Split-bolt connectors are used to splice large cables.*

Screw Terminals. Screw terminals provide a mechanically and electrically secure connection. Since wiring is always attached to electrical equipment with right-hand screws, the wire should be bent around a screw in a clockwise direction. **See Figure 4-16.** When the screw method of wire connections is used, the screw draws the wire tight without pushing the wire away from the terminal.

Leviton Manufacturing Co., Inc.

Figure 4-16. *Conductors attached to screw terminals must be bent so that the wire can be tightened in a clockwise direction.*

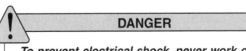

DANGER

To prevent electrical shock, never work on energized equipment when connecting conductors to screw terminals.

Back-Wired (Quick) Connectors

A *quick connector* is a mechanical connection method used to secure wires to the backs of switches and receptacles. The wires are held in place by either spring or screw tension, with screw tension being the most secure. **See Figure 4-17.**

Back-Wired (Quick) Connectors

SCREW TENSION QUICK CONNECT

INSERTED WIRE

PRESS TO RELEASE

PULL TO REMOVE WIRE

Figure 4-17. *The conductor attached to a back-wired receptacle is held in place by spring tension or screw tension.*

To remove a wire from a spring-type quick connector, individuals must insert a screwdriver or a stiff piece of wire into the spring opening next to the connection. Pressing down the spring through the opening releases the wire. Screw-type connectors release a wire as the screw is loosened.

⚠ **CAUTION**

Spring and screw tension connectors are used with copper wire only.

Wire Nut Installation

Wire nuts have almost eliminated the need for soldering and taping. Wire nuts are manufactured in a variety of sizes and shapes. For the most effective use of wire nuts, the wires are twisted together clockwise before the wire nut is twisted on and taped. **See Figure 4-18.** When solid and stranded wires are joined together, the solid wire is bent back over the stranded wire. **See Figure 4-19.**

Wire Nut Installation

WIRE NUT

TWISTED CONDUCTORS

TAPE STRETCHED DURING WRAPPING

Figure 4-18. *To ensure a proper connection, conductors are twisted together before the wire nut and tape are applied.*

A voltage indicator can be used to check if a receptacle is energized.

Connecting Stranded and Solid Wires

STRIP WIRES

TWIST WIRES TOGETHER

NEEDLE NOSE PLIERS

BEND SOLID WIRE OVER STRANDED WIRE

INSTALL WIRE NUT

Figure 4-19. *The technique used to connect solid and stranded wires together is used to ensure a mechanically and electrically sound connection.*

The size of wire nuts is determined by the size and number of wires to be connected. Shape is an individual preference and is determined by the manufacturer. To ensure safe connections, every wire nut is rated for minimum and maximum wire capacity. Wire nuts are used to connect both conducting wires and grounding wires. Green wire nuts are used only for grounding wires.

Crimp-Type Solderless Connectors

A *crimp-type solderless connector* is an electrical device that is used to join wires together or to serve as terminal ends for screw connections. **See Figure 4-20.** Crimp connectors are manufactured as insulated or noninsulated. Noninsulated crimp connectors are less expensive and are used where there is no danger of shorting the connector to a metal surface. When working with crimp-type solderless connectors, identification can be a problem. To avoid confusion, a wire marker is used to identify each conductor.

Crimp Connector Types

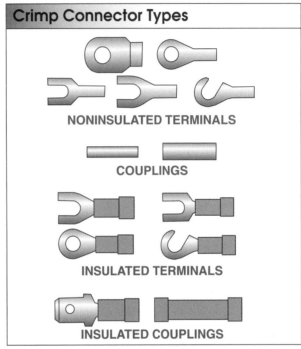

NONINSULATED TERMINALS

COUPLINGS

INSULATED TERMINALS

INSULATED COUPLINGS

Figure 4-20. *Crimp-type solderless connectors are designed for a variety of applications.*

Electrical connector categories are based on shape, function, and smallest size contact in the series. Over 1000 companies worldwide manufacture electrical connectors.

Crimp connectors are secured into place with a multipurpose crimp tool. Crimping tools are also used to cut and strip wire. **See Figure 4-21.**

SOLDERING CONNECTIONS

Soldering is the process of joining metals by using filler metal and heat to make a strong electrical and mechanical connection. The parts to be soldered must be clean, fluxed, and hot enough to melt solder for the solder to properly adhere.

Installing Crimp Connectors

INSERT WIRE INTO CORRECT WIRE GAUGE HOLE SIZE ❶

SQUEEZE AND ROTATE STRIPPER AROUND WIRE ❷

STRIP INSULATION OFF END OF WIRE ❸

CUTTING AND STRIPPING WIRE

TWIST WIRE ❹

ENSURE EXPOSED WIRE IS IN CONNECTOR ❺

CRIMP CONNECTOR SECURELY TO WIRE ❻

ATTACHING SOLDERLESS CRIMP CONNECTOR

Figure 4-21. *The male stub of the crimping tool is placed on the seam of the crimp connector during crimping.*

In addition to surface dirt, oil, and corrosion, the metal surfaces must be cleaned of all surface oxides. Oxide is formed on metal surfaces by oxygen in the air. For example, when copper is exposed to air long enough, the oxide appears as a green tarnish. Flux is used with solder to remove surface oxides. **See Figure 4-22.** Flux removes the oxide by making the oxide soluble and evaporating the oxide as the flux boils off during heating.

A soldered connection must be mechanically strong before soldering. Heat is applied until the materials are hot, allowing solder to be applied.

Solder must be melted by the heat of the material to be joined, not by the heat of the soldering tool.

Flux

SOLDERING PASTE (FLUX)

SOLID SOLDER

Figure 4-22. *When the solder being used is solid, flux is purchased in a separate container to be brushed on to the connection for soldering.*

Only a small amount of solder should be used. The connection should appear smooth and shiny. **See Figure 4-23.** When the solder appears dull and crackly, the connection is a cold solder joint. A *cold solder joint* is a soldered joint with poor electrical and mechanical properties. Cold solder joints are typically caused by insufficient heat during soldering or the parts being moved after the solder is applied but before cooling has finished.

Care must be taken not to damage surrounding parts by overheating them. Semiconductor components, such as transistors and ICs, are very sensitive to heat. A heat sink, such as an alligator clip, is used to help prevent heat damage. The heat sink is placed between the soldered connection point and component that requires protection. The heat sink absorbs the heat produced during soldering.

TESTING CONNECTIONS

Resistance measurements using a DMM are useful in isolating problems from loose connections, corrosion, or shorts. With all power OFF, the test leads of a DMM are connected across a connection, splice, load, or circuit. **See Figure 4-24.** The resistance of the connection or circuit being tested is displayed. When a DMM is set to measure resistance, the measurement should not change with a proper connection. When a varying high-resistance measurement is recorded, there is probably a loose connection. For a connection with a high fixed-resistance value (150.0 Ω or greater) the measurement indicates there is probably a bad connection. A DMM can be left for long-term measurements as long as the batteries are in good condition (typically 1000 hr).

Solder Appearance

SOLDER REMOVED AS SOLDER FLOWS ON JOINT

SOLDER

SOLDERING TIP

SMOOTH AND SHINY SOLDERED JOINT

CONDUCTORS

SOLDERING CONDUCTORS

GOOD SOLDER JOINTS

COLD SOLDER JOINT

SOLDERING CONDUCTORS TO DEVICE

Figure 4-23. *A properly soldered connection looks smooth and shiny while a cold solder connection has a dull grainy texture.*

Tech Tip: Cold and Hot Resistance

COLD RESISTANCE MEASURED WITH POWER OFF

16.4 Ω

SCREW BASE

CENTER CONTACT

COLD RESISTANCE MEASUREMENT

.5 A

120 V

TO 120 VAC POWER SUPPLY

$R = \dfrac{E}{I}$

$R = \dfrac{120}{.5}$

$R = \mathbf{240}\ \Omega$

HOT RESISTANCE CALCULATED FROM VOLTAGE AND CURRENT MEASUREMENTS

HOT RESISTANCE MEASUREMENT

Testing Connections

Resistance Problems

LOOSE SCREW
} RESISTANCE CHANGES FROM VERY HIGH TO VERY LOW WHEN MOVED

LOOSE CONNECTION

CORRODED TERMINAL

CORROSION

} EXCESSIVE RESISTANCE PRESENT. RESISTANCE CHANGES WHEN MOVED

TERMINAL CONNECTOR

CORROSION

CABLE STRAP GROUNDED

SHORT TO GROUND

WIRE INSULATION DAMAGE

} RESISTANCE DROPS TO VERY LOW OR ZERO

CABLE DAMAGE

WIRE-TO-WIRE SHORT

SHORT

RESISTANCE OF CIRCUIT BEING TESTED

RESISTANCE SHOULD NOT CHANGE WHEN CIRCUIT COMPONENT(S) MOVED

NEW MAXIMUM READING INDICATES BAD CONNECTION

POWER FROM CIRCUIT OFF

Figure 4-24. *Resistance measurements are useful when testing a connection for improper splicing or soldering.*

Chapter 4
Test

Name _____ **Date** _____

Making Electrical Connections

_____ **1.** Solder used in electrical work is usually an alloy of ___.
   A. 60% tin and 40% lead
   B. 60% lead and 40% tin
   C. 50% tin and 50% lead
   D. none of the above

_____ **2.** The amount of ___ in solder determines its melting point.

_____ **3.** The amount of ___ in solder determines its strength.

_____ **4.** Flux removes ___ and other small impurities from metal surfaces.

_____ **5.** ___ solder should never be used on electrical connections.

_____ **6.** The ___ splice is the most commonly used electrical splice.

   T   F   **7.** Splices are designed to stop the flow of electricity.

   T   F   **8.** Wire ends are cut off when a solderless connector is used for a splice.

_____ **9.** ___ may be added to solder to ensure proper solder adhesion.

_____ **10.** Plastic tape insulates against voltages up to ___ V.

_____ **11.** Melting solder flows toward the source of ___.

_____ **12.** Taping a splice protects the splice from ___.

_____ **13.** Taping a splice protects personnel against ___.

_____ **14.** A quick connector holds the wire in place by ___ or screw tension.

_____ **15.** Quick connectors are used to secure wires on the backs of switches and ___.

_____ **16.** ___ are used to join large cables together.

_____   **17.** Wiring is always connected to electrical equipment with ___ screws.

T   F   **18.** When solid and stranded wires are spliced together, the solid wire should be bent back over the stranded wire.

T   F   **19.** Rapid cooling is preferred for developing strong solder joints.

T   F   **20.** Solder should always be applied on the side opposite from where the heat is applied.

_____   **21.** Solder is commercially available in ___ form.
     A. liquid or bar
     B. wire or liquid
     C. bar or wire
     D. none of the above

_____   **22.** Cord splices are ___.
     A. weak connections
     B. staggered
     C. soldered for additional strength
     D. all of the above

_____   **23.** The ___ splice is strong enough to support long lengths of heavy wire.

_____   **24.** ___ core solder contains no flux.

_____   **25.** ___ core solder contains flux within the solder.

T   F   **26.** Solder joints should be dipped in water to stop the cooling process.

T   F   **27.** Wires on screw terminals should always bend and tighten in a clockwise direction.

T   F   **28.** Solderless connectors are used extensively to save time when making splices.

_____   **29.** A(n) ___ splice may be used to connect into an uncut wire.

_____   **30.** A(n) ___ may be used to heat solder joints if electricity is not available.

Taping Splices

_____ 1. Technique for taping cord splice in an emergency only

_____ 2. Technique for taping a solderless connector

_____ 3. Technique for taping a pigtail splice

_____ 4. Technique for taping a Western Union splice

Pigtail Splice with Wire Nut

_____ 1. ___ is the first step.   _____ 4. ___ is the fourth step.

_____ 2. ___ is the second step.   _____ 5. ___ is the last step.

_____ 3. ___ is the third step.

Pigtail Splice with Tape

_____ 1. ___ is the first step.   _____ 4. ___ is the fourth step.

_____ 2. ___ is the second step.   _____ 5. ___ is the fifth step.

_____ 3. ___ is the third step.   _____ 6. ___ is the last step.

Screw Terminals

_____ **1.** Correct

_____ **2.** Wrong; end not looped

_____ **3.** Wrong; end too long

_____ **4.** Wrong; end too short

_____ **5.** Wrong; wire in counterclockwise direction

_____ **6.** Wrong; too much insulation stripped off wire

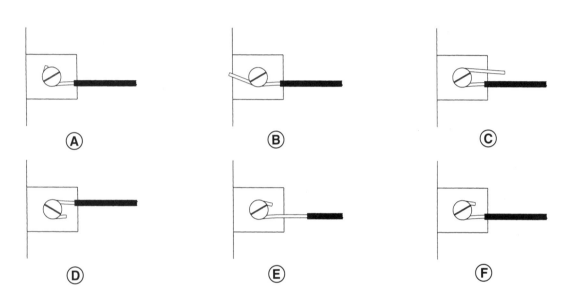

Electrical Tools and Materials

_____ 1. Tightens clockwise

_____ 2. Cuts bolts and wire and removes insulation

_____ 3. Repairs large stranded cables

_____ 4. Twists wires and insulates

_____ 5. Common alloy of tin and lead used in solder

_____ 6. Connection without cutting the main line

_____ 7. Used to apply heat

_____ 8. Should be stretched

_____ 9. Used in emergency only

_____ 10. Released with a screwdriver or stiff wire

A. Solderless connectors

B. T-tap

C. Soldering iron

D. Tape

E. Portable cord splice

F. Screw terminal

G. Spring-type (quick) connectors

H. Stripper/crimping tool

I. 60/40

J. Cable splice

Chapter 5

Switches and Receptacles

Important rating information is printed or embossed on switches and receptacles that must be understood prior to use. Chapter 5 provides an overview of the types of switches and receptacles that are available for residential use. Commonly used switches and receptacles are shown, and selection of appropriate switches and receptacles for an application is explained.

SWITCHES

In most residential electrical circuits, individuals should expect to find some type of control device such as a switch. A *switch* is an electrical device used to control loads in a residential electrical circuit. **See Figure 5-1.**

Originally, the switches used to open and close circuits had to be physically changed by hand to either the ON (closed) or OFF (open) condition. Modern technology and the demand for convenience have greatly expanded the role of switches.

Today, switches can be activated by light, heat, water, smoke, and radio waves. Switches can turn lights ON and OFF or vary the intensity (brightness) of lights. Switches are classified as simple or complex depending on the requirements of the user.

Switches

Cooper Wiring Devices

Figure 5-1. *Switches control loads by opening and closing circuits.*

Switch Markings

When an individual picks up a switch, a great deal of information is found marked on the switch. Information provided can be in the form of color-coding or abbreviations. **See Figure 5-2.** Individuals must pay careful attention to the information because the information determines where and how a switch can be used.

Switch Markings

COPPER/COPPER-CLAD WIRES ONLY

NOTE: BLACK TERMINAL INDICATES COMMON ON THREE-WAY SWITCHES

MAXIMUM AMPERAGE = 15 A
MAXIMUM VOLTAGE = 120 V
RESTRICTED TO AC ONLY

UNDERWRITERS LABORATORY INC.® LISTING

FRONT

ELONGATED HOLES FOR ALIGNMENT IN SWITCH BOX

PLASTER EARS

GROUND TERMINAL (GREEN)

HOLES FOR BACK WIRING

STRIP GAUGE

BACK

Figure 5-2. *A great deal of information is indicated on the body of a switch.*

Color Coding. *Color coding* is a technique used to identify switch terminal screws through the use of various colors. Switches use black, steel, and green colors to identify certain screw terminals. Black is used on three-way switches to indicate the screw that is the common terminal for the switch. Power will always come into a switch at the common and leave the switch by the traveler terminal. **See Figure 5-3.** The common screw terminal is typically black or darker than other screws. Green always indicates a ground terminal screw. Switches are constructed with a green ground screw attached to the metallic strap of the switch for grounding.

Printed Information. In addition to color coding, abbreviated words and symbols printed on a switch provide important information. Printed information is typically found on the front of a switch, but some information can be found on the back. **See Figure 5-4.**

UL Label. A *UL label* is a stamped or printed icon that indicates that a device or material has been approved for consumer use by Underwriters Laboratories Inc.® Underwriters Laboratories (UL) was created by the National Board of Fire Underwriters to test electrical materials and devices. Manufacturers,

Switch Color Coding

GROUND TERMINAL (GREEN)

STRAP

COMMON TERMINAL

TRAVELER TERMINAL

FRONT   RIGHT SIDE
SINGLE-POLE SWITCH

GROUND TERMINAL (GREEN)

TRAVELER A TERMINAL

TRAVELER B TERMINAL

COMMON TERMINAL (DARK OR BLACK)

FRONT   RIGHT SIDE
THREE-WAY SWITCH

Figure 5-3. *The color of the common and traveler screw terminals are the same on single-pole switches. Three-way switches have a darker or black common terminal.*

who wish to obtain UL approval, must submit samples to a UL testing laboratory in New York, Chicago, or Santa Clara, California. When a sample passes an extensive testing program, the sample is listed in a UL category as having met the minimum safety requirements.

A UL label indicates the minimum safety requirements and is not meant to serve as a quality comparison between manufacturers. Two switches, both with UL approval, can differ greatly in quality and performance.

CSA Label. A *Canadian Standard Association (CSA) label* is a marking that indicates that extensive tests have been conducted on a device by the Canadian Standards Association. Both CSA and UL labels are found on many devices to indicate that the device is accepted in both Canada and the United States.

Conductor Symbols. A *conductor symbol* is an electrical symbol that represents copper and aluminum respectively. Certain electrical devices are made to work with copper only and some devices with

Switch Inscribed Information

SPECIFICATIONS

UL LABEL

CSA LABEL

CONDUCTOR SYMBOLS

USE CU (COPPER) WIRE ONLY

CURRENT AND VOLTAGE RATINGS

AC ONLY
20 A – 120/277 V

Cooper Wiring Devices

Figure 5-4. *Switch specifications are typically found on the front of a switch.*

aluminum or copper. When a device is specified CU/AL, the device can be used with copper or aluminum wires.

When aluminum wire is used with copper connectors, the typical result is overheating, but electrical fires due to the chemical reaction between the dissimilar metals are also possible.

Current and Voltage Ratings. Current and voltage ratings are always provided on a switch. The maximum current rating of a switch for residential use is 15 A or 20 A. The maximum voltage rating is typically 120 V. In addition, some switches are specified for alternating current (AC) use only. Failure to follow current and voltage ratings along with other specifications reduces the useful life of a switch.

T Ratings. Switches used to control loads with a tungsten filament (such as standard incandescent lamps) must be marked with the letter T. A *T rating* is special switch information that indicates a switch is capable of handling the severe overloading created by a tungsten load as the switch is closed. **See Figure 5-5.** Tungsten has a very low resistance when cold and increases in resistance as heated. At the moment a switch is closed, the low resistance of a tungsten load causes the current draw to be 8 to 10 times the normal operating current. Once the switch is closed, the tungsten filament (load) heats up and the current flow drops immediately. The process of heating up a tungsten filament takes about $\frac{1}{240}$ of a second. Failure to observe the T rating of a switch will reduce the life expectancy of the switch.

Strip Gauges. Strip gauges are found on the rear portion of a back-wired switch. **See Figure 5-6.** A *strip gauge* is a short groove that indicates how much insulation must be removed from a wire so the wire can be properly inserted into a switch. When a wire has not had enough insulation removed, a proper connection is not made. When too much insulation is removed, bare wire is left exposed allowing a short to possibly occur.

T Rating

T RATING (T5 OR T8)

Figure 5-5. *A T rating is a special rating given to switches that are capable of handling the severe overloading created by a tungsten load as the switch is closed.*

Strip Gauge

STRIP GAUGE

Figure 5-6. *A strip gauge is a marker on the back of a switch that identifies the amount of insulation that must be removed from a wire so the wire can be attached to the switch.*

Types of Switches

Switches are designed for a variety of applications. **See Figure 5-7.** Common switches used in residences are the single-pole, three-way, four-way, and double-pole switches. Some modern residential-use switches are the timer, programmable, and motion sensor switches. A timer switch is set to the times that the switch is turned ON and OFF. A programmable switch allows a sequence of events to be established, such as turning lights ON when no one is home. Motion sensor switches are used as security devices or energy savers. As a security device, motion sensor switches turn ON lights when someone enters an area. As an energy saver, motion sensor switches turn lights OFF when no one is detected in an area.

Switch Types . . .

Cooper Wiring Devices

SINGLE-POLE SWITCH

Standard ON/OFF switch provides control from one location; a three-way switch used with another three-way switch provides control from two locations (has no ON/OFF markings)

Leviton Manufacturing Co., Inc.

THREE-WAY SWITCH

Leviton Manufacturing Co., Inc.

FOUR-WAY SWITCH

Used with two three-way switches to provide control from three or more locations

Cooper Wiring Devices

DOUBLE-POLE SINGLE-THROW SWITCH

Equivalent to two single-pole switches. May open and close two circuits or wires at the same time; Looks identical to a four-way switch except double-pole switch is marked with an ON/OFF

Cooper Wiring Devices

DUPLEX

Useful when space is a problem; duplex switch allows two single pole switches to be placed in a standard switch box

Cooper Wiring Devices

SWITCH/RECEPTACLE COMBINATION

Switch may be wired to control receptacle or receptacle can be hot while the switch controls another circuit

Cooper Wiring Devices

DIMMER

Provides light adjustment from low levels to full brilliancy; Available in single-pole or three-way operation.

Leviton Manufacturing Co., Inc.

KEY

Used where access to the switch is to be restricted

Cooper Wiring Devices

AC PUSHBUTTON

Replaces old and loud snap action switches; Quiet switches are also available with toggle operation

Copper Wiring Devices

WEATHERPROOF

Suitable for outside use

Leviton Manufacturing Co., Inc.

TIMER

Used to turn ON and OFF lights or appliances at predetermined times

Cooper Wiring Devices

MOTION SENSOR

Allows a circuit to be turned ON and OFF according to any movement within a 400 to 1600 sq ft distance

... Switch Types

Cooper Wiring Devices	Cooper Wiring Devices	Cooper Wiring Devices	Broan-NuTone LLC
PILOT LIGHT/SWITCH COMBINATION	**FUSE/SWITCH COMBINATION**	**LOW-VOLTAGE**	**DOOR-BELL**
Provides an indicator for equipment not seen in attics or basements	Provides fused ON/OFF protection for individual equipment like furnaces	Switch designated to operate low voltage switching systems. Usually 24 V	A type of low voltage switch used to operate chimes and door buzzers. Usually limited to 12 V to 24 V operation

Figure 5-7. *Common switches used in residences are the single-pole, three-way, four-way, and double-pole switches.*

Per NEC® Section 404.2(A), Switch Connections, switches shall be wired so that all switching is done only in the ungrounded circuit conductor. Switches shall not disconnect the grounded conductor of a circuit. Per Section 404.4, Wet Locations, switches in a wet location or outside a building shall be enclosed in a weatherproof enclosure or cabinet that shall comply with 312.2(A). Switches shall not be installed within wet locations in tub or shower spaces unless installed as part of a listed tub or shower assembly.

Single-Pole Switches. A *single-pole switch* is an electrical control device used to turn lights or appliances ON and OFF from a single location. Switches are connected into a circuit in the positive or hot side (leg) of a circuit.

As a general rule, neutral conductors (white wires) are not switched or used as a leg in a switch loop. Not switching the neutral conductor is an easy rule to follow for conduit systems but does not apply to armored and nonmetallic-sheathed cable. When armored or nonmetallic cable is used, an identified white conductor can be used as the feeder conductor from a switch. **See Figure 5-8.** The NEC® allows this exception. Some applications require that a load (lamp) be controlled from two separate locations.

Single-Pole Switch Circuit

ARCHITECTURAL PLAN

LINE DIAGRAM

Figure 5-8. *Color of wire can vary when wiring with armored or nonmetallic cables.*

Three-Way Switches. A *three-way switch* is an electrical control device used in pairs to control a light or load from two locations. The term "three-way" is the name given to the switch and in no way describes the operation of the switch. The terminals of a three-way switch are identified as common, traveler A, and traveler B. **See Figure 5-9.** The single terminal at one end of the switch is the common. The common terminal is easily identified because the terminal is darker than the other terminals or is black. The positive or hot wire of a circuit is always connected to the darkened terminal. The remaining two terminals are the connecting points for the two traveler wires that connect paired switches together.

Three-Way Switch Terminals

TRAVELER A
TERMINAL

TRAVELER B
TERMINAL

GROUND
TERMINAL
(GREEN
COLOR)

COMMON
TERMINAL
(DARK OR
BLACK COLOR)

Cooper Wiring Devices

Figure 5-9. *The terminals of a three-way switch are identified as common, traveler A, and traveler B.*

A three-way switch operates by moving a pole between two positions. A three-way switch is really 2 two-position switches. When the handle is down, contact is made with terminal 1; when the handle is up, contact is made with terminal 2. Three-way switches have no ON or OFF markings because the handle indicates the position of the contacts from 1 three-way switch in relation to another three-way switch. The pole position of each switch determines whether or not the circuit is complete (load ON). **See Figure 5-10.**

WARNING

When using nonmetallic cable a white wire is possible on the load side of three-way switches.

Three-Way Switch Operation

Figure 5-10. *A three-way switch operates by moving a pole between two positions.*

When the same respective traveler of each switch is connected, a conducting path is completed, which allows a load (light) to turn ON. When either switch contact is moved, the light will turn OFF because the conducting path is broken. Because either switch can break the conducting path, the load can be turned OFF from two locations. When the light must be turned back ON, either switch can be moved to allow a flow path to be completed. Two three-way switches are typically used for hallways, stairways, and rooms with two entrances.

A lamp that is used to light a staircase (six steps or more) must have a three-way switch at the top and bottom of the staircase. Rooms that have two entrances (or exits) require 2 three-way switches to control the light(s) from each location. Two three-way switches must be used to control a lamp from two locations. **See Figure 5-11.**

Figure 5-11. *Two three-way switches are used to control a lamp from two locations.*

Three-way switch circuits have the common terminal of 1 three-way switch connected to the hot power supply at all times. The common point of the other three-way switch is connected directly to the load (lamp) at all times. The traveler terminals of both three-way switches are connected together. A black wire is used to connect the hot power line to the first three-way switch. Red wires are used for the travelers. The load wire connecting the second three-way switch to the lamp is typically red or black with colored tape or marker used to distinguish the load wire from others.

Residential circuits typically use a green or bare wire for the ground when nonmetallic cable is used. A ground wire is required to ground all non-current-carrying metal to earth. Metal conduit may be used to maintain a solid ground connection when metal conduit is used. Some applications require a load (lamp) to be controlled from more than two locations.

Four-Way Switches. A *four-way switch* is a control device that is used in combination with 2 three-way switches to allow control of a load from three locations. One or more four-way switches are used with 2 three-way switches to provide control of a load from three or more locations. The two types of four-way switches are the through-wired type and crossed-wired type. **See Figure 5-12.** The through-wired type of a four-way switch is the most popular. Any number of four-way switches can be connected into a circuit, but all four-way switches must be connected between 2 three-way switches.

The positions of the switch contacts in relation to each other determine whether a load (lamp or receptacle) is ON or OFF. To completely understand all combinations of three-location control, electricians should sketch all possible combinations of the contacts. **See Figure 5-13.** With 2 three-way switches and 1 four-way switch, there are six possible combinations.

Tech Tip: Switch Contacts

CONTACTS OPEN

SWITCH OFF

Cooper Wiring Devices

Four-Way Switches

HANDLE UP

HANDLE DOWN

THROUGH-WIRED

TRAVELER 1 TERMINAL

TRAVELER 2 TERMINAL

GROUND TERMINAL

TRAVELER 3 TERMINAL

TRAVELER 4 TERMINAL

ON

Cooper Wiring Devices

HANDLE UP

HANDLE DOWN

CROSS-WIRED

Figure 5-12. *Four-way switches provide multiple switch locations for controlling loads such as lamps.*

Four-Way Switch Locations

Figure 5-13. *Operation of a four-way switch requires that four-way switches be installed between 2 three-way switches.*

For example, a room that contains three entrances requires a switch to turn a lamp ON from any of the three entrances. A four-way switch is placed between 2 three-way switches to control the lamp from three locations. **See Figure 5-14.**

Two three-way switches and 2 four-way switches can be used to control a light from four locations. The 2 four-way switches must always be wired between 2 three-way switches. Any number of four-way switches can be added to a lamp control circuit to increase the number of control locations.

Double-Pole Switches. A *double-pole switch* is a control device that is two switches in one for controlling two separate loads. Double-pole switches are designed to connect or disconnect (open or close) at the same time. **See Figure 5-15.** Double-pole switches are common for 230 V circuits where both conductors are hot conductors. Double-pole switches open or close the dual path to the 230 V load, turning the load ON or OFF. Double-pole switches look similar to four-way switches, however double-pole switches are distinctly marked with an ON and OFF position.

Use a commercial-grade switch for extra protection or longer service. Commercial-grade switches increase voltage capability from 120 V to 277 V, horsepower capability from ½ HP to 2 HP, and amperage capability from 15 A to 20 A or 30 A.

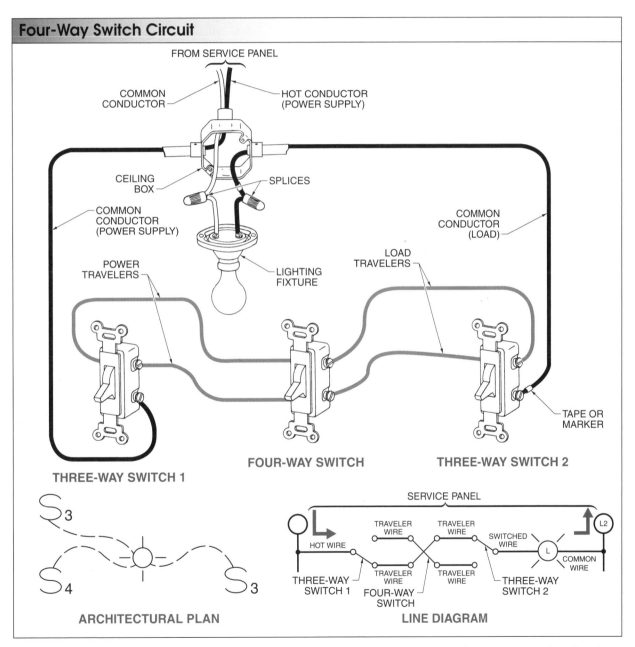

Figure 5-14. *Four-way switches add as many control locations to a circuit as required: 1 four-way equals three locations, 2 four-ways equal four locations, 3 four-ways equal five locations, etc.*

Double-Pole Switches

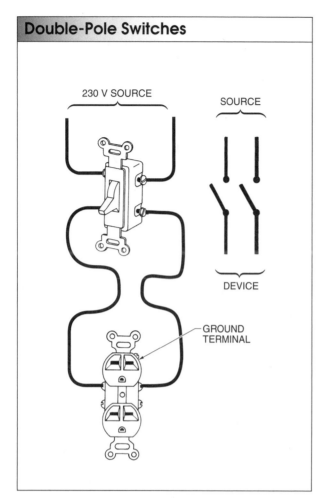

Figure 5-15. *Double-pole switches open two lines or circuits simultaneously.*

TESTING SWITCHES

A continuity tester or test instrument with a continuity test setting is used to test a switch for a complete path for current flow. A closed switch that is operating correctly has continuity, while an open switch does not have continuity. **See Figure 5-16.** A continuity tester or test instrument with a continuity test setting indicates when a switch has a complete path by emitting an audible beeping sound. Some test instruments with a continuity test setting display the resistance of a device while beeping. Indication of a complete path is used to determine the condition of a switch as open.

A quad box, or four-gang, is the largest switch box that is typically used with residential construction. Larger boxes are available but are rarely used for residential applications for aesthetic reasons. A four-gang connection can be used at the main entrance of a residence to control entry lights, outdoor lights, ceiling fans, room lights, spotlights, hallway lights, and closet lights from one location. A four-gang arrangement can be separated into two double-gang arrangements either for ease in wiring or for memorization of which circuit is controlled by the switch. All switches should be clearly marked when installed in a quad box.

Testing Switches

Figure 5-16. *Switches should be tested prior to installation using continuity testing.*

RECEPTACLES

Receptacles are often called convenience outlets. A *receptacle* is a contact device installed for the connection of plugs and flexible cords to supply current to portable electrical equipment.

Receptacle Markings

Receptacles, like switches, convey important information by colors and symbols. In addition, the shapes and positions of the openings (slots) in a receptacle also determine proper use. **See Figure 5-17.**

Shape and Position. The shape and position of the connection slots are used to differentiate between a 15 A, 125 V receptacle and a 15 A, 250 V receptacle. A 125 V receptacle has connection slots that are vertical and typically different lengths. A 250 V receptacle has connection slots that are horizontal and the same size. **See Figure 5-18.**

A 125 V receptacle with different size connection slots is a polarized receptacle. A *polarized receptacle* is a receptacle where the size of the connection slots determines the plug connection. The short connection slot is the hot connection and the long connection slot is the common (neutral) connection. Because the slots are designated and a plug can only be connected one way, the receptacle is a polarized receptacle. **See Figure 5-19.**

Shapes and Positions of Connection Slots

15 A, 125 V RECEPTACLE

15 A, 250 V RECEPTACLE

CONNECTION SLOTS VERTICAL AND DIFFERENT LENGTHS

CONNECTION SLOTS HORIZONTAL AND SAME LENGTH

Cooper Wiring Devices

Figure 5-18. *The shape and position of the connection slots are used to differentiate between various amperage and voltage rated receptacles.*

Receptacle Markings

BREAK-OFF TAB

LONG SLOT INDICATES COMMON ON POLARIZED RECEPTACLE

STEEL-COLORED SCREWS INDICATE COMMON SIDE OF RECEPTACLE

UNDERWRITERS LABORATORIES LISTING

COPPER OR ALUMINUM WIRES

115 V

230 V   CU/AL

SMALLER SLOT INDICATES HOT ON POLARIZED RECEPTACLE

GREEN-COLORED SCREW INDICATES GROUNDING CONNECTION

BRONZE-COLORED SCREWS INDICATE HOT SIDE OF RECEPTACLE

BREAKAWAY TAB NORMALLY CONNECTS TOP AND BOTTOM RECEPTACLE

CANADIAN STANDARDS ASSOCIATION

GROUNDING (HOLE)

Figure 5-17. *A great deal of information is indicated on the body of a receptacle.*

Polarized Receptacles

Cooper Wiring Devices

Figure 5-19. *Because the slots of a polarized receptacle are designated, a plug can only be connected one way.*

Ratings determine the number of contacts and the configuration in which the slots are positioned in the receptacle. **See Figure 5-20.** There are a large number of configurations and diagrams for receptacles encountered in residential construction work. **See Appendix.**

Low Electric Fittings Co.

Floor-mount boxes can be used when routing telecommunications or electrical conductors to specially designed locations such as a home office.

Receptacle Connection Slot Configurations

Figure 5-20. *Receptacle amperage and voltage ratings determine the number of connection slots and the configuration in which the slots are positioned.*

Receptacles are designed for straight blade or locking type plugs. Locking type receptacles are more common in commercial and industrial applications than in residential work. **See Figure 5-21.**

Straight and Locking Blade Receptacles

THREE-PRONG   THREE-PRONG

FOUR-PRONG   FOUR-PRONG
STRAIGHT BLADE   **LOCKING BLADE**

Cooper Wiring Devices

Figure 5-21. *Straight blade receptacles are typically used for residential applications while locking blade receptacles are typically used for commercial and industrial applications.*

Color Coding. Steel, bronze, and green colors are typically used on receptacle terminal screws. A silver-colored screw indicates the neutral terminal, a bronze-colored screw indicates the hot terminal, and a green colored screw indicates the ground terminal.

Printed Information. The markers "UL", "CSA", "CU/AL", "15 A", and "125 V" have the same meaning for receptacles as they do for switches: Underwriter Laboratories, Canadian Standards Association, copper/aluminum wire connections, maximum current, and maximum voltage rating.

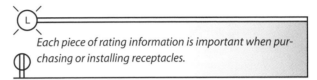

Each piece of rating information is important when purchasing or installing receptacles.

Types of Receptacles

Receptacles are found in a variety of shapes and sizes depending on the application. Typical receptacles found in residences are standard, isolated ground, split-wired, and GFCI. **See Figure 5-22.**

Standard Receptacles. Standard receptacles include a long neutral slot, a short hot slot, and a U-shaped ground hole. **See Figure 5-23.** Wires are attached to the receptacle at screw terminals or push-in fittings. A connecting tab between the two hot and two neutral screw terminals provides an electrical connection between the terminals. The electrical connection allows for both terminals to be powered when one wire is connected to either terminal screw.

Receptacles are marked with ratings for maximum voltage and amperes. Standard receptacles are marked 15 A, 125 or 20 A, 125 V (maximum values). Receptacles marked 20 A, 125 V are typically required for laundry and kitchen circuits. Other 125 V receptacles found in a residence are 15 A.

Receptacles marked CU are used with solid copper wire only. Receptacles marked CU-CLAD are used with copper-coated aluminum wire. Receptacles marked CO/ALR are used with solid aluminum wire.

DANGER

Receptacles require a grounding jumper if not automatically grounded.

Receptacle Types . . .

STANDARD DUPLEX

A grounded receptacle commonly used for 15 A, 115 V appliances in the home

STANDARD DUPLEX

A grounded receptacle commonly used for 20 A, 115 V appliances in the home

COMBINATION HIGH/LOW VOLTAGE

Used to provide a 230 V circuit and a 115 V circuit in one receptacle

SINGLE GROUNDED 115 V

Maximum load is 15 A

30 A

Used on clothes dryers for 120/240 V operation; maximum load is 30 A

TWIST-LOCK

Used with twist-lock plugs in areas where positive connection is to be maintained

SINGLE GROUNDED 115 V

Maximum load is 20 A

50 A

Used on electric ranges to supply 120/240 V operation; maximum load is 50 A

NOTE: Four-wire can be required by local code

50 A SURFACE MOUNT

Used on electric devices to supply 120/240 V operation; maximum load is 50 A

... Receptacle Types

FUSE/RECEPTACLE COMBINATION

Offers direct fuse protection of receptacle at workbenches, etc.

ISOLATED-GROUND DUPLEX

Isolating the ground protects communication circuits from noise; receptacle ground bonded to service entrance grounding system

GROUND FAULT CIRCUIT INTERRUPTER

Used to protect electricians (all persons) from electrical shock due to ground faults in electrical devices

WEATHERPROOF

Standard grounded duplex receptacle with protective waterproof cover attached

SURGE PROTECTION (TVSS)

Used to provide surge protection for hot to neutral, hot to ground, and neutral to ground

SWITCH/GFCI COMBINATION

Used to protect persons from ground faults with switch disconnect and indicator light

Cooper Wiring Devices

Figure 5-22. *Receptacles are found in a variety of shapes and sizes depending on the application.*

Standard Receptacles

LONG (NEUTRAL) SLOT

GROUNDING HOLE

SILVER (NEUTRAL) SCREW TERMINALS

VOLTAGE AND AMERAGE RATING

GREEN (GROUNDING) SCREW TERMINAL

MOUNTING STRAP

SHORT (HOT) SLOT

CONNECTING TAB

MOUNTING STRAP

BRASS (HOT) SCREW TERMINALS

PUSH-IN FITTING

WIRE RATINGS

WIRE TYPE

FRONT

BACK

Figure 5-23. *Local codes must be checked for the exact requirements for installation and use of standard receptacles.*

When wiring a 120 V duplex receptacle, the black or red (hot) wire is connected to the brass-colored screw, the white wire is connected to the steel-colored (common) screw, and the green or bare wire is connected to the green screw. **See Figure 5-24.**

Figure 5-24. *Most local codes require that a standard receptacle be installed as a polarized receptacle.*

Split-Wired Receptacles. A *split-wired receptacle* is a standard receptacle that has had the tab between the two brass-colored (hot) terminal screws removed. The tab between the two steel-colored (neutral) terminals has not been removed. Split-wired receptacles are used to provide a standard and switched circuit or two separate circuits at the same duplex outlet. **See Figure 5-25.**

Figure 5-25. *Split-wired receptacles provide a standard-wired receptacle and a switched-circuit receptacle or two separate circuits at the same duplex receptacle.*

Isolated-Ground Receptacles. In a standard receptacle, the receptacle ground is connected to the common grounding system when the receptacle is installed in a metal outlet box. A common grounding system normally includes all metal wiring, boxes, conduit, water pipes, and the non-current-carrying metal parts of most electrical equipment. The receptacle ground becomes part of the larger grounding system when a piece of electrical equipment is plugged into the receptacle.

The common grounding system acts as a large antenna and conducts electrical noise. This electrical noise causes interference in computers, medical, security, military, and communication equipment.

An isolated-ground receptacle is used to minimize problems in sensitive applications or areas of high electrical noise. An *isolated-ground receptacle* is a special receptacle that minimizes electrical noise by providing a separate grounding path for each connected device. Isolated-ground receptacles are identified by an orange color. **See Figure 5-26.** A separate ground conductor is run with the circuit conductors in an isolated grounding system.

Figure 5-26. *Isolated-ground receptacles minimize noise by providing a separate grounding path for each receptacle.*

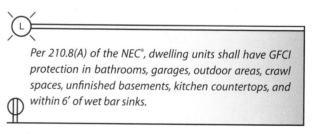

Per 210.8(A) of the NEC®, dwelling units shall have GFCI protection in bathrooms, garages, outdoor areas, crawl spaces, unfinished basements, kitchen countertops, and within 6′ of wet bar sinks.

GFCI Receptacles. A *ground fault circuit interrupter (GFCI)* is a fast-acting receptacle that detects low levels of leakage current to ground and opens the circuit in response to the leakage (ground fault). A *ground fault* is any current above the level that is required for a dangerous shock. GFCIs provide greater protection than standard or isolated-ground receptacles. **See Figure 5-27.**

Testing Standard Receptacles — Test Lights

Figure 5-28. *A test light illuminates when a standard receptacle is energized.*

GFCI Receptacles

RESET BUTTON

TEST BUTTON

Figure 5-27. *A GFCI receptacle is a fast-acting receptacle that detects low levels of leakage current to ground and opens the circuit in response to the leakage.*

TESTING RECEPTACLES

A test light or test instrument with a voltage setting is used to test a receptacle for voltage. A receptacle that is operating correctly has 120 V between the hot slot and the common slot or ground, while an open switch does not have continuity. **See Figure 5-28.** Indication of correct voltage is used to determine the condition of a receptacle.

Cover receptacle terminal screws with several layers of electrical tape prior to installation in a metal box to prevent electrical shock or a short circuit to the system.

Receptacles are sometimes located inside cabinets to serve specific appliances such as microwave ovens.

Testing receptacles is also possible with a receptacle tester. A *receptacle tester* is a test instrument that is plugged into a standard receptacle to determine if the receptacle is properly wired and energized. **See Figure 5-29.** Some receptacle tester models include a ground fault circuit interrupter or ground fault interrupter test button that allows the receptacle tester to be used on GFCI or GFI receptacles. **See Figure 5-30.**

Figure 5-29. *Receptacle testers are plugged into a standard receptacle to determine if the receptacle is properly wired and energized.*

Figure 5-30. *GFCI receptacle testers are plugged into a GFCI receptacle to determine if the receptacle is properly grounded, wired, and energized.*

Milwaukee Electric Tool Corporation

A drywall saw is used to cut holes in drywall for placement of electrical boxes.

SWITCH AND RECEPTACLE COVERS

To properly trim out a switch or receptacle, the device must be properly covered. **See Figure 5-31.** Switches can be combined with receptacles and trimmed out by using the correct cover plate configuration. Switches and receptacles can also be located outside. For outdoor applications, weatherproof covers are required.

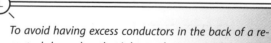

To avoid having excess conductors in the back of a receptacle box, a box that is larger than required should be used. The largest size single-gang, nonmetallic receptacle box has a volume of 22.5 cu in.

Switch and Receptacle Covers

Figure 5-31. *Switches and receptacles must be properly covered according to the NEC ®.*

Cooper Wiring Devices

Name_____   Date _____

Switches and Receptacles

_____   **1.** The ___ screw on a three-way switch indicates the common pivot point for the switch.

_____   **2.** Printed information is generally found on the ___ side of a switch.

_____   **3.** The UL label indicates that an item meets ___ and NEC® safety requirements.

_____   **4.** The letters ___ on a device indicate copper or aluminum wires can be used.

_____   **5.** If a device is not specified as copper or aluminum, ___ should be used.

T   F   **6.** Current and voltage ratings are always provided on a switch.

_____   **7.** Switches that are used to operate devices with a tungsten filament must be marked with the letter ___.

_____   **8.** ___ switches open two circuit conductors at the same time.

_____   **9.** A single-pole switch is connected in the ___ leg of a circuit.

_____   **10.** A(n) ___ on the back of a switch or receptacle indicates what length of insulation must be removed from a wire.

T   F   **11.** As a general rule, the neutral conductor should not be switched or used as one leg in a switch loop.

T   F   **12.** Three-way switches do not have ON and OFF markings.

_____   **13.** Receptacles are also known as ___ outlets.

_____   **14.** Receptacles are rated by their ___.

A. physical size   **C.** type of material
B. color   **D.** amperage and voltage

_____ **15.** The ___ tests electrical devices in Canada.

_____ **16.** ___ switches are used to control a light or device from two locations.

T   F   **17.** One or more four-way switches may be used with 2 three-way switches to provide control of a device from three or more locations.

T   F   **18.** Receptacles are designed as straight blade or locking blade.

_____ **19.** A(n) ___ plug is identified by the size of the openings, which determines which blade opening is the hot and which opening is the neutral.

_____ **20.** Silver-colored screws on a receptacle indicate the ___ terminal.

_____ **21.** Bronze-colored screws on a receptacle indicate the ___ terminal.

_____ **22.** Green-colored screws on a receptacle indicate the ___ terminal.

_____ **23.** A(n) ___ plug and receptacle may be used where a positive connection is to be maintained.

_____ **24.** A(n) ___ switch may be used where access to the switch is to be restricted.

_____ **25.** A(n) ___ switch provides light adjustment from low levels to full brilliancy.

_____ **26.** A(n) ___ switch is used to turn ON and OFF devices at predetermined times.

_____ **27.** A(n) ___ switch may be used where space is a problem.

_____ **28.** A(n) ___ switch is used to turn circuits ON and OFF according to movement within a specified distance.

_____ **29.** Receptacles marked CO/ALR are used with ___ wire only.

_____ **30.** Color coding, abbreviations, and ___ are used to provide information about switches.

Receptacles

_____ 1. Breakaway tab normally connects top and bottom receptacle

_____ 2. Canadian Standards Association

_____ 3. Underwriters Laboratories

_____ 4. Breakoff tab

_____ 5. Grounding slot

_____ 6. Hot on polarized receptacle

_____ 7. Neutral on polarized receptacle

_____ 8. Neutral screw (silver)

_____ 9. Hot screw (bronze)

_____ 10. Ground screw (green)

Light Controlled by Single-Pole Switch-Conduit

_____ 1. Splices

_____ 2. Outlet box

_____ 3. Switch

_____ 4. Source

_____ 5. Light bulb

_____ 6. Switch loop

_____ 7. Switch leg

_____ 8. Hot leg

_____ 9. Lighting fixture

Switches

_____ 1. Canadian Standards Association   _____ 7. Strip gauge

_____ 2. Copper/copper-clad wires only   _____ 8. Maximum amperage/voltage

_____ 3. Colored screw   _____ 9. Elongated holes

_____ 4. Plain screw   _____ 10. Back wiring holes

_____ 5. Plaster ears   _____ 11. Underwriters Laboratories

_____ 6. Captive mounting screw

FRONT

BACK

15 A Receptacles, 2-Pole, 3-Wire

_____ 1. 125 V

_____ 2. 250 V

_____ 3. 277 V

20 A Receptacles, 2-Pole, 3-Wire

_____ **1.** 125 V

_____ **2.** 250 V

_____ **3.** 277 V

Ⓐ

Ⓑ

Ⓒ

30 A Receptacles, 2-Pole, 3-Wire

_____ **1.** 125 V

_____ **2.** 250 V

_____ **3.** 277 V

Ⓐ

Ⓑ

Ⓒ

50 A Receptacles, 2-Pole, 3-Wire

_____ **1.** 125 V

_____ **2.** 250 V

_____ **3.** 277 V

Ⓐ

Ⓑ

Ⓒ

AWG — AMERICAN
WIRE
GAUGE (WIRE SIZE)

Chapter 6

Working with Nonmetallic-Sheathed Cable

Chapter 6 provides an overview of the characteristics of nonmetallic-sheathed cable and the procedures for preparing and routing the cable. The safe, economical, and effective installation of nonmetallic-sheathed cable is shown. The mounting of common types of boxes is covered in detail.

NONMETALLIC-SHEATHED CABLE

A *nonmetallic-sheathed cable* is an electrical conductor (cable) that has a set of insulated electrical conductors held together and protected by a strong plastic jacket. **See Figure 6-1.** The plastic jacket can contain any number of conductors; however, the typical cable contains two or three insulated conductors and a separate bare ground wire. Nonmetallic-sheathed cable is very popular in residential wiring because it is inexpensive and easy to install.

Nonmetallic-Sheathed Cable

BLACK WIRE
GROUND WIRE (CAN BE BARE)
14/2 W/GR TYPE NM
PLASTIC JACKET
WHITE WIRE

Figure 6-1. *The electrical conductors in nonmetallic-sheathed cable are protected by a rugged plastic jacket.*

INFORMATION PRINTED ON NONMETALLIC-SHEATHED CABLE

Important information is printed on the outside jacket of nonmetallic-sheathed cable. The printed information typically includes size of conductors (wire), number of conductors (with or without ground), and type of jacket.

Numbers

A considerable amount of information is printed on the outside jacket of nonmetallic-sheathed cable. The numbers, which are printed first, provide information about the size of the wire and the number of conductors in the cable, such as cable that is marked 14/2 or 12/3. The first number (in this case 14 or 12) indicates the size of the wire. The smaller the number, the larger the wire size. The second number (in this case 2 or 3) refers to the number of current-carrying conductors in the cable, not counting the ground wire. **See Figure 6-2.** To determine the load carrying capacity of any wire, the National Electrical Code® (NEC®) should be referred to for wire size and ampacity.

Over 185 companies produce nonmetallic-sheathed cable.

14 GAUGE → 15 AMPS
12 " → 20
10 " → 30
8 " → 50

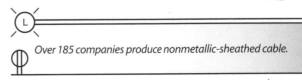
6 GAUGE → 65
4 " → 85
3 " → 100
2 " → 115
1 " → 130

1/0 GAUGE → 150 (1 ALT)
2/0 " → 175
3/0 " → 200
4/0 " → 230

Nonmetallic-Sheathed Cable Numbers

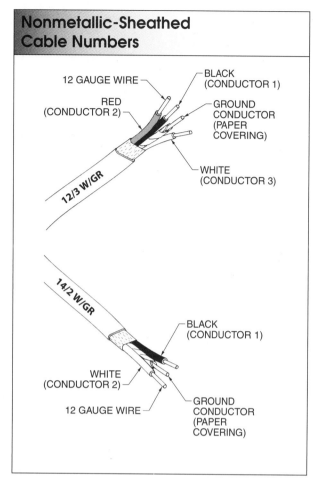

Figure 6-2. *Nonmetallic-sheathed cable is manufactured in various wire sizes and with a specified number of conductors.*

Letters

The letters NM and NMC indicate specific types of nonmetallic cable and what characteristics the cable has. *Type NM cable* is a nonmetallic-sheathed cable that has the conductors enclosed within a nonmetallic jacket and is the type typically used for dry interior wiring. *Type NMC cable* is a nonmetallic-sheathed cable that has the conductors enclosed within a corrosion-resistant, nonmetallic jacket. Article 334 of the NEC® contains detailed information on NM and NMC cable.

The letters WITH GR (with ground) indicate that a separate grounding conductor is present. **See Figure 6-3.** When a nonmetallic-sheathed cable does not clearly specify WITH GR, the cable will not contain a grounding wire.

Nonmetallic-Sheathed Cable Letters

Figure 6-3. *The identification letters and numbers of a nonmetallic-sheathed cable are found on the jacket of the cable and on the packaging that the cable is sold in.*

BUYING NONMETALLIC-SHEATHED CABLE

Nonmetallic-sheathed cable is found at electrical supply houses, hardware stores, and in some large retail stores with home repair centers. Nonmetallic-sheathed cable is typically sold in boxed rolls of 250 ft. **See Figure 6-4.** For small jobs, smaller quantities are available at hardware stores and at some electrical supply stores.

Nonmetallic-Sheathed Cable Packaging

Figure 6-4. *Nonmetallic-sheathed cable is typically packaged in rolls of 250′.*

When purchasing nonmetallic-sheathed cable, electricians must specify the length and type of cable required. For example, when an application requires 100′ of cable that has two conductors of 14 gauge wire with a separate ground wire, the cable is specified as 100′ of 14/2 WITH GR Type NM or NMC.

PREPARING NONMETALLIC-SHEATHED CABLE

Nonmetallic-sheathed cable must be prepared. Typically the cable must be cut to length, have the outer jacket removed to a distance from the end, and have a specified amount of insulation removed from the individual conductors.

Plastic Jacket Removal

Nonmetallic-sheathed cable is easy to install and requires few tools to perform a quality job. Lineman side cutting pliers are capable of cutting NM cable quickly to length. **See Figure 6-5.**

Figure 6-5. *Lineman side cutting pliers easily cut through nonmetallic-sheathed cable.*

When NM cable has been cut to length, the ends of the plastic jacket must be removed before the cable is inserted into outlet or junction boxes. To open the plastic jacket of an NM cable, a knife is used to cut through the center of the jacket where the ground wire is located. **See Figure 6-6.** The bare ground wire will guide the path of the knife blade. At least 8″ of the jacket should be removed from each end of the cable.

Figure 6-6. *The plastic jacket of nonmetallic-sheathed cable can easily be removed with a pocketknife.*

When great lengths of cable must be prepared, cable rippers are used to save time. **See Figure 6-7.** Cable rippers have a small, razor-sharp blade designed to penetrate a short distance into the cable to remove only the outer plastic cover.

ITT Holub Industries

Figure 6-7. *Cable rippers are useful where large quantities of cable are being used.* Note: *There is a small blade (not shown) that cuts the jacket.*

Cable Conductor Insulation Removal

When the outer jacket is cut away, insulation from the individual conductors (wires) can be removed. Various multipurpose wire-stripping tools are used to remove insulation from individual conductors. **See Figure 6-8.**

⚠	CAUTION

Never use a pocketknife to remove insulation from individual wires.

ROUGHING-IN NONMETALLIC CABLE

Roughing-in is a phrase that refers to the placement of electrical boxes and wires before wall coverings and ceilings are installed. Roughing-in must be performed in such a way that the entire electrical system (wires and boxes) can be easily traced after walls and ceilings are in place. All rough-in work must be carefully checked by the Authority having Jurisdiction (AHJ). Errors in the roughing-in process are compounded once the wall coverings are in place.

When roughing-in the electrical system of a residence, the integrity of the wood studs and joists must be taken into consideration. Care should be taken to not drill too many large-diameter holes. Consult local codes prior to drilling and cutting studs and joists.

Receptacle Boxes

A *receptacle box* is an electrical device designed to house electrical components and protect wiring connections. Depending on the specific application, number of wires, and size of wires, receptacle boxes can have various shapes, sizes, and standard accessories.

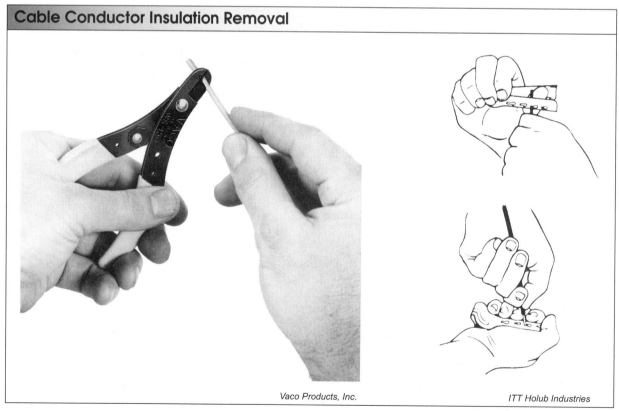

Cable Conductor Insulation Removal

Vaco Products, Inc.

ITT Holub Industries

Figure 6-8. *Wire-stripping tools can be used to remove insulation from individual cable conductors.*

Uses for Receptacle Boxes. Receptacle boxes and junction boxes must be installed at every point in the electrical system where NM cable is spliced or terminated. receptacle boxes are installed so that every point in the system is accessible for future repairs or additions. Boxes must never be completely covered to the point that a box becomes inaccessible.

Shapes and Sizes of Receptacle Boxes. Typically three shapes of receptacle boxes are used in residential wiring. The three boxes are square, octagonal, and rectangular. **See Figure 6-9.** Square, octagonal, and rectangular boxes come in various widths and depths, and with various knockout arrangements.

Never use a nonmetallic box for hanging lights or ceiling fans. A metal ceiling-mount box has large attachment screws and will be more secure than a nonmetallic box.

Boxes come in various sizes as well as various shapes. Rectangular boxes for switches are available in one-, two-, three-, or four-gang box sizes.

Box Shapes

SQUARE BOX

SWITCH AND RECEPTACLE BOX

CEILING LIGHT FIXTURE BOX

OCTAGONAL BOX

RECTANGULAR BOX

Figure 6-9. *Typical boxes found in residential wiring are square and rectangular (for switches and receptacles) and octagonal (for ceiling fixtures).*

Per the NEC®, luminaire outlet boxes must provide adequate space for conductors.

Although there is no hard-and-fast rule regarding the shape of a box, octagonal boxes are typically used in ceilings for lighting fixtures. Square and rectangular boxes are typically used for switches and receptacles. Any of the three are used for junction boxes.

The size of an outlet box is based on the number and the size of the wires entering the box. More wires and larger size wires require a larger or deeper box. Manufacturer specification sheets must be consulted when ordering boxes to find the appropriate volume (cubic inch capacity) box. Additional information can be obtained from the NEC®.

A *knockout* is a round indentation punched into the metal of a box and held in place by unpunched narrow strips of metal. Knockouts (abbreviated KO) are located in the sides and bottoms of outlet boxes and provide ready access from any direction. **See Figure 6-10.** Knockouts must be removed to attach fittings for wiring.

Mounting Boxes. Boxes are typically secured by nails. The nails may be part of the box or driven through straps in the box. **See Figure 6-11.** When a box must be mounted between studs and joists, hangers are used. Almost all ceiling outlet boxes are mounted with bar hangers.

Removing Box Knockouts

Klein Tools, Inc.

Figure 6-10. *Box knockouts must be removed to attach fittings for wiring.*

Mounting Plastic Boxes

When mounting plastic boxes, the box should be positioned against the stud so that the front of the box will be flush with the finished surface of the wall. **See Figure 6-12.** For example, if the finished wallboard is ½″ drywall, the box should be positioned ½″ past the face of the stud. When the wallboard will be covered by tile, the thickness of the tile must be taken into account.

Too many conductors in a box are known as a "cable fill violation." Refer to NEC® Article 314.16, Number of Conductors in Outlet, Device, and Junction Boxes and Conduit Bodies, for proper box size. Boxes must have enough volume to account for the receptacle and incoming and outgoing conductors. Nonmetallic boxes are available in sizes of 16, 18, 20.3, and 22.5 cu in. and have the volume stamped on the inside of the box. Check the manufacturer's catalog for the volume of metal boxes.

Knockout Holes. In each plastic box there is an area where knockout holes can be created. The knockouts can be removed before or after a box is mounted. **See Figure 6-13.** Any sharp edges that might penetrate the plastic sheathing that surrounds the NM cable should be removed. Burrs or sharp edges can typically be removed by rotating a screwdriver around the knockout hole. **See Figure 6-14.**

Mounting Boxes

SIDE NAILS

FRONTAL STRAP

SIDE STRAP

SIDE BRACKET

SIDE STRAP

BAR HANGER

Midland Ross Corp., Electrical Products Div.

Bowers, Division of Norris Industries

BOXES WITH MOUNTING ACCESSORIES

BAR HANGER

MOUNTED ON WOOD

SIDE STRAP

FRONT STRAP

WALL MOUNTINGS

BAR HANGER

CEILING MOUNTING

Figure 6-11. *A variety of box mounting accessories and methods are used for mounting (securing) boxes.*

Plastic Box Depth Positioning

⅜" OR ½"
DRYWALL
ALLOWANCES

Figure 6-12. *When mounting plastic boxes, the box should be positioned against the stud so that the front of the box is flush with the finished surface of the wall.*

Deburring Plastic Box Knockout Holes

Figure 6-14. *Burrs and sharp edges can be removed from knockout holes by rotating a screwdriver around the hole.*

Receptacle and switch boxes must be installed to allow enough room for the drywall to be flush with the front section of the box.

Plastic Box Knockouts

Figure 6-13. *Plastic box knockouts are typically removed with a screwdriver.*

When securing cables to a box, at least 8" of wire must extend beyond the bottom of the box to allow enough wire for making connections to receptacles and switches. **See Figure 6-15.** When securing nonmetallic cables to studs and joists, a wide range of staples are available. **See Figure 6-16.**

Determining Length of Conductors to Plastic Box

Figure 6-15. *At least 8″ of wire must extend beyond the bottom of a box to allow for connections to receptacles and switches.*

Mounting Plastic Boxes between Studs. To mount a plastic box between studs a cross block is used. Cross blocks are installed with the top edge 46″ above the floor so that when the box is attached, the face of the box is flush with the finished wall. The box is attached to the cross block with nails or screws. **See Figure 6-17.**

Drilling Holes

There is some difference of opinion on whether holes should be drilled before or after boxes are mounted. For the beginner, it is best to mount the boxes first according to the plan and then drill the holes. Mounting the box first reduces the number of unnecessary holes and saves time.

Large-diameter holes (½″ and larger) can be cut into wooden joists and studs by using a power drill and either a spade bit, auger bit, self-feed wood borer, or hole saw attachment.

NM Cable Staples

STAPLES

Figure 6-16. *NM cables must be secured with staples at various positions of the cable run.*

Mounting Plastic Boxes between Studs

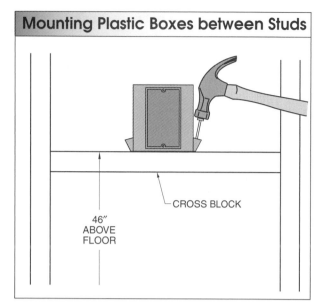

Figure 6-17. *Plastic boxes are mounted to cross blocks when located between studs.*

Holes in studs or floor joists can be made most effectively with an offset drill. **See Figure 6-18.** Electricians use offset drills almost exclusively because offset drills easily fit between studs and joists. When an offset drill is not available, a heavy-duty electric drill with a spade power bit is substituted. **See Figure 6-19.** All holes should be drilled as straight as possible to aid in pulling wires through multiple studs. **See Figure 6-20.**

Heavy-Duty Electric Drills

Milwaukee Electric Tool Corp.

Figure 6-19. *A heavy-duty electric drill with a hole saw is used for drilling holes when a right angle drill is not available.*

Offset Drills

Milwaukee Electric Tool Corp.

Figure 6-18. *Offset or right angle drills are ideal for drilling in tight spots between studs.*

Drilling Holes in Studs

Figure 6-20. *Holes in studs should be drilled at the same height to aid in running cables.*

Installing Cable Runs

When all holes have been properly drilled, NM cable can be installed quickly and easily. To obtain the proper length of cable required, the cable should be pulled into position before cutting. Positioning the cable ensures that enough, but not an excessive amount of, cable is pulled. **See Figure 6-21.**

Figure 6-21. *Cable should be pulled to the proper positions and cut to length to avoid waste.*

Cable and conductors should be stripped before being installed in a box. **See Figure 6-22.** Stripping the wire before installing the wire into a box saves time later when outlets and switches are being installed.

Figure 6-22. *Cable jacket and conductor insulation should be removed from the wire before it is installed in the box.*

Stripping cable is much easier to perform from outside a box than from inside a box. When stripping the cable, leave at least 8″ of wire for rough-in purposes. It is easier to cut off excess wire later than to try to add wire.

Routing through Studs and Joists. Running nonmetallic cable through stud walls and through floor joists is the most popular way of routing. **See Figure 6-23.** Typically, holes are drilled through the center of the studs and joists. This practice reduces the possibility of a nail penetrating deep enough to puncture the cable. When cable is run through drilled holes, no additional support is required.

Figure 6-23. *Generally cable is run through holes in studs or floor joists.*

In some instances, studs may have to be notched instead of drilled. **See Figure 6-24.** When notches are substituted for holes, the cable run must be protected from nails by a steel plate at least ¹⁄₁₆″ thick.

Figure 6-24. *When notches are substituted for holes, a cable must be protected by a minimum of a ¹⁄₁₆″ steel plate.*

When installing runs of cable 2′ and longer, do not bundle the cables together because the heat generated from the flow of current within the bundle may damage the insulation of the cables.

Routing around Corners. Routing cables through solid corners can sometimes be complicated. Various methods are used to overcome the problem of solid corners.

One method is to drill holes from each side at an angle to accommodate a cable run. **See Figure 6-25.** Drilling holes from each side will save wire but may be time-consuming if the holes do not line up properly. Another method is to notch the corner studs, using steel plates for protection.

Milwaukee Electric Tool Corp.
A jab saw can be used to notch studs when routing cables.

Routing over or under a corner is another method of routing cable. At first glance, the looping under method appears to be the most economical method, but looping under requires extra time. The extra time is due to someone being required to go into the basement or crawl space to send the wire back up through the floor. The over method is accomplished rapidly by one electrician without leaving the room.

Routing through Masonry Walls. Type NM cable may be fished through masonry walls if no moisture is present and the wall is above grade. **See Figure 6-26.** When moisture is present, type NMC cable must be used. Neither NM nor NMC cable can be embedded in poured cement, concrete, or aggregate.

Securing Cable

NM and NMC cable must be supported or secured (stapled) every 4½′ of cable run and within 12″ of a box. NM and NMC cables can also be secured using guard strips.

Routing Cables around Studded Corners

DRILLING HOLES FROM
EACH SIDE OF THE SOLID CORNER
AT AN ANGLE

NOTCHING CORNER STUDS

ROUTING OVER CORNER

ROUTING UNDER CORNER

METHODS OF ROUTING CABLES AROUND CORNERS

Figure 6-25. *Cables can be run through holes or notches in corner studs, or run over or under the corner.*

Cable Run Stapling. When cable has been pulled into position, the cable must be securely fastened with special staples. Nonmetallic cable staples typically have a plastic strap that reduces the possibility of damage to the cable. **See Figure 6-27.** The NEC® requires that all cables be secured near an outlet box.

Using a hammer or piece of wood cut to the proper length as a height gauge ensures that all holes drilled through studs for cable runs are at the same height.

Routing Cable through Masonry Walls

Figure 6-26. *Type NM cable may be fished in masonry walls when no moisture is present and the cable run is above grade; when moisture is present, type NMC must be used.*

Stapling NM and NMC Cables

Figure 6-27. *NM and NMC cable is firmly secured using staples designed for nonmetallic cable.*

When cable is not supported by holes or notches, but rests along the sides of joists, studs, or rafters, the cable must be stapled every 4½′. **See Figure 6-28.** Cables must also be stapled under

floor joists in such a way that the cables do not present problems later when the basement ceiling is being installed.

Cable Stapling Distance

Figure 6-28. *Horizontal cable runs not supported by holes must be stapled every 4½′. Cable runs on the sides of joists, studs, or rafters require no additional protection.*

Placing Guard Strips. Nonmetallic cables must be protected when routed across the face of roof rafters, studs within 7′ of the floor, or attics accessible by stairs. A quick method of protection is the use of wooden guard strips. **See Figure 6-29.** Wooden guard strips must be at least as thick as the cable being protected.

Placing Guard Strips

Figure 6-29. *When cable is run across the face of roof rafters, across studding within 7′ of the floor, or in attics accessible by stairs, it must be protected by guard strips at least as high as the cable.*

Securing Ground Wires. When a cable is secured, a good mechanical and electrical ground must be established to provide electrical protection. **See Figure 6-30.** The three widely accepted methods of proper residential grounding are component, pigtail, and clip.

Component grounding is a grounding method where the ground wire is attached directly to an electrical component such as a receptacle. Component grounding requires that the grounding wire be attached before the electrical component is permanently mounted.

Ground wires are installed to help protect equipment and wiring from electrical power surges. The main cause of these surges is lightning strikes. The magnetic field created by a lightning strike can induce voltage into both current-carrying conductors, such as those found in appliances and electronics, and noncurrent-carrying conductors, such as water pipes. If the current from the surge cannot find a path from the appliance to ground, it will take a path through electronic equipment or a phone line, or arc through the air.

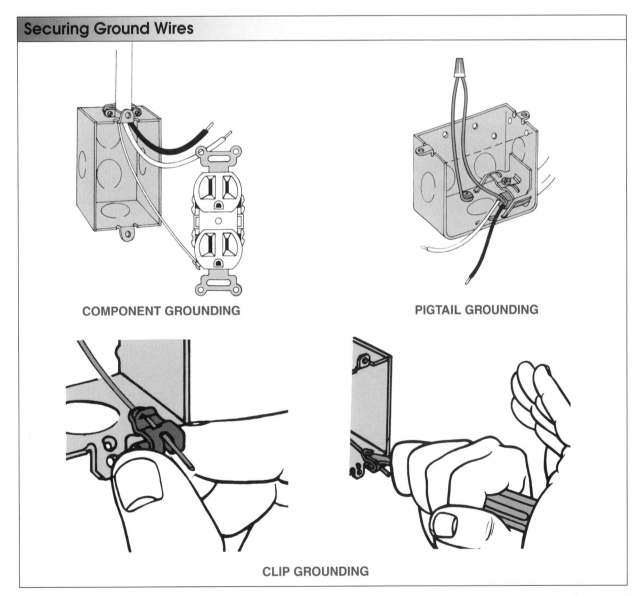

Securing Ground Wires

COMPONENT GROUNDING

PIGTAIL GROUNDING

CLIP GROUNDING

Figure 6-30. *The three widely accepted methods of proper residential grounding are component grounding, pigtail grounding, and clip grounding.*

Pigtail grounding is a grounding method where two grounding wires are used to connect an electrical device to a grounding screw in the box and then to system ground. The box ground wire is secured to a threaded hole in the bottom of the box. Once secured, the cable ground wire is pigtailed to the box ground wire.

Clip grounding, like pigtail grounding, can be secured as the cable is put in place. *Clip grounding* is a grounding method where a grounding clip is merely slipped over the grounding wire from the electrical device. The grounding wire and grounding clip are secured with pressure using a screwdriver.

Securing Cables in Outlet Boxes

Cables are secured to outlet boxes by clamps. The three types of clamps typically available for nonmetallic cables are saddle, straight, and cable connectors. **See Figure 6-31.** Saddle clamps and straight clamps are part of an outlet box when manufactured. Cable connectors are installed by electricians. **See Figure 6-32.** Locknuts are installed so that the points of the nut point inward to dig firmly into the metal box.

Box Cable Clamps

NONMETALLIC CABLE CLAMPS

Figure 6-31. *Various types of cable clamps are used to secure nonmetallic cable to outlet and junction boxes.*

Tech Tip: Cord-and-Plug-Connected Equipment

CORD-AND-PLUG-CONNECTED EQUIPMENT

RECEPTACLE OUTLET INSTALLED WHEREVER CORD-AND-PLUG-CONNECTED EQUIPMENT IS TO BE USED
• 210.50(B)

6'
MAXIMUM
• 210.50(C)

6'
MAXIMUM
• 210.50(C)

When inserting cable through clamps, care must be taken not to damage any insulation by scraping the cable on the rough surfaces and edges. Care must also be taken when tightening cable clamps. Too much pressure can cause the clamp to penetrate the insulation and cause a short circuit.

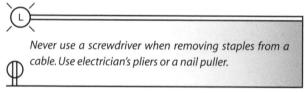

Never use a screwdriver when removing staples from a cable. Use electrician's pliers or a nail puller.

Folding Back Wires

Many wires have been needlessly damaged because they were left exposed. The very last roughing-in task is to tuck the wires neatly into the outlet boxes. **See Figure 6-33.** The time taken to fold back wires helps to avoid damage to the wires as wall coverings are being placed and other construction is being performed.

Fitting Locknuts

START LOCKNUT BY HAND   **TIGHTEN LOCKNUT**

Figure 6-32. *The points of the locknut dig firmly into the metal box.*

Folding Back Wires

FOLDED WIRES

Figure 6-33. *Wires that are neatly folded into a box avoid being damaged as other construction is performed.*

Chapter 6

Test

Name_____ Date _____

Working with Nonmetallic-Sheathed Cable

_____ 1. NMC is protected by a strong ___ jacket.

_____ 2. NMC usually contains two or three insulated conductors and a bare ___ wire.

_____ 3. The first number identifying nonmetallic-sheathed cable provides the ___ size.

_____ 4. The second number identifying nonmetallic-sheathed cable provides the number of ___ conductors.

_____ 5. The letters NM and NMC indicate ___ of nonmetallic-sheathed cable.

_____ 6. Type NMC cable is ___ -resistant and fungus-resistant.

_____ 7. Type ___ cable is typically used for interior (dry) wiring.

_____ 8. The letters ___ on nonmetallic-sheathed cable stand for "with ground."

_____ 9. Nonmetallic cable is typically sold boxed in ___' rolls.

_____ 10. An outlet box or junction box is installed when NM cable is ___ or terminated.

T　　　F 11. Boxes in walls can be completely covered for appearance.

T　　　F 12. The size of an outlet box is generally based on the number and size of wires entering the box.

_____ 13. The three shapes of outlet boxes are ___, ___, and ___.
- **A.** square; round; rectangular
- **B.** square; hexagonal; octagonal
- **C.** square; rectangular; octagonal
- **D.** none of the above

T　　　F 14. Only square boxes are used for junction boxes.

143

_____ 15. ___ are round indentations punched into a metal box and held in place by narrow strips of metal.

_____ 16. Almost all ceiling outlet boxes are mounted with ___.

T   F   17. NM cable should be cut before being pulled through a wall.

T   F   18. NM cable should be stripped before being installed in a box.

_____ 19. When stripping NM and NMC cable, at least ___″ should be left outside the box.

_____ 20. Cable routed through notches in stud walls is protected by a(n) ___″ steel plate.

T   F   21. Types NM and NMC cable can be embedded in concrete.

T   F   22. Component grounding is the direct attachment of the component grounding wire to a box.

T   F   23. Cables are secured in outlet boxes by clamps.

_____ 24. Cable must be supported within ___″ of a box.

T   F   25. Type NM cable may be fished in masonry walls when no moisture is present.

T   F   26. Type NM cable can be routed through the corners of stud walls by notching the corner studs.

_____ 27. ___ refers to the placement of electrical boxes and wires before wall coverings and ceilings are installed.

T   F   28. Pocketknives should not be used to remove insulation from wires.

T   F   29. Cable rippers are used to remove the outer cover of cables efficiently.

T   F   30. Outlet boxes are generally secured by nails.

Mounting Square Boxes

_____ 1. Brace

_____ 2. Side strap

_____ 3. Bar hanger

_____ 4. Front strap

(A)

(B)

(C)

(D)

Cables

_____ 1. Clamp

_____ 2. Stripping

_____ 3. NMC

_____ 4. Octagonal box

_____ 5. Notching

_____ 6. NM

_____ 7. Pigtail ground

_____ 8. Knockout

_____ 9. Ground

_____ 10. Guard strip

A. Corrosion-resistant cable

B. Provides electrical protection

C. Secures cable in outlet box

D. Used for lighting outlets

E. Round indentation

F. Cable for dry interior wiring

G. Must be at least as thick as cable

H. Removing insulation

I. Ground wire secured to box

J. Requires 1/16" steel plate for cable protection

145

Cables in Walls and Floors

_____ 1. Cable through drilled studs

_____ 2. Cable through drilled floor joists

_____ 3. Cable protected by guard strips within 7' of floor, in attics, or across roof rafters

_____ 4. Cable through notched studs protected by ¹⁄₁₆″ steel plate

_____ 5. Cable supported every 4½' on sides of joists, studs, or rafters

Electrical Boxes

_____ 1. Octagonal box,
side strap

_____ 2. Rectangular box,
side nails

_____ 3. Rectangular box,
frontal strap

_____ 4. Octagonal box,
side bracket

_____ 5. Octagonal box,
bar hanger

_____ 6. Rectangular box,
side strap

Ⓐ

Ⓑ

Ⓒ

Ⓓ

Ⓔ

Ⓕ

147

Grounding

_____ 1. Component grounding

_____ 2. Clip grounding

_____ 3. Pigtail grounding

Ⓐ

Ⓑ

Ⓒ

NM and NMC

_____ 1. #14 wire, two conductor, with ground, corrosion-resistant

_____ 2. #14 wire, three conductor, with ground

_____ 3. #12 wire, two conductor, with ground

_____ 4. #12 wire, three conductor, with ground

_____ 5. #14 wire, two conductor

_____ 6. #12 wire, two conductor, with ground, corrosion-resistant

14/3 W/GR TYPE NM

Ⓐ

14/2

Ⓑ

14/2 W/GR TYPE NMC

Ⓒ

12/3 W/GR TYPE NM

Ⓓ

12/2 W/GR TYPE NM

Ⓔ

12/2 W/GR TYPE NMC

Ⓕ

Chapter 7

Creating Electrical Systems from Electrical Plans

Chapter 7 provides an overview of how complete electrical circuits are installed. Combining electrical components and wires into circuits is the most rewarding part of electrical construction. Various symbols and schematics are used to design systems to fit specific needs. Chapter 7 provides information on how electrical plans are developed into actual system wiring, how various switching circuits are wired, and how switches, receptacles, and lights are installed.

ROOM LAYOUTS

The ultimate objective of learning to read and follow electrical plans is the finished product, an electrical system that is ready to use. All the knowledge of electrical components and installation is expressed in the finished electrical system. The use of standard plans and private plans result in a full-scale house plan and electrical system that meets the needs of the occupants.

Component Layout

Electrical components are installed in locations typically shown on the floor plans. An isometric drawing (construction layout) can help to clarify the approximate location of all switches, receptacles, and light fixtures. **See Figure 7-1 through Figure 7-15.** Component layouts are directly coordinated to the actual construction layout which includes the stud walls and electrical boxes.

Electrical Layouts

An electrical layout is a drawing that indicates how the component parts of a circuit will be connected to one another and where the wires will be run. Careful planning of the electrical layout results in substantial savings by eliminating long runs of wire. Electrical layouts are used by individuals to determine where to place electrical boxes and how many boxes are required. Electrical layouts are helpful in determining a bill of material and approximate costs of an electrical project.

Wire runs shown on actual construction drawings should indicate the most economical use of wire.

Wire runs are laid out on a wiring layout in a very smooth and definite pattern to make the drawing easier to follow. In many cases, wire runs shown at right angles on the wiring layout could have been run diagonally in the room to conserve wire. When any cable runs are routed on a job site, shortening the wire runs always results in lower installation costs.

Bedroom Wiring

FROM SWITCH

COMPONENT
LAYOUT

TO LIGHT

COMPONENT LAYOUT

FROM
RECEPTACLE

ISOMETRIC DRAWING
(CONSTRUCTION LAYOUT)

TO RECEPTACLE

GROUND

FROM RECEPTACLE

COMPONENT LAYOUT

ELECTRICAL LAYOUT

S₁

L

Figure 7-1. *A typical bedroom wiring layout shows receptacles, a switch, and a ceiling fixture.*

Exploded Views

Exploded views or component layouts provide key points for the construction of an electrical circuit by providing detailed representations of how each component is actually wired into the system. When component wiring is duplicated, the component can be given a letter designation to indicate the device is wired exactly the same way.

Wiring Methods

Although it is assumed that conduit is being used in most construction layouts, all circuits can be wired with metallic sheathed cable or nonmetallic cable.

The NEC® lists 38 different wiring methods that apply to construction and remodeling projects. Of these 38 methods, 21 may be used in residential construction. Of these 21 methods, 14 methods are typically used in single-family home construction. Of the 14 methods, 6 are for wiring with cable assemblies, 4 are for wiring with metallic conduits, and 4 are for wiring with flexible and rigid nonmetallic conduits.

Use of Room Designs

Wiring layouts provide enough information to successfully wire each room. Wiring layouts must be studied carefully to determine how each component will be connected. All residential electrical systems vary, but all systems have items in common. The design of an electrical circuit for one room might require only minor changes to be used for another room.

When performing remodeling work, it is important to locate the studs behind a finished wall without damaging the wall. This can be done by either using a battery-operated stud finder or by drilling a ¼" hole and inserting a wire bent to a 90° angle and then rotating the wire until you feel the stud.

Tech Tip: Passing Cable through Forced-Air HVAC Systems

NONMETALLIC CABLE

NM CABLE MAY PASS HORIZONTALLY THROUGH CLOSED-IN STUD/JOIST SPACE WHEN USED AS RETURN IN FORCED-AIR HVAC SYSTEM

AIR DUCT FORMED BY STUDS AND DRYWALL

TO FURNACE

DRYWALL

RETURN AIR GRILLE

DRYWALL

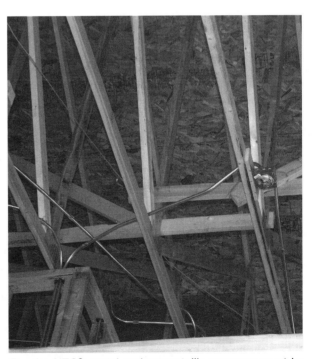

Per the NEC®, metal and nonmetallic raceways must be continuous between all cabinets, boxes, fittings, or other enclosures and outlets.

Bedroom and Closet Wiring

POWER FROM
RECEPTACLE

TO
CEILING
LIGHT

FROM SWITCH

FROM
SWITCH

COMPONENT
LAYOUT

COMPONENT
LAYOUT

COMPONENT LAYOUT

TO
CLOSET
LIGHT

COMPONENT
LAYOUT

ISOMETRIC DRAWING
(CONSTRUCTION LAYOUT)

TO
RECEPTACLE

FROM RECEPTACLE

COMPONENT LAYOUT

ELECTRICAL LAYOUT

Figure 7-2. *A typical bedroom with closet wiring layout shows receptacles, two ceiling lights, and switches for the two ceiling lights.*

Bathroom Wiring

FROM RIGHT
WALL LIGHT BOX

WALL LIGHT
FIXTURE

TO LEFT
WALL LIGHT BOX

COMPONENT
LAYOUT

TO RIGHT
WALL LIGHT BOX

FROM
SWITCH

COMPONENT
LAYOUT

GFCI

FROM SWITCH

COMPONENT
LAYOUT

BOX CAN BE
PART OF FAN AND
LIGHT HOUSING

ISOMETRIC DRAWING
(CONSTRUCTION LAYOUT)

GFCI   TO SWITCH

FROM SUPPLY

COMPONENT
LAYOUT

TO FAN AND LIGHT

FROM
GFCI
BOX

PER NEC® 210.11(C)(3)
BATHROOM BRANCH
CIRCUITS, AT LEAST ONE
20 A BRANCH CIRCUIT
SHALL BE PROVIDED.

COMPONENT
LAYOUT

GFCI   (L)   S₁   (L)

(L)
(F)

S₁ S₁   GFCI

ELECTRICAL LAYOUT

Figure 7-3. *A typical bathroom wiring layout shows two lighting fixtures, a combined fan and ceiling light, and two GFCI receptacles.*

Hallway and Light Wiring

FROM LIGHT

COMPONENT LAYOUT

POWER IN

FROM SWITCH

FROM SWITCH

COMPONENT LAYOUT

FROM LIGHT

COMPONENT LAYOUT

TO LIGHT

POWER IN

COMPONENT LAYOUT

ISOMETRIC DRAWING
(CONSTRUCTION LAYOUT)

TRAVELERS

RED

BLACK

3-WAY
SWITCH

3-WAY
SWITCH

BLACK

WHITE

WHITE

WIRING DIAGRAM

S_3

S_3

L

ELECTRICAL LAYOUT

Figure 7-4. *One wiring layout for a hallway shows a single light controlled from two locations.*

Hallway and Two-Light Wiring — Two Switches

TO LIGHT

FROM SWITCH

TO LIGHT #2

FROM SWITCH

FROM LIGHT

COMPONENT LAYOUT

COMPONENT LAYOUT

COMPONENT LAYOUT

TO SWITCH

FROM RECEPTACLE

TO SWITCH

FROM SUPPLY

COMPONENT LAYOUT

COMPONENT LAYOUT

ISOMETRIC DRAWING (CONSTRUCTION LAYOUT)

S_3

L

L

S_3

ELECTRICAL LAYOUT

Figure 7-5. *A wiring layout for a hallway with a light controlled from two locations shows use of two switches.*

Hallway and Two-Light Wiring—Three Switches

FROM SWITCH — — TO LIGHT

COMPONENT LAYOUT

FROM SWITCH

TO LIGHT

FROM LIGHT

COMPONENT LAYOUT

COMPONENT LAYOUT

FROM RECEPTACLE

TO SWITCH

COMPONENT LAYOUT

TO JUNCTION BOX

FROM SUPPLY

COMPONENT LAYOUT

ISOMETRIC DRAWING (CONSTRUCTION LAYOUT)

FROM SWITCH

TO LIGHT

COMPONENT LAYOUT

TRAVELERS

BLACK   BLACK

RED   RED

3-WAY SWITCH   3-WAY SWITCH

4-WAY SWITCH

BLACK   WHITE

HOT

WHITE   COMMON

WIRING DIAGRAM

S_3

L

L

S_4 S_3

ELECTRICAL LAYOUT

Figure 7-6. *A wiring layout for a hallway with two lights controlled from three locations shows use of three switches.*

Living Room Wiring

FROM RECEPTACLE

COMPONENT LAYOUT

COMPONENT LAYOUT

FROM RECEPTACLE

TO SWITCH

TO RECEPTACLE

POWER IN

SPLIT-WIRED RECEPTACLE

COMPONENT LAYOUT

ISOMETRIC DRAWING (CONSTRUCTION LAYOUT)

TO RECEPTACLE

SPLIT-WIRED RECEPTACLE

COMPONENT LAYOUT

FROM RECEPTACLE

S_1

ELECTRICAL LAYOUT

Figure 7-7. *A living room wiring layout with split-wired receptacles controlled from one location uses one switch.*

Living Room Wiring—Two Switches

SPLIT-WIRED RECEPTACLE

FROM RECEPTACLE

COMPONENT LAYOUT

TO RECEPTACLES

3-WAY SWITCH

FROM RECEPTACLE

COMPONENT LAYOUT

TO SWITCH

SPLIT-WIRED RECEPTACLE

POWER IN

COMPONENT LAYOUT

TO RECEPTACLES

3-WAY SWITCH

COMPONENT LAYOUT

FROM RECEPTACLE

SPLIT-WIRED RECEPTACLE

TO RECEPTACLE

COMPONENT LAYOUT

ISOMETRIC DRAWING (CONSTRUCTION LAYOUT)

S_3

S_3

ELECTRICAL LAYOUT

NOTE: BREAKING TABS MUST BE REMOVED FOR USE AS SPLIT-WIRED RECEPTACLE

Figure 7-8. *A living room wiring layout with split-wired receptacles controlled from two locations uses two switches.*

Garage Wiring

Figure 7-9. *A garage wiring layout has two lights and uses one 1-way switch and two 3-way switches.*

Outdoor Garage Lighting Wiring

Figure 7-10. *In this wiring layout, the outdoor lighting is controlled from either the foyer or the kitchen area.*

Kitchen Wiring

GFCI RECEPTACLES REQUIRED FOR EVERY 4′ OF CONTINUOUS COUNTER SPACE (12″ WIDE OR GREATER)

RECEPTACLE HEIGHT ABOVE COUNTERTOP CANNOT EXCEED 18″

ANY WALL SPACE THAT IS 2′ IN LENGTH BUT LESS THAN 6′, REQUIRES A RECEPTACLE

RECEPTACLES FOR COOKTOPS, OVENS, COMPACTORS OR REFRIGERATORS CANNOT BE MORE THAN 4′ FROM APPLIANCE

GARBAGE DISPOSAL RECEPTACLE OR JUNCTION BOX CANNOT BE MORE THAN 3′ FROM GARBAGE DISPOSAL

DISHWASHER RECEPTACLE OR JUNCTION BOX CANNOT BE MORE THAN 4′ FROM DISHWASHER

NOTE: ALL OTHER WALL BOXES MUST BE WITHIN 18″ OF FLOOR (12″ TYPICAL) FOR HANDICAP 36″

REFRIGERATOR RECEPTACLES ARE TYPICALLY 40″ ABOVE FLOOR (15 A OR 20 A DEDICATED CIRCUIT)

Figure 7-11. *A pictorial kitchen layout shows the locations of all electrical appliances and receptacles specified by building and electrical codes.*

When installing GFCI receptacles near a kitchen countertop, consideration must be given to the height of the backsplash, which is installed to prevent water from getting between the countertop and the wall, at the back of the wall countertop space. Typical backsplash height is 4″ but can vary from one house to another. Check with the builder or check the blueprints before installing receptacles near a kitchen counter.

Leviton Manufacturing Co., Inc.

GFCI receptacles are available in a variety of colors to help coordinate with kitchen and bathroom decor.

Kitchen Wiring — 230 V Receptacles

ISOMETRIC DRAWING
(CONSTRUCTION
LAYOUT)

WHITE

RED

BLACK

GREEN

HIGH-VOLTAGE (230 V)
RECEPTACLE FOR
DOUBLE OVEN
OR COOKTOP

COMPONENT LAYOUT

ELECTRICAL LAYOUT

Figure 7-12. *A kitchen oven and cooktop wiring layout shows the locations of 230 V receptacles.*

Kitchen Wiring — GFCIs

ISOMETRIC DRAWING (CONSTRUCTION LAYOUT)

FROM GFCI

TO GFCI

FROM SUPPLY

TO GFCI

GFCI

GFCI

COMPONENT LAYOUT

GFCI   GFCI

GFCI

GFCI

ELECTRICAL LAYOUT

Figure 7-13. *A kitchen wiring layout shows the ground fault circuit interrupters (GFCIs).*

Kitchen Wiring — Lighting and Exhaust

FROM RECEPTACLE/SWITCH

TO OVERHEAD LIGHT

TO SWITCH

TO FAN

FROM BOX TO BOX

FROM BOX TO BOX

TO OVERHEAD LIGHT

FROM BOX

ISOMETRIC DRAWING (CONSTRUCTION LAYOUT)

FROM SUPPLY

TO BOX

COMPONENT LAYOUT

ELECTRICAL LAYOUT

Figure 7-14. *A kitchen wiring layout shows lighting and exhaust fan wiring.*

Kitchen Wiring — Dishwasher, Garbage Disposal, and Refrigerator

FROM
SWITCH

FROM
SUPPLY

TO
GARBAGE
DISPOSAL

SWITCH FOR
GARBAGE
DISPOSAL

**ISOMETRIC DRAWING
(CONSTRUCTION
LAYOUT)**

FROM
SUPPLY

DISHWASHER CAN
BE HARDWIRED

COMPONENT LAYOUT

S S

ELECTRICAL LAYOUT

Figure 7-15. *A kitchen wiring layout shows dishwasher and garbage disposal wiring.*

Lighting Fixtures

Although lighting fixtures differ greatly in outward appearance, most fixtures are wired to the electrical system of a residence in the same way. **See**

Figure 7-16. Most lighting fixtures will have black and white wires from the manufacturer. The black and white wires are typically connected to the corresponding black and white wires found in the cable or conduit run.

Lighting Fixtures

OUTDOOR LIGHT FIXTURE

CHANDELIERS

FLUORESCENT LIGHTING FIXTURE

CEILING FIXTURE

RECESSED LIGHTING FIXTURE

Figure 7-16. *All common light fixtures are wired in a similar manner.*

Chapter 7

Test

Name_____ **Date** _____

Wiring Electrical Systems

Connect the components as shown on the wiring diagrams and schematics. Use the following to indicate wires:

_____   -------------------------   +++++++++++++++++

        BLACK   WHITE   RED

1.

WIRING DIAGRAM   SCHEMATIC

2.

WIRING DIAGRAM   SCHEMATIC

3.

WIRING DIAGRAM   SCHEMATIC

4.

WIRING DIAGRAM   SCHEMATIC

5.

WIRING DIAGRAM   SCHEMATIC

6.

ELECTRICAL LAYOUT **SCHEMATIC**

7.

ELECTRICAL LAYOUT **SCHEMATIC**

8.

ELECTRICAL LAYOUT **SCHEMATIC**

169

9.

ELECTRICAL LAYOUT   SCHEMATIC

10.

ELECTRICAL LAYOUT   SCHEMATIC

170

Chapter 8

Working with Metallic-Sheathed Cable

Chapter 8 provides an overview of how to install metallic-sheathed cable. Metallic-sheathed cable is similar to nonmetallic-sheathed cable but provides more protection and requires more attention when cutting. The proper installation of metallic-sheathed cable results in an electrical system that meets most local residential electrical codes.

Metallic Sheathed Cable

TRW Crescent Wire and Cable

Figure 8-1. *Metallic-sheathed cable consists of two or more insulated wires protected by a flexible metal jacket.*

METALLIC-SHEATHED CABLE

Metallic-sheathed cable is a type of cable that consists of two or more individually insulated wires protected by a flexible metal outer jacket. **See Figure 8-1.**

Metallic-sheathed cable is often referred to as armored cable or BX. Armored cable provides additional protection to wires by using a metal outer jacket. The trade name BX was used to denote the armored cable produced by one specific manufacturer. The BX trade name became so popular that even armored cable produced by other manufacturers was called BX.

Armored cable has a typical construction. **See Figure 8-2.** In addition to insulation, each current-carrying conductor has a paper wrapping. The paper provides additional protection within the cable but is removed from the conductors when the cable is being installed into boxes.

A *bonding wire* is an uninsulated conductor in armored cable that is used for grounding. The bonding wire is in contact with the flexible metal outer jacket to assure a proper conducting (ground) path along the entire length of an armored cable. Bonding wires are typically made of aluminum or copper.

BX Cable Construction

INSULATION
PAPER WRAPPER
BONDING STRIP
FLEXIBLE METAL JACKET
CONDUCTORS

Figure 8-2. *BX cable has a bonding strip, and each insulated conductor of the cable is wrapped with paper for extra protection.*

PURCHASING ARMORED CABLE

As with nonmetallic cable, armored cable is purchased with a specific number of current-carrying conductors. Armored cable is typically sold in coils of 250′. **See Figure 8-3.** When armored cable is ordered, the cable is typically specified as 12/3 or 14/2 to indicate the wire size (8, 10, 12, or 14) and the number of current carrying conductors (2, 3, 4, or 5) required. When designating armored cable, the phrase "with ground" is not required because the outer metal jacket and bonding wire automatically establish a conductive grounding path.

Armored Cable Coils

Figure 8-3. *Armored cable (BX) is typically sold in coils of 250′.*

Types of Armored Cable

The NEC® recognizes three types of armored cable for residential work: AC, ACT, and ACL. AC and ACT armored cables are used in dry locations. Both AC and ACT may be fished through the air voids of masonry walls when the walls are not exposed to excessive moisture. Both AC and ACT may be used for under-plaster electrical extensions. ACT armored cable is used for either exposed work or concealed work.

ACL armored cable is embedded in concrete or masonry, run underground, or used where gasoline or oil is present. **See Figure 8-4.** ACL armored cable is lead-covered to provide additional protection for masonry and underground applications. Article 332 of the NEC® contains detailed information on ACL armored cabling.

ACL Armored Cables

— LEAD COVERING

Figure 8-4. *ACL armored cable is covered with a layer of lead.*

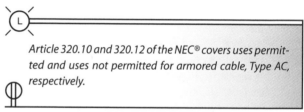

Article 320.10 and 320.12 of the NEC® covers uses permitted and uses not permitted for armored cable, Type AC, respectively.

PREPARING ARMORED CABLE

Installing armored cable requires many of the same techniques and equipment used when working with nonmetallic cable. However, armored cable requires more attention when cutting and splicing because of the sharp metal edges.

Cutting Armored Cable

Most electricians use a hacksaw to cut through the metal jacket of armored cable. **See Figure 8-5.** The first step is to cut through the outer armor (one of the convolutions) at a 45° angle about 6″ to 8″ from an end. To avoid damage to the insulation of conductors, care must be taken not to cut too deeply into the jacket of the cable. When the armored cable is cut, the cable is separated by twisting the two sections apart. The armored cable must be carefully flexed until the cable breaks.

Cutting Armored Cable — Hacksaw

CUT CABLE AT 45° ANGLE

FLEX CABLE UNTIL CABLE BREAKS

CONVOLUTION

Figure 8-5. *A hacksaw must cut across one of the convolutions of the cable at a 45° angle for the cable to separate properly.*

Twisting the cable can open the convolutions enough so that tin snips or cable cutters can be inserted. **See Figure 8-6.** Armored cable cutters are used to avoid damaging the insulation on the conductors. The use of protective gloves helps protect hands from cuts and scratches. When the outer armor and conductors are cut, a second trimming cut may be required to remove any of the metal outer jacket that is bending outward.

A center cut is used to separate the armored cable while side cuts prepare each end for mounting the cable to electrical boxes.

Installing Anti-Short Bushings

Whenever armored cable is cut, an unavoidable sharp edge remains on the ends of the metal armor. To avoid any damage to the insulation of the conductors, anti-short bushings must be installed. **See Figure 8-7.**

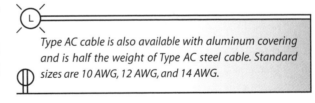

Type AC cable is also available with aluminum covering and is half the weight of Type AC steel cable. Standard sizes are 10 AWG, 12 AWG, and 14 AWG.

Cutting Armored Cable — Cable Cutters

CABLE CUTTER

OUTER JACKET

Figure 8-6. *When using armored cable cutters, care must be exercised not to pinch the conductor insulation.*

Anti-Short Bushings

Figure 8-7. *To protect conductors from the sharp edges of cut armored cable, plastic anti-short bushings must be used.*

An *anti-short bushing* is a plastic or heavy fiber paper device used to protect the conductors of armored cable. The bushing covers the sharp edges at the ends of the armor to reduce the possibility of damage to conductor insulation.

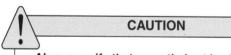

⚠️ **CAUTION**

Always verify that an anti-short bushing has been installed on the end of armored cable before installing the cable.

ROUGHING-IN ARMORED CABLE

To rough-in armored cable, the cable must be pulled, cut, secured, and grounded properly.

Pulling Armored Cables

When roughing-in armored cable into studded walls, the cable must be pulled into position first and then cut to length. **See Figure 8-8.** Pulling the armored cable into position, then cutting to length, reduces

waste. To avoid twisting and kinking the cable, it should be unwound from the center of the coil. After the cable has been pulled into position, three cuts are made in the armor about 6″ to 8″ apart. The entire cable is cut through with a center cut.

Pulling and Cutting Armored Cables to Length

Figure 8-8. *To install armored cable, three cuts must be made to the armored jacket. A center cut is used to separate the cable, and two side cuts prepare each end for mounting to electrical boxes.*

The two side cuts are cut through the metal armor (sheath) only; the conductors and insulation are left intact. One end of the cable is used to terminate the run previously started, and the other end is used to start the next run. When wires are concealed in walls, cable runs can be shortened by allowing the cable to run wild, thus saving an amount of cable. **See Figure 8-9.**

⚛️ **Tech Tip: AC Cable Installation Requirements**

Armored Cable Running Wild

Figure 8-9. *The length of an armored cable that is concealed in a wall can be shortened by allowing the cable to run wild.*

To avoid breaking armored cable, sharp bends should not be made. **See Figure 8-10.** Typically a bend in armored cable must have a minimum radius at least 5 times the diameter of the cable. Armored cable installations have a typical appearance when work is completed. **See Figure 8-11.**

Bending Armored Cable

Figure 8-10. *Armored cable cannot be bent tighter than the recommended bending radius without causing damage to conductors.*

Tech Tip: AC Cable Support Requirements

The outer sheathing and terminal connectors of Type AC cable can be used as a grounding path for the equipment it is connected to. Type AC cable is also available with a separate equipment grounding conductor (EGC). The bonding strip is not considered an EGC and can be removed with a cable cutter at the ends of the cable sheathing. Type AC cable is available with three current-carrying conductors and either with or without an EGC.

Armored Cable Installation

Figure 8-11. *Armored cable installations have a typical appearance when work is completed.*

Securing Armored Cables

Armored cable is secured in place with cable clamps or cable connectors. **See Figure 8-12.** Cable clamps are typically part of a box, while cable connectors are installed before a box is wired. A right angle connector (90° connector) is used where the radius bend of the armored cable would be so tight that the cable would snap if forced into the bend. **See Figure 8-13.**

Grounding Armored Cables

Grounding armored cable requires that the metal jacket and bonding wire be firmly secured. **See Figure 8-14.** A typical method used to ground armored cable is to secure the bonding wire of the cable between the connector and box. Other methods of grounding armored cable are the same as with grounding nonmetallic cable.

An armored cable cutter is used to cut a notch in Type AC cable by cutting only the material covering of the cable without damaging the conductors inside the cable.

Armored Cable Box Clamps and Connectors

Figure 8-12. *Armored cables can be secured to a box with cable clamps, which are part of the box, or cable connectors, which are installed at wiring.*

Armored Cable Box Connectors

STRAIGHT-ON BOX ENTRY

90° BOX ENTRY

OFFSET

Figure 8-13. *Armored cable connectors are used for straight-on box entry and for 90° box entry.*

Grounding Armored Cable

BONDING WIRE

ARMOR

BUSHING

PAPER

SHOULDER ON CONNECTOR

BONDING WIRE

ARMOR

BONDING WIRE

ARMOR

BONDING WIRE

Figure 8-14. *The bonding wire of armored cable is secured between the box connector and the box to create a proper grounding path.*

Name_____ Date _____

Working with Metallic-Sheathed Cable

T	F	**1.**	Armored cable is also known as BX.

_____   **2.** Each current-carrying conductor of armored cable has a(n) ___ wrapping over the insulation.

_____   **3.** The ___ wire used for grounding in armored cable can be Cu or Al.

    T   F   **4.** The 3 in the armored cable designation 12/3 refers to the gauge of the conductors.

_____   **5.** The 14 in the armored cable designation 14/2 refers to wire ___.

    T   F   **6.** Type ACL cable may be embedded in concrete.

    T   F   **7.** Type ACT cable may be used for exposed work.

    T   F   **8.** Type ACL cable may be embedded in masonry.

_____   **9.** ___ cable is lead-covered.

_____   **10.** ___ cable is only for use in dry, concealed locations.

_____   **11.** Types AC and ACT cable may be fished through air voids of masonry walls when the walls are not exposed to excessive ___.

    T   F   **12.** Type ACL cable may be run underground.

_____   **13.** When gasoline or oil is present, ___ type of cable must be used.

_____   **14.** When cutting the jacket of armored cable with a hacksaw, the cut should be made at a(n) ___° angle.

_____   **15.** An anti-short bushing for armored cable is made of ___ or heavy fiber paper.

    T   F   **16.** Armored cable should be cut to length before being pulled into position.

_____   **17.** ___ are placed on the cut ends of armored cable to avoid any damage to conductor insulation.

_____ **18.** A bend (radius) in armored cable should be at least ___ times the diameter of the cable.

_____ **19.** Armored cable must be secured within ___″ of receptacles or switch boxes.

T   F   **20.** Cable clamps are typically part of a box.

T   F   **21.** Cable connectors are typically part of the box.

_____ **22.** Grounding armored cable requires that the metal jacket and the ___ be firmly secured.

T   F   **23.** The paper wrapper of armored cable should be removed from the individual conductors contained within boxes.

T   F   **24.** Armored cable is typically sold in 100′ coils.

_____ **25.** The ___ recognizes three types of armored cable.

T   F   **26.** AC and ACT cables are used for underplaster extensions.

_____ **27.** To avoid twisting and kinking, armored cable should be removed from the ___ of the coil.

_____ **28.** A ___ cut is used to separate armored cable.

_____ **29.** Metallic ___ are used to fasten armored cable to studs and joists.

T   F   **30.** Armored cable connectors may be used for straight-on or 90° entry into a box.

Armored Cable

_____ **1.** Fished in masonry walls	**A.** Metallic cable	
_____ **2.** Secures metallic cable	**B.** Bonding wire	
_____ **3.** Exposed or concealed work	**C.** 14/2 or 12/3	
_____ **4.** BX	**D.** AC	
_____ **5.** Wire size and number of conductors	**E.** ACL	
_____ **6.** Protects conductor insulation	**F.** ACT	
_____ **7.** Continuous electrical path	**G.** Anti-short bushing	
_____ **8.** Copper or aluminum	**H.** Metallic cable bend	
_____ **9.** Embedded in concrete	**I.** Cable connector	
_____ **10.** At least 5 times the cable diameter	**J.** Grounding	

Metallic-Sheathed Cable Components

_____ 1. Conductors

_____ 2. Insulation

_____ 3. Flexible metallic jacket

_____ 4. Paper wrapper

_____ 5. Bonding wire

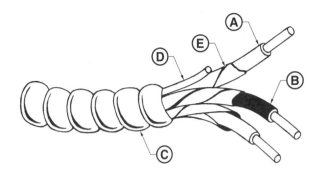

Armored Cable Connectors and Clamps

_____ 1. Straight armored cable connector

_____ 2. Armored cable clamp in place

_____ 3. Armored cable connector in place

_____ 4. 90° armored cable connector

Metallic-Sheathed Cable Parts

_____ 1. Armored cable

_____ 2. BX

_____ 3. ACL

_____ 4. Bonding wire

_____ 5. Anti-short bushing

A. Lead-covered armored cable

B. Serves same purpose as grounding conductor

C. Trade name for armored cable

D. Protects conductor's insulation

E. Two or more insulated wires protected by a flexible metal jacket

181

Installing Armored Cable

_____ **1.** Octagonal box

_____ **2.** Support required if over 12″

_____ **3.** Inner radius of bends is not less than 5 times the diameter

_____ **4.** Bar hanger

_____ **5.** Cable secured within 12″ of box

_____ **6.** Top plate

_____ **7.** Bridging

_____ **8.** Stud

_____ **9.** Receptacle box

_____ **10.** Staple

Chapter 9

Wiring with Conduit

Chapter 9 provides an overview of how to install electrical metallic conduit. A conduit (metal pipe) wiring system is probably the most challenging of residential electrical systems because of the extra planning, special tools, and basic skill required to create a professional-looking system. Chapter 9 provides several tips and techniques for additions and repairs to existing conduit systems. Any design layout, however, must be performed in accordance with the National Electrical Code® and local building inspector.

TYPES OF CONDUIT

Conduit is a rugged protective tube (typically metal) through which wires are pulled. Although several types of conduit are used in the electrical industry, only three types are commonly found in residential installations. The three most common types of conduit are electrical metallic tubing (EMT), rigid conduit, and flexible metal conduit. **See Figure 9-1.**

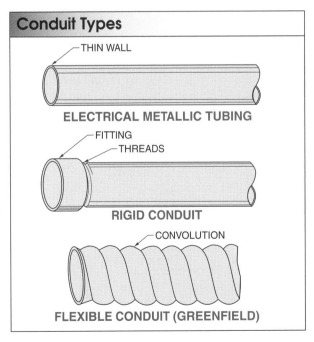

Conduit Types

THIN WALL

ELECTRICAL METALLIC TUBING

FITTING

THREADS

RIGID CONDUIT

CONVOLUTION

FLEXIBLE CONDUIT (GREENFIELD)

Figure 9-1. *Electrical metallic tubing (EMT) is the most common conduit used in residential wiring.*

The primary function of the conduit is to provide protection for conductors.

Electrical Metallic Tubing (EMT)

Electrical metallic tubing (EMT) is a light-gauge electrical pipe often referred to as thin-wall conduit. EMT has a wall thickness that is about 40% the thickness of rigid conduit. Because EMT is lighter, easier to bend, and requires no threading, EMT is typically used for a complete residential layout. Additional information on the installation of EMT can be found in Article 358 of the NEC®.

Rigid Metal Conduit (RMC)

Rigid metal conduit (RMC) is a heavy-duty pipe that is threaded on the ends much like standard plumbing pipe. For residential use, rigid conduit is limited mainly to risers for service entrances. Rigid conduit can be cut with a standard hacksaw and must be threaded with a standard cutting die (plumbing die) providing ¾″ per foot taper. Many electrical supply houses carry a number of conduit sizes in various lengths that are prethreaded and ready for use. Additional information on the installation of rigid metal conduit can be found in Article 344 of the NEC®.

Flexible Metal Conduit (FMC)

Flexible metal conduit (FMC) is a conduit that has no wires, and can be bent by hand. The conductors (wires) are not installed until the system is complete. Generally, flexible metal conduit is used where some type of movement or vibration is present. For example, flexible conduit is suited for wiring to a motor. Flexible conduit (Greenfield) is also used where other conduits might be difficult to bend. Additional information on the installation of flexible metal conduit can be found in Article 348 of the NEC®.

Conduit benders are available in hydraulically powered models to help reduce fatigue of the electrician. Hydraulic-powered conduit benders can bend conduit with diameters of 1″ through 4″ and are available with a hand-powered hydraulic pump or a ½ HP electric motor driven pump.

INSTALLING EMT

To install EMT conduit, an individual must purchase, cut, bend, and secure the conduit.

Purchasing EMT

EMT is typically purchased in bundles of 100′. The bundles contain ten lengths of conduit, each 10′ long. **See Figure 9-2.** Most electrical supply houses warehouse conduit; therefore, individual lengths of 10′ can typically be purchased. The trade sizes for conduit range from ½″ to 4″. **See Figure 9-3.** All sizes of conduit have limitations on the size and number of conductors that are allowed in the conduit for an application such as residential wiring. Further information on the allowable number of conductors per size of conduit can be obtained from Annex C of the NEC®. **See Figure 9-4.**

Figure 9-2. *EMT and rigid conduit are typically sold in 100′ bundles.*

EMT Conduit Specifications

Inside Diameter Nearest ¹⁄₁₆″	Inside Diameter	Outside Diameter	Trade Size in Inches
⅝	0.622	0.706	½
¹³⁄₁₆	0.824	0.922	¾
1¹⁄₁₆	1.049	1.163	1
1⅜	1.380	1.508	1¼
1⅝	1.610	1.738	1½
2¹⁄₁₆	2.067	2.195	2
2¾	2.731	2.875	2½
3⅜	3.356	3.500	3
3¹³⁄₁₆	3.834	4.000	3½
4⁵⁄₁₆	4.334	4.500	4

Figure 9-3. *EMT conduit is typically specified by nominal size.*

Maximum Number of Conductors Allowed

NO. 14   NO. 12

NO. 10   NO. 8

½″ CONDUIT

EMT and RIGID CONDUIT

SIZE THHN AWG WIRE	½″ CONDUIT	¾″ CONDUIT
14	6*	11*
12	4*	8*
10	3*	5*
8	2*	3*

*Half the wire amount indicated by the NEC® for some applictions due to typical residental amperage ratings

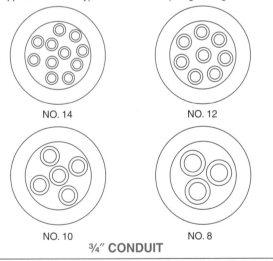

NO. 14   NO. 12

NO. 10   NO. 8

¾″ CONDUIT

Figure 9-4. *Each conduit size has a maximum number of wires allowed.*

Cutting EMT

Conduit is typically cut to length using a hacksaw. **See Figure 9-5.** However, all the rough edges from cutting must be removed before wire can be pulled through conduit. Removing the rough edges is called "deburring" and is accomplished with a conduit deburring tool designed for this purpose. **See Figure 9-6.** Conduit can also be deburred with a file or a special deburring tool called a reamer.

Cutting EMT

Republic Steel Corp.

Figure 9-5. *EMT conduit is typically cut with a hacksaw.*

Conduit Deburring Tool

CONDUIT FITTING AND REAMING SCREWDRIVER

Klein Tools, Inc.

Figure 9-6. *When conduit has been cut, the conduit must be deburred to remove rough edges.*

Bending EMT

EMT conduit bends and offsets require a certain amount of planning and practice. Using proper procedures, techniques, and tools, bends and offsets can be successfully created.

Conduit Benders. Bending EMT conduit properly requires the aid of a hand conduit bender. **See Figure 9-7.** A hand rigid or heavywall conduit bender is sometimes referred to in the trade as a "hickey." A hand conduit bender has high supporting sidewalls to prevent flattening or kinking of the EMT conduit. **See Figure 9-8.**

Hand Conduit Benders

HIGH SIDEWALL

Klein Tools, Inc.

Figure 9-7. *Hand conduit benders are specifically designed to bend EMT conduit.*

Bending Conduit Forty-Five Degrees

45° ANGLE CREATED WHEN HANDLE OF BENDER IS IN VERTICAL POSITION

EMT (THINWALL) CONDUIT

45°

HIGH SIDEWALL

Figure 9-8. *EMT conduit is bent to 45° when the handle of the hand conduit bender is exactly vertical.*

Forty-Five Degree Bends. To create a 45° angle (bend), a hand bender is placed on EMT conduit. The handle of the bender is raised until the handle is in the vertical position. The handle is pulled until the angle required (45°) is completed. The hand bender is removed, releasing the EMT conduit with a smooth-flowing 45° bend. Hand benders also have a long arc that permits making 90° bends in a single sweep without moving the bender to a new position.

Ninety Degree Bends. Ninety degree bends are used to turn corners or to form a predetermined length for use as a stub up through a floor that will be added onto later. **See Figure 9-9.** The typical method for laying out a 90° bend requires that the conduit be marked to a predetermined measurement.

Note: The distance marked on the tubing must be visually lined up with the hand bender by the individual.

Bending Conduit Ninety Degrees

10 ¾″

10 ¾″

Figure 9-9. *A typical method of creating a 90° bend in EMT conduit is to bend the conduit to a predetermined measurement.*

The accuracy to which an individual lines up the marks on the bender determines how accurate the conduit bend will be. For the novice, it is recommended that the accuracy of bends be checked using a level. **See Figure 9-10.**

Using proper technique to secure conduit during bending assures conduit bends are made to the needed requirements. **See Figure 9-11.**

Checking Ninety Degree Bends

CONDUIT HORIZONTAL

BEAD VERTICAL

2

1

Klein Tools, Inc.

Figure 9-10. *A level is typically used to check conduit for a properly created 90° bend.*

Technique for Bending Conduit Ninety Degrees

Republic Steel Corp.

Figure 9-11. *Proper technique for securing conduit while making a bend with a hand conduit bender is critical.*

Back-to-Back Bends. When running conduit from one outlet box to another box, the run can require that two 90° bends be made to one piece of conduit. The use of two 90° bends is called back-to-back bending. To make back-to-back bends, the first bend is made as a regular 90° bend. **See Figure 9-12.** Then the distance between the boxes is laid out on the conduit as distance *D*. The direction of the hand bender is reversed and point A of the bender is placed over the mark at distance *D*. Raising the hand bender to form a normal 90° bend finishes the second right angle. When creating back-to-back bends, individuals must take care to ensure that both bends line up with each other (are on the same plane or flat).

Creating Back-to-Back Ninety Degree Bends

BEND WHEN COMPLETED

THINWALL CONDUIT

"D"

POINT "A" ON BENDER SET AT DISTANCE "D"

Figure 9-12. *When creating back-to-back bends, electricians must ensure that both bends line up with each other (are on the same plane or flat).*

Offsets. If all conduit bends were as simple as 45° and 90° bends, conduit forming would be a relatively simple art. Unfortunately, conduit runs are often interrupted by obstructions requiring changes in direction that cannot be accomplished by using just 45° and 90° bends. An offset is a compound bend in conduit used to bypass many types of obstructions. **See Figure 9-13.** An *offset* is laid out with the aid of parallel lines drawn on a floor or other smooth surface. Always double-check all dimensions for an offset bend on the floor layout. The hand bender must be repositioned on the conduit to create both offset bends. **See Figure 9-14.** A simple method for checking the accuracy of an offset bend uses a pocket level. **See Figure 9-15.**

Offset Bends

Figure 9-13. *The second bend of an offset is readily determined by using parallel lines drawn on the floor.*

A hickey conduit bender is typically used when making a series of short-radius bends in rigid and heavywall conduit with diameters of ½″, ¾″, and 1″.

Checking Offset Bends

Klein Tools, Inc.

Figure 9-15. *Pocket levels are used to check the accuracy of offset bends.*

Double Offsets (Saddles). A *double offset* or saddle is a common complex bend made in conduit to bypass obstructions. **See Figure 9-16.** Standard procedures are used in creating a double offset. **See Figure 9-17.**

Note: Use parallel lines to provide a frame of reference for a double offset. Parallel lines on each side of the conduit are used to help eliminate any deviation from center.

Creating Offset Bends

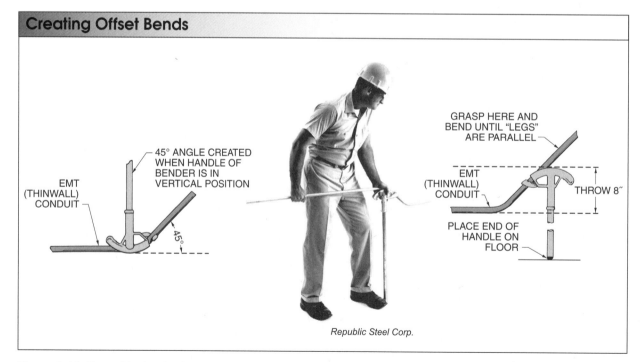

Republic Steel Corp.

Figure 9-14. *Repositioning the hand bender and conduit is required to make the second bend of an offset.*

Double Offsets (Saddles)

Figure 9-16. *Double offsets or saddles are used to clear obstructions.*

> Standard hand conduit benders are made of aluminum or iron and include angle markings of 22½°, 25°, 45°, 60°, and 90° on both sides of the bender.

Creating Double Offsets (Saddles)

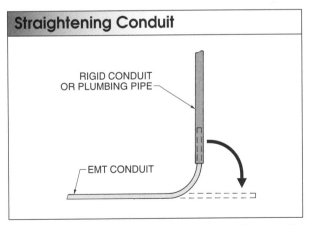

Figure 9-17. *A standard procedure is used to create double offsets (saddles).*

An alternative method can occasionally be used to create a saddle. Typically, the alternative method of creating a saddle is used where the bend will not be seen. **See Figure 9-18.**

Alternating Method for Creating a Saddle

Figure 9-18. *The alternative method of creating a saddle is used where the saddle will not be seen, such as in a drop ceiling.*

Straightening Conduit. When electricians are first learning to bend conduit, some bends will miss the mark. To avoid scrapping the conduit, the conduit can sometimes be rebent to straightness. A common technique is used to straighten incorrect bends. **See Figure 9-19.** A piece of rigid conduit, the handle of a conduit bender or plumbing pipe, is typically used as a straightening tube.

Straightening Conduit

Figure 9-19. *When straightening bent conduit, place the conduit on a hard surface.*

Rules Concerning Conduit Bends. Per Article 358.24 of the NEC®, *Bends – How Made,* bends in tubing shall be made so that the tubing will not be damaged and that the internal diameter of the tubing will not be effectively reduced.

In addition, per Article 358.26 of the NEC®, *Bends – Number in One Run,* a run between pull points (between outlet and outlet, between fitting and fitting, or between outlet and fitting) shall not contain more than the equivalent of four 90° bends (360° total), including bends located immediately at the outlet box or fitting. The NEC® table Annex –

Table 2, *Radius of Conduit and Tubing Bends,* indicates the minimum acceptable radius for various sizes of conduit.

Securing EMT

The NEC® requires that EMT be installed as a complete system and be securely fastened in place at least every 10′ and within 3′ of each outlet box, junction box, cabinet, or fitting. **See Figure 9-20.** Conduit must be installed into smooth-flowing pathways through which wires can be easily pulled. **See**

Securing EMT

ONE HOLE PUSH-ON CONDUIT STRAP

TWO HOLE CONDUIT STRAP

TOP PLATE

COMPRESSION COUPLINGS

HEADER

DOOR OPENING

SWITCH

SET SCREW BOX CONNECTIONS

ONE HOLE STRAP

NAIL-UP STRAP

SOLE PLATE

BRIDGING

STUD

OUTLET

NAIL-UP CONDUIT STRAP

Figure 9-20. *Conduit straps secure conduit in position. Straps must be used for every 10′ of conduit run and within 3′ of a box.*

Figure 9-21. Conduit is secured in place and attached to electrical boxes and other conduit using straps, connectors, and couplings.

Conduit Connectors

EMT is firmly secured to electrical boxes using compression, indenter, and set screw connectors. **See Figure 9-22.** Each type of connector has a distinctly different technique for holding the conduit securely. Various types of connectors are accepted by the NEC® for residential use.

Compression Connectors. A *compression connector* is a type of box fitting that firmly secures conduit to a box by utilizing a nut that compresses a tapered metal ring (ferrule) into the conduit. **See Figure 9-23.** As the compression nut is tightened, the nut forces the ferrule into the conduit, locking the conduit in position. Compression connectors can be loosened to remove the conduit and reused multiple times to attach the same piece of conduit.

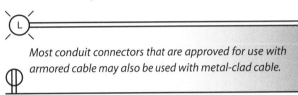

Most conduit connectors that are approved for use with armored cable may also be used with metal-clad cable.

Figure 9-21. *Conduit and fittings that are properly installed form a smooth-flowing pathway through which wires can be run.*

Conduit Connectors

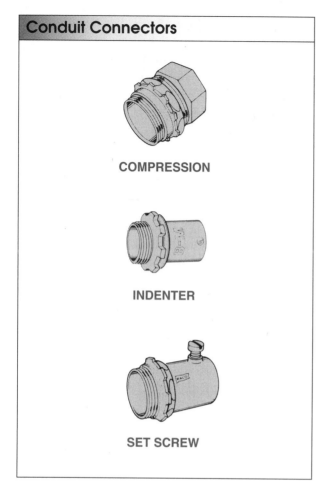

COMPRESSION

INDENTER

SET SCREW

Figure 9-22. *Conduit connectors hold conduit securely to boxes.*

Compression Connectors

LOCKNUT

COMPRESSION NUT

Figure 9-23. *Compression connectors are held in place by a locknut, and secure conduit in place with a compression nut and ferrule.*

Indenter Connectors. An *indenter connector* is a type of box fitting that secures conduit to a box with the use of a special indenting tool. **See Figure 9-24.** Indenter coupling connectors are not reusable and must be cut off with a hacksaw to be removed.

Indenter Connectors

INDENTER CONNECTOR

INDENTING TOOL

INDENTATION

Raco Inc.

Figure 9-24. *Indenter connectors require a special indenting tool for installation.*

Set Screw Connectors. A *set screw connector* is a type of box fitting that relies on the pressure of a screw against the conduit to hold the conduit in place. **See Figure 9-25.** Set screw connectors are also reusable.

Conduit Couplings. Unlike metallic and nonmetallic cable, conduit must be joined together using conduit couplings when a run exceeds 10′. A *conduit coupling* is a type of fitting used to join one length of conduit to another length of conduit and still maintain a smooth inner surface. **See Figure 9-26.** Conduit couplings are similar in design to back-to-back conduit connectors and operate on the same principles of compression, indentation, and pressure.

Set Screw Connectors

CONNECTOR — CONDUIT

Raco Inc.

CONDUIT CONNECTOR

Figure 9-25. *Set screw connectors are quickly and securely installed with a screwdriver.*

Compression and set-screw connectors and couplings are designed for use with all rigid conduit and compresion fittings are impervious to rain, moisture, and concrete.

Conduit Couplings

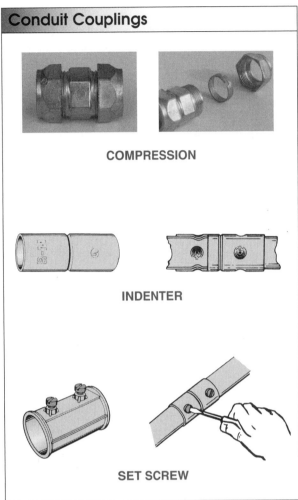

COMPRESSION

INDENTER

SET SCREW

Figure 9-26. *Conduit couplings use the same techniques as conduit connectors (compression, indenting, and set screw) to join two lengths of conduit.*

Tech Tip: RMC Installation

EXPOSED THREADS
PROHIBITED

COUPLING

BENDS NOT TO
TOTAL MORE THAN
360° IN ONE RUN

RMC

Applications that require conduit to be run where water is present require that special liquid-tight conduit and watertight conduit couplings be used. **See Figure 9-27.**

Article 350 of the NEC® provides guidelines for liquid-tight flexible metal conduit (LFMC) which is used to connect equipment that vibrates during normal operation and is located outdoors or near wet locations.

Liquid-Tight Conduit Connector

HARDENED STEEL LOCKNUT
HAS TANGS THAT DIG INTO BOX FOR EXCELLENT CONTINUITY OF GROUND. LOCKNUT WILL NOT SLIP OR SPIN.

INSULATED THROAT
PROTECTS INSULATION ON WIRE AND EASES WIRE PULLING. YELLOW COLOR EASILY SEEN BY INSPECTORS

STEEL GROUNDING FERRULE
EASILY THREADED BY HAND. FITS CONVOLUTIONS OF CONDUIT SECURELY TO ELIMINATE PULL-OUTS AND ENSURE CONTINUITY OF GROUND. DISTORTION FREE TO REMAIN REUSABLE.

HEXAGONAL COMPRESSION NUT
IS SCREW MACHINED STEEL THROUGH 1" AND MALLEABLE IRON ON LARGER SIZES.

"O" RING ASSEMBLY
GIVES BETTER LIQUID-TIGHT PROTECTION AROUND KNOCKOUT OF SHEET METAL BOX. NEOPRENE GASKET SEALS OUT LIQUIDS AND STEEL RETAINING RING PROTECTS GASKET FROM DISTORTION. "O" RING ASSEMBLY MUST BE ORDERED SEPARATELY.

BODY
IS VIRTUALLY UNBREAKABLE. STRAIGHT CONNECTORS THROUGH 1" ARE SCREW MACHINED STEEL; OTHER SIZES MALLEABLE IRON. THREADS AT LEFT ARE TAPERED TO ENSURE LIQUID-TIGHT SEAL IN THREADED HUB.

NYLON GLAND RING
IS SPLIT FOR EASE OF INSTALLATION AND GREATER COMPRESSION. REVERSIBLE DESIGN CANNOT BE INSTALLED FACING THE WRONG WAY. NYLON IS IMPERVIOUS TO LIQUIDS, UNAFFECTED BY TEMPERATURE EXTREMES AND RESISTS ABRASION.

LIQUID-TIGHT CONDUIT
CUTAWAY VIEW SHOWS FELXIBLE STEEL CORE UNDER PLASTIC JACKET.

Figure 9-27. *Specifically designed (watertight) conduit connectors and couplings must be used when liquid-tight conduit is being used in a wet environment.*

INSTALLATION OF RIGID METAL CONDUIT

Bending rigid metal conduit requires many of the skills used to bend EMT. The primary difference is that rigid metal conduit is heavier and much more difficult to bend, requiring use of heavy-duty hydraulic machinery. Due to the difficulty in bending, rigid metal conduit is typically threaded. The threads allow threaded fittings such as elbows to be used instead of bending the conduit. **See Figure 9-28.**

Fortunately, very little rigid metal conduit is used in residential construction. For residences, rigid metal conduit is typically only used for overhead service risers and for underground services. For service installations, rigid metal conduit can be purchased precut and prethreaded. Electrical supply houses or hardware stores typically stock a variety of lengths and sizes of rigid metal conduit ready for use. Electrical supply houses or stores also carry stock fittings such as 45° and 90° bends. When special lengths are required, rigid metal conduit can be cut and threaded by a supply house for an additional fee.

INSTALLATION OF FLEXIBLE METAL CONDUIT

Flexible metal conduit (Greenfield) uses the same techniques for installation as metallic sheathed cable. Flexible metallic conduit is a metal conduit, with no wires, that can be bent by hand. Flexible metal conduit differs from metallic sheathed cable in that wires must be pulled through flexible metal conduit after installation. **See Figure 9-29.**

Pulling Wires through Conduit

Fishing is the term used for the process of pulling wires through conduit. **See Figure 9-30.** A *fish tape* is a device used to pull wires through conduit. The fish tape is extended and pushed through the conduit until the tape reaches an opening. At the opening the wires being installed are firmly secured to the fish tape. The fish tape is retrieved by pulling the tape out of the conduit with the wires attached. The fish tape must be pulled evenly and smoothly to allow the wires to move easily through the conduit. Typically, one electrician operates the fish tape while another electrician feeds the wires into the conduit.

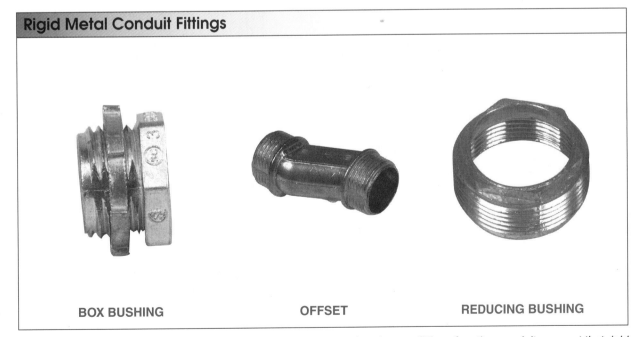

Rigid Metal Conduit Fittings

BOX BUSHING   OFFSET   REDUCING BUSHING

Figure 9-28. *The fittings for rigid metal conduit perform the same functions as fittings for other conduits, except that rigid metal conduit has threads for connections.*

Flexible Metal Conduit Installation

FLEXIBLE METAL CONDUIT (NO WIRE)

Figure 9-29. *Flexible metal conduit requires that wires be pulled through the conduit after installation.*

Pulling Wire through Conduit

Figure 9-30. *Always securely fasten wires to a fish tape before pulling the wires through conduit.*

Two types of fish tapes are typically used by electricians. **See Figure 9-31.** One type of fish tape is made of a rigid steel ribbon while the other type is a more flexible polyethylene tape. A *rigid fish tape* is a wire-pulling device used for pulling wires through conduit, and pulling wires through walls and ceilings during remodeling. A *polyethylene fish tape* is a wire-pulling device typically used to pull wire within conduit systems.

Occasionally, wires being pulled through conduit can become difficult to pull. Two aids are used by electricians when pulling wires through conduit, pulling grips and lubricants. **See Figure 9-32.** A *pulling grip* is a device that is attached to a fish tape to allow

more leverage. A *lubricant* is a wet or dry compound that is applied to the exterior of wires to allow the wires to slide better. If pulling the wires is still difficult with a hand grip and lubricant, compare the number and size of wires in the conduit to NEC® standards.

Fish Tapes

RIGID STEEL RIBBON

POLYETHYLENE

Klein Tools, Inc.

Figure 9-31. *Steel ribbon fish tapes are the more common tape used by electricians because of their suitability for general use.*

Underground conduit frequently fills with moisture, and even interior conduit saturated with wire pulling lubricants can rust a steel fish tape. A nylon-coated tape is impervious to moisture and will last longer under these conditions.

Wire Pulling Aids

**FLEXIBLE - EYE
PULLING GRIP**

SQUEEZE
BOTTLE

LUBRICANT

Klein Tools, Inc.

Figure 9-32. *Wire pulling aids are helpful when pulling wires through conduit.*

Rigid metal conduit can be grounded to the water system piping of a dwelling.

Trimming Out a Conduit System

For the most part, installing switches and receptacles in a conduit system is the same as in any other system. In a properly installed metal conduit system, switches and receptacles are grounded through the conduit. However, an additional green wire pulled through the system and attached to the green grounding screw provides additional grounding security. **See Figure 9-33.** Conduit is also used to add on to or extend existing systems. **See Figure 9-34.**

Trimming Out Conduit System

RECEPTACLE

GROUNDING
HOLES

GREEN HEX NUT
GROUNDING SCREWS

GROUNDING WIRE

Harvey Hubbell, Inc.

Figure 9-33. *Pulling and connecting a separate ground wire can establish additional switch and receptacle grounding security.*

A power cable puller is used to pull large cables and wires into place. Power cable pullers are similar to fish tapes but use a gas- or electric-powered motor to pull wire. This reduces the strain and fatigue of the operator. Power cable pullers can pull cables up to distances of 200′ and use up to 2000 lb of force.

Extending Existing Conduit Systems

**CONDUIT RUN TO
OUTSIDE LAMP-POST**

**UNDERGROUND CONDUIT CONNECTING
HOME TO GARAGE**

SECURING OUTDOOR WEATHERPROOF RECEPTACLE

Figure 9-34. *Conduit with weatherproof connectors, couplings, and boxes is required for all outside conduit systems.*

Chapter 9

Test

Name_____ Date_____

Wiring with Conduit

_____ 1. Electrical metallic tubing is also known as ___ conduit.

_____ 2. ___ metal conduit is threaded on the ends.

_____ 3. ___ metal conduit is similar to armored cable but without the wires.

_____ 4. EMT is typically sold in ___' bundles.

_____ 5. EMT is ___.
   A. lighter than rigid conduit　　**C.** threaded conduit
   B. 10' in length per piece　　　**D.** both A and B

_____ 6. EMT shall be securely fastened ___.
   A. within 36" of boxes　　　**C.** at every bend
   B. at least every 10'　　　　**D.** both A and B

_____ 7. A run of EMT shall not contain more than four quarter bends totaling ___°.

_____ 8. Pulling wire through conduit is also known as ___.

T　　　　F 9. Lubricants may be used to facilitate wire pulls through EMT.

T　　　　F 10. Receptacles are typically grounded by metal piping when using EMT.

T　　　　F 11. Compression connectors are firmly secured through tightening by hand.

T　　　　F 12. EMT shall be securely fastened in place within 5' of a junction box.

_____ 13. A pocket ___ may be used to check the accuracy of an offset.

_____ 14. A hand conduit bender is also known as a(n) ___.

_____ 15. The trade sizes for EMT range from ½" to ___" in diameter.

_____ 16. Conduit must be ___ after being cut to length.

_____ 17. Conduit ___ are used to join pieces of EMT together.

_____		**18.** Bends in tubing must not reduce the ___ diameter.
T	F	**19.** A compression connector may be used to secure EMT to an electrical box.
T	F	**20.** A compression connector can only be used one time.
T	F	**21.** Set screw connectors can be reused.
T	F	**22.** An indenter connector can only be used one time.
_____		**23.** A total of ___ bends are required to produce a saddle bend.
_____		**24.** A total of ___ bends are required to produce an offset bend.
_____		**25.** A(n) ___° angle is produced when the bender handle is raised to the vertical position.

Conduit Straps

_____ **1.** One hole push-on

_____ **2.** One hole

_____ **3.** Two hole

_____ **4.** Nail-up

Allowable Number of Conductors

_____ **1.** ½″ conduit; No. 14 conductors

_____ **2.** ½″ conduit; No. 12 conductors

_____ **3.** ¾″ conduit; No. 10 conductors

_____ **4.** ¾″ conduit; No. 12 conductors

_____ **5.** ¾″ conduit; No. 14 conductors

Installing Conduit

_____ 1. Outlet

_____ 2. Sole plate

_____ 3. Stud

_____ 4. Headers

_____ 5. Top plate

_____ 6. Bridging

Conduit Bends

_____ 1. Double offset bend

_____ 2. 45° bend

_____ 3. Back-to-back bend

_____ 4. Offset bend

_____ 5. Alternate double offset bend

_____ 6. 90° bend

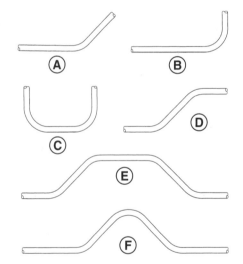

Conduit Types

_____ 1. Flexible conduit

_____ 2. Electrical metallic tubing

_____ 3. Rigid conduit

201

Conduit Connectors and Couplings

_____ 1. Indenter connector

_____ 2. Compression connector

_____ 3. Set screw connector

_____ 4. Compression coupling

_____ 5. Set screw coupling

_____ 6. Indenter coupling

(A)

(B)

(C)

(D)

(E)

(F)

Liquid-Tight Conduit Connector

_____ 1. O-ring assembly

_____ 2. Steel grounding ferrule

_____ 3. Hexagonal compression nut

_____ 4. Hardened steel locknut

_____ 5. Nylon gland ring

_____ 6. Flexible steel core

_____ 7. Insulated throat

_____ 8. Body

Chapter 10

Service Entrances

Chapter 10 provides an overview of how service entrance equipment is installed. The local building inspector and power company must be consulted before installing service equipment. Properly installed service equipment will provide years of maintenance-free service.

Installers of electrical service equipment should verify that the equipment is suitable for use as service equipment. There are many types of identification used to mark the suitability of service equipment. Equipment should be marked "Suitable only for use as service equipment." Use of the wrong equipment violates the NEC® requirements and could introduce the possibility of a fire and/or shock hazard.

RESIDENTIAL SERVICE ENTRANCES

Installing a service entrance is typically the first priority when wiring a new home. A *service entrance* is the connecting link between a residence and the power company. Service entrances provide all the equipment necessary to obtain electricity and distribute it throughout a residence.

Electrical service to a residence is provided by wires that run overhead from a utility pole to the residence, or by wires to the residence that are buried in the ground. The two methods of electrical service to a residence are the service drop and underground lateral. The *service drop* method of electrical service runs wires from a utility pole to a service head on or above the residence. The *underground (service lateral)* method of electrical service buries the wires to a residence in the ground. **See Figure 10-1.**

Clearance requirements are provided to protect the service-drop conductors from physical damage and to protect personnel from contact with conductors.

Figure 10-1. *The two service entrance methods used for residences are the service drop and underground (service lateral).*

Placement of Service Entrances

Placement of a service entrance must take into consideration both cost and convenience. Electricians must try to make the service panel of the residence as accessible as possible using the minimum of materials. The three tips that are useful in determining the placement of a service entrance are the following:

- Keep the service wires as short as possible.
- Locate the service panel as close to the kitchen as possible to avoid costly wire runs to major appliances.
- Avoid having the meter socket placed on the outside of a bedroom wall.

Sizing Service Entrances

Service entrances for single family dwellings require a minimum 100 A capability. For larger residences and structures using electric heat, a 200 A or larger service entrance can be required. Residential service entrances are typically rated in amperes because voltage is typically a standard (115/230 V).

Further information concerning service entrances can be obtained from Article 230 of the NEC® or the local building inspector.

ROUGHING IN SERVICE ENTRANCES

Electricians need not be apprehensive about installing an electrical service. To make service installation to a residence easier, manufacturers provide service entrance installation kits. **See Figure 10-2.** Depending on local codes and the specific power company, service entrances can be installed by anyone safely, with a professional look and at minimal cost.

Types of Service Entrances

Not all electrical services are installed in the same manner. Services differ because of the application or because of the place in which the service is located. Typically four methods are used to bring electrical service to a residence.

Service Entrance Parts

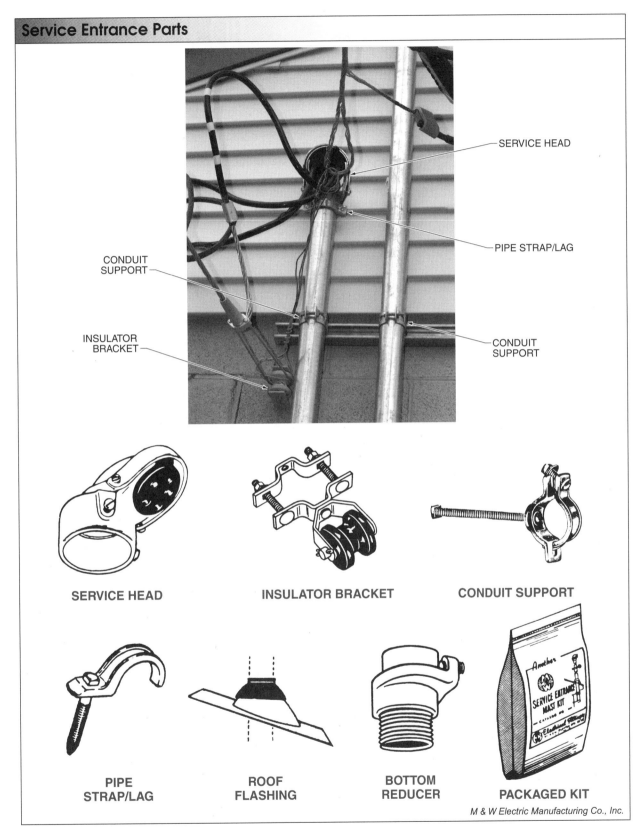

Figure 10-2. *To make service installation to a residence easier, manufacturers provide service entrance installation kits for electricians.*

Overhead Riser Service Entrances

Many established neighborhoods and urban areas use the overhead riser method of electrical service. See Figure 10-3. The *overhead riser service entrance* has wires running from a utility pole to a service head, where the meter socket and riser are firmly secured to the exterior of a dwelling, while the service panel is placed inside. An appropriate-size conduit typically connects the meter socket and meter to the service panel. Several methods are used to connect the meter and socket to the service panel with conduit.

Overhead Service Entrances

SERVICE HEAD

3' CABLE

12' MIN— RESIDENTIAL DRIVEWAYS
18' MIN— PUBLIC STREETS AND ROADS

5'-6" TO CENTER

METER SOCKET BOX

GROUND FROM SERVICE PANEL

DUCT SEAL

6"

8' TO 10'

12"

GROUNDING ROD

SERVICE PANEL

COMPONENT LAYOUT

SERVICE HEAD

METER SOCKET BOX

SERVICE PANEL

WIRING DIAGRAM

100 AMP 115V/230V SINGLE PHASE				
Conductor Type	Wire Size	Conduit Size	Ground Wire Size	Ground Rod Size
Copper	#4	1 ¼"	#8	⅝"
Aluminum	#2	1 ¼"	#6	⅝"

200 AMP 115V/230V SINGLE PHASE				
Conductor Type	Wire Size	Conduit Size	Ground Wire Size	Ground Rod Size
Copper	2/0	2"	#4	⅝"
Aluminum	4/0	2 ½"	0	⅝"

ALTERNATE METHODS OF ENTERING SERVICE PANEL

Figure 10-3. *The overhead riser method of electrical service wiring has the meter socket and riser firmly secured to the exterior of a dwelling, while the service panel is placed inside.*

Lateral Service Entrances (Conduit)

In most new developments it is customary to bury all service wires underground. **See Figure 10-4.** A *lateral service entrance (conduit)* is a service entrance where all service wires are buried underground, creating a condition where the wires are subjected to less damage from the environment (weather) and allowing unsightly poles and service wires to be removed from streets and alleys. Typically, underground services are built using conduit.

Lateral Service Entrances (Conduit)

100 AMP 115V/230V SINGLE PHASE				
Conductor Type	Wire Size	Conduit Size	Ground Wire Size	Ground Rod Size
Copper	#4	1 ¼″	#8	⅝″
Aluminum	#2	1 ¼″	#6	⅝″

200 AMP 115V/230V SINGLE PHASE				
Conductor Type	Wire Size	Conduit Size	Ground Wire Size	Ground Rod Size
Copper	2/0	2″	#4	⅝″
Aluminum	4/0	2 ½″	0	⅝″

Figure 10-4. *A lateral service entrance is a service entrance where all service wires are buried underground, creating a condition where the wires are subjected to less damage from the environment (weather) and allowing unsightly poles and service wires to be removed from streets and alleys.*

Lateral Service Entrances (Cabinet)

The cabinet type of underground service is another method of installing an underground service to a residence. **See Figure 10-5.** A *lateral service entrance* (cabinet) utilizes a cabinet that encloses the service wires, meter socket, and meter. The entire enclosure is then covered with a metal cover that is typically locked. A cabinet type of underground service is very neat and makes the routing of wires much easier.

Lateral Service Entrances (Cabinet)

METER SOCKET CABINET

WIRING DIAGRAM

SERVICE PANEL

HEIGHT SUBJECT TO LOCAL CODES

METER SOCKET CABINET

5'-6" MAX 3'-6" MIN TO CENTER

6"

8' TO 12'

GROUNDING ROD

SERVICE PANEL

COMPONENT LAYOUT

100 AMP 115V/230V SINGLE PHASE				
Conductor Type	Wire Size	Conduit Size	Ground Wire Size	Ground Rod Size
Copper	#4	1 ¼"	#8	⅝"
Aluminum	#2	1 ¼"	#6	⅝"

200 AMP 115V/230V SINGLE PHASE				
Conductor Type	Wire Size	Conduit Size	Ground Wire Size	Ground Rod Size
Copper	2/0	2"	#4	⅝"
Aluminum	4/0	2 ½"	0	⅝"

ALTERNATE METHODS OF ENTERING SERVICE PANEL

Figure 10-5. *A lateral service entrance (cabinet) utilizes a cabinet that encloses the service wires, meter socket, and meter.*

Mobile Home Service Entrances

Mobile homes present a unique problem for service entrances because the service is not typically attached directly to the mobile home. Instead, the service is permanently mounted near the mobile home and a cable is run to the mobile home.

See Figure 10-6. Overhead and lateral methods are used to connect electrical service to a mobile home. A cable from the meter runs to a disconnect, then a cable from the disconnect runs to the service panel of the mobile home. The service panel then distributes electricity throughout the mobile home.

Mobile Home Service Entrances

100 AMP 115V/230V SINGLE PHASE				
Conductor Type	Wire Size	Conduit Size	Ground Wire Size	Ground Rod Size
Copper	#4	1 ¼″	#8	⅝″
Aluminum	#2	1 ¼″	#6	⅝″

200 AMP 115V/230V SINGLE PHASE				
Conductor Type	Wire Size	Conduit Size	Ground Wire Size	Ground Rod Size
Copper	2/0	2″	#4	⅝″
Aluminum	4/0	2 ½″	0	⅝″

NOTE: SERVICE EQUIPMENT CANNOT BE MOUNTED IN OR ON A MOBILE HOME

COMPONENT LAYOUT OVERHEAD SERVICE ENTRANCE

COMPONENT LAYOUT LATERAL SERVICE ENTRANCE

Figure 10-6. *Overhead and lateral methods are used to connect electrical service to a mobile home.*

Securing Service Equipment

Typically, the service wires are not connected to the power company until the service and inside of the residence are properly wired. All boxes, panels, conduit, and wires must be securely held in place to avoid problems from wind, rain, snow, hail, and other environmental concerns.

Knockouts. During the installation of a service entrance, large and small box knockouts must be removed from the service panel. Whenever possible, large knockouts should be removed before the service panel is mounted. Removing the knockouts before mounting reduces any chance of loosening the panel. **See Figure 10-7.** Knockouts are removed using standard procedures.

Fasteners. Meter sockets and service panels must be firmly secured before any wires (cables) are pulled or conduit attached. When service equipment is mounted on wood, wood screws or lag bolts are used to hold the equipment in place. When service equipment is mounted to masonry, drills and special bolts with anchors are used. **See Figure 10-8.** Plastic anchors support a considerable amount of weight when properly installed.

An enclosure is a device that protects electrical control devices. Enclosures are categorized by the protection they provide. An enclosure is selected based on the location of the equipment and the NEC® requirements. For example, a Type 3 enclosure is used outdoors for applications subjected to windblown dust, rain, sleet, and ice. Type 3 enclosures must pass rain, external icing, windblown dust, and rust resistance tests. Type 3 enclosures, however, do not protect against internal condensation or internal icing.

Concentric Knockout Removal

LARGE KNOCKOUTS REMOVED

SMALL KNOCKOUTS REMOVED

SERVICE PANEL

Square D Company

CONCENTRIC KNOCKOUT REMOVAL

Figure 10-7. *Removing knockouts before mounting a panel reduces any chance of loosening the panel.*

Tech Tip: Single-Ring Knockout

SERVICE PANEL

SINGLE-RING KNOCKOUT

Mounting Service Equipment to Masonry

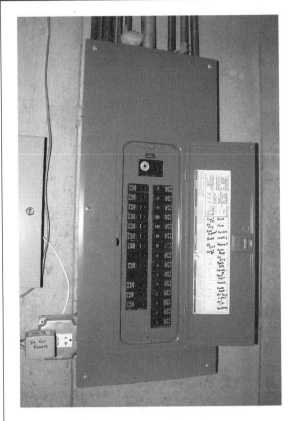

Klein Tools, Inc.

CARBIDE-TIPPED MASONRY DRILL BIT

DRILL HOLE

POSITION INSERT (HAMMER)

START SCREW

TIGHTEN SCREW

SETTING BOLTS IN MASONRY

Figure 10-8. *When service equipment is mounted to masonry, drills and special bolts with anchors are used.*

SERVICE PANELS

The electric power brought to a residence is typically a three-wire 115 V/230 V, 1φ system. Red, black, and white wires for the service panel enter the residence through a service head. **See Figure 10-9.** The red and black wires represent the hot or live wires, and the white wire represents the neutral. As with most residential services, 230 V can be obtained between the red and black hot wires. One hundred and fifteen volts can also be obtained between either of the hot wires and neutral. The 115 V and 230 V voltages are constant throughout the meter socket and into the service panel.

Inside the service panel, where the wires are terminated, metal conductors called bus bars continue the system. Bus bars distribute the power to the circuit breakers in an organized manner. **See Figure 10-10.** Service panel bus bars convey power to single-pole and double-pole circuit breakers to form 115 V and 230 V circuits.

Service Equipment Voltages

Figure 10-9. *A standard 115 V/230 V system consists of two incoming hot lines (red and black) and a neutral (white).*

Busbar Electrical Distribution

DOUBLE-POLE 230 V BREAKER

SINGLE-POLE 115 V BREAKER

Figure 10-10. *Busbars alternately supply circuit breakers with phase 1 and phase 2 to form 115 V and 230 V circuits.*

Any single circuit breaker can only furnish power to one 115 V circuit. Two consecutive circuit breakers are used to provide power for a 230 V circuit. The circuit breakers must be consecutive so that the breaker handles can be fastened together as one unit. Fastening the handles of two circuit breakers together ensures that, in the event of a 230 V overload, both hot lines are disconnected simultaneously. **See Figure 10-11.** Circuit breakers are snapped into position when being installed to the busbars of a service panel.

230 V Circuit Breakers

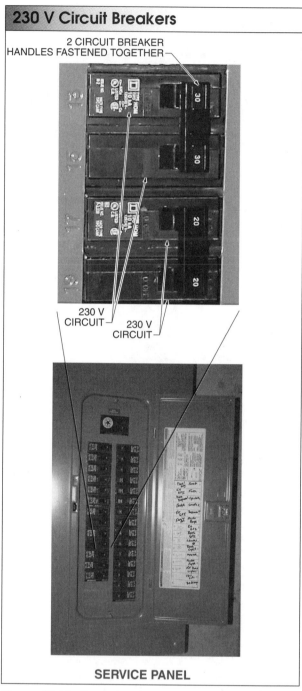

SERVICE PANEL

Figure 10-11. *Fastening the handles of a circuit breaker together ensures that, in the event of a 230 V overload, both hot lines are disconnected simultaneously.*

Service Entrance Cables

Instead of individual wires being pulled through conduit, quite often service entrance cables are used. **See Figure 10-12.** Service entrance cables have a bare conductor that is wound around the insulated conductors. The spiral winding prevents tampering with the conductors ahead of the meter and also serves as the neutral conductor.

Service Entrance Cable Parts

BARE CONDUCTOR
HELICALLY WOUND
ON CABLE

INSULATED
CONDUCTORS

YPE SE CABLE

TWISTED BASE
CONDUCTOR

Figure 10-12. *The twisted bare conductor in a service cable protects the current-carrying wires and serves as the neutral wire.*

Service entrance cables are accepted in many areas and require no special tools to install. Service entrance caps are shaped to accept oval service cables. **See Figure 10-13.** The sill plate covers the cable and the cable opening where the service enters the dwelling. Sealing compound or caulking is applied to make the sill plate watertight. Service cable connectors are available as standard box connectors or as watertight connectors when used on top of the meter socket. Mounting straps are used to secure service cables in place. No matter who performs the work, the service entrance cable and devices must be installed as if an electrician performed the work. **See Figure 10-14.**

A service head or gooseneck should be installed at a point that is above the point of attachment for the service-drop conductors. This ensures that water does not enter the service raceway or service-entrance cable. There are installations where it is impractical to locate the service head or gooseneck above the point of attachment. NEC® Article 230.54(C) Ex. permits the point of attachment not to be located above the service head or gooseneck, but the service head or gooseneck must be located less than 24" from the point of attachment.

Service Entrance Cable Parts

SERVICE ENTRANCE CAP
USED WITH
OVAL SERVICE CABLE

SILL PLATE USED WITH
SERVICE ENTRANCE
CABLE

OVAL SERVICE
CABLE CONNECTOR

OVAL SERVICE
CABLE STRAP

Figure 10-13. *Service entrance cables are accepted in many areas and require no special tools to install.*

Complete Service Entrance Cable

DUAL SERVICE
ENTRANCE
CAP

SERVICE
ENTRANCE
CABLE

METER

MOUNTING
STRAPS

Figure 10-14. *Service cable connectors are available as standard box connectors or as watertight connectors when used on top of the meter socket.*

SERVICE DROPS

A *service drop* consists of overhead wires and devices that connect the power company power lines to a residence. Service drops are owned and maintained by the power company. Homeowners and electricians must be aware of the important rules governing the placement and elevation of service drops for new installations. The National Electrical Code® (NEC®) provides guidelines for the installation of service drops in relation to platforms, windows, service heads, and structure elevations.

Platforms

To comply with NEC® standards, a service head must be at least 10′ above and 3′ to the side of any platform. **See Figure 10-15.**

Figure 10-15. *NEC® standards govern service drops in relation to platforms (porches).*

Windows

The NEC® has standards governing service drops in relation to windows. **See Figure 10-16.** Service conductors must be at least 3′ from the bottom and sides of a window. Conductors that run above a window are considered out of reach from the window.

Figure 10-16. *NEC® standards govern service drops in relation to windows.*

Elevations

NEC® standards governing the elevation of service conductors specify a 3′ clearance over adjacent buildings, and various elevations are required for sidewalks, private drives, alleys, and streets. **See Figure 10-17.**

Service Heads

The NEC® has standards relating to the use of service heads. **See Figure 10-18.** Very explicit specifications are in place to ensure the performance and safety of service head installations. Careful consideration of each NEC® standard during installation ensures a permanent weatherproof connection out of the reach of potentially destructive obstacles.

Service Drop Standards for Elevations

SERVICE DROP (NOT OVER 300 V BETWEEN CONDUCTORS)

10′ MIN

3′ MIN

10′ MIN

18′ MIN

12′ MIN

SIDEWALK

PRIVATE DRIVE

ALLEY OR STREET

Figure 10-17. *Depending on the type of structure, service drops are required to maintain specific heights above grade.*

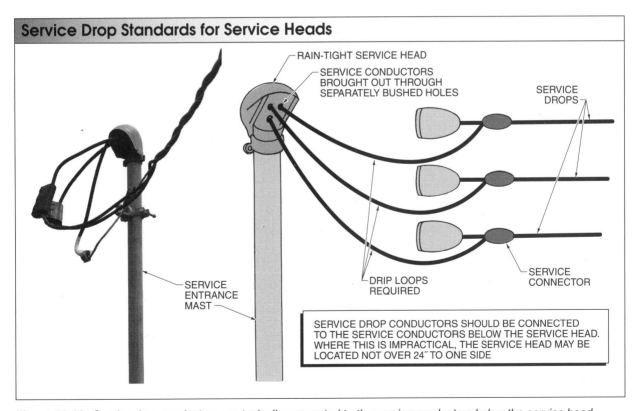

Service Drop Standards for Service Heads

RAIN-TIGHT SERVICE HEAD

SERVICE CONDUCTORS BROUGHT OUT THROUGH SEPARATELY BUSHED HOLES

SERVICE DROPS

SERVICE ENTRANCE MAST

DRIP LOOPS REQUIRED

SERVICE CONNECTOR

SERVICE DROP CONDUCTORS SHOULD BE CONNECTED TO THE SERVICE CONDUCTORS BELOW THE SERVICE HEAD. WHERE THIS IS IMPRACTICAL, THE SERVICE HEAD MAY BE LOCATED NOT OVER 24″ TO ONE SIDE

Figure 10-18. *Service drop conductors are typically connected to the service conductors below the service head.*

SERVICE LATERALS

A *service lateral* is any service to a residence that is achieved by burying the wires underground. The four types of service laterals used for residences are the following:

- from utility manhole in street to service panel disconnect.
- from utility sidewalk handhole to service panel disconnect.
- from pole riser to service panel disconnect.
- from transformer pad to service panel disconnect.

When service originates in a manhole, the work to be performed must be arranged with the utility company for joint installation of all conduit and wires. The manhole requirement is necessary because a manhole is a potentially dangerous space and is restricted to utility workers.

When service originates in a sidewalk handhole, electricians are typically permitted to run conduit and wires into the handhole. **See Figure 10-19.** The utility company will make the appropriate connections in the handhole.

When a pole riser is used, the service installation is shared by the homeowner and utility company. **See Figure 10-20.** In many instances, electricians simply install conduit to a point at least 8′ above grade and pull enough wire to reach the crossarm at the top of the pole. The utility company extends the protection for the drop cables with approved molding to the crossarm upon final connection. In some cases a short piece of conduit with a service head is used to terminate the run at the crossarm. When the utility company extends protection, the homeowner furnishes the conduit and service head. In other cases, homeowners must furnish conduit all the way with a service head at the end. For this type of service, see the utility company to avoid waste and delay.

When a service entrance originates from a transformer pad, special direct-burial cable is used to make the installation. **See Figure 10-21.** Transformer pad service entrances require the homeowner to furnish a transformer pad in addition to the regular electrical service equipment. The utility company typically creates the trench from the transformer pad to the dwelling, buries the cable, and makes all final connections. Always check with the utility company ahead of time to avoid delays and problems.

Figure 10-19. *Underground service can be provided to a dwelling by running wires through buried conduit from a sidewalk handhole.*

Figure 10-20. *Service laterals can originate from a pole riser.*

Figure 10-21. *Transformer pad service entrances require the homeowner to furnish a transformer pad and service equipment.*

TRIMMING OUT A SERVICE ENTRANCE

Trimming out or finishing a service entrance requires the installation of internal service conductors, circuit breakers, and branch circuit wiring. Wires must be bent to shape to fit some service heads. **See Figure 10-22.** Similar bends are required when wiring the meter socket and service panel.

⚠️ **CAUTION**

Never force a wire into a connection; always bend and shape wires to fit.

Bending Wires for Service Caps

PROPERLY BENT WIRES

SERVICE MAST

ITT Holub Industries

Figure 10-22. *Service wires must be properly bent and fitted into service caps for maximum protection.*

Wire (cable) coming from branch circuits must also be bent to fit the configuration of the service panel. **See Figure 10-23.** Electricians should always take care and provide a professional appearance and organization to the wires to each circuit breaker. Although a novice may not be able to accomplish a professional look immediately, the professional look can be achieved given time and practice.

Service Panel Neatness

Figure 10-23. *Taking care to route wires in a service panel in an organized manner makes it easier to distinguish one wire from another.*

After all the circuit breakers have been properly installed and each circuit tested, electricians must prepare the trim cover to the service panel. **See Figure 10-24.** Proper technique must be used to remove the breaker openings from the service panel trim cover. Remove only the openings necessary for the circuit breakers installed. The service panel cover is installed to finish trimming out a service panel. **See Figure 10-25.**

The cover panel will have a directory on the inside of the door. The directory is filled out to indicate the location and use of each circuit breaker.

Removing Service Panel Breaker Knockouts

Figure 10-24. *Circuit breaker knockouts should only be removed for the positions where circuit breakers are installed.*

Service Panel Breaker Directory

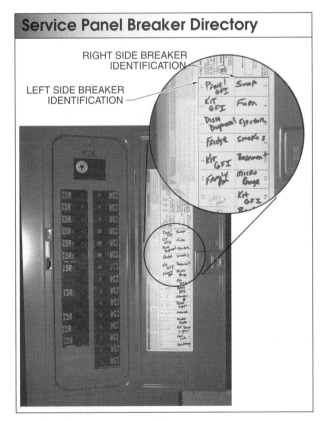

Figure 10-25. *A service panel is finished when the cover is installed and each breaker is labeled according to position and operation (circuit).*

AC GENERATORS

A *generator* is an electromechanical device that converts mechanical energy into electrical energy by means of electromagnetic induction. AC generators (alternators) convert mechanical energy into AC voltage and current. AC generators consist of field windings, an armature, slip rings, and brushes. **See Figure 10-26.**

AC Generators

Figure 10-26. *AC generators consist of field windings, a coil (armature), slip rings, and brushes.*

Field windings are magnets used to produce the magnetic field in a generator. The magnetic field in a generator can be produced by permanent magnets or electromagnets. Most generators use electromagnets, which must be supplied with current. An *armature* is the movable coil of wire in a generator that rotates through the magnetic field. The armature may consist of many coils. The ends of the coils are connected to slip rings. *Slip rings* are metallic rings connected to the ends of the armature and are used to connect the induced voltage to the generator brushes. When the armature is rotated in the magnetic field, a voltage is generated in each half of the armature coil. A *brush* is the sliding contact that rides against the slip rings and is used to connect the armature to the external circuit (power grid).

AC generators are similar in construction and operation to DC generators. The major difference between AC and DC generators is that DC generators contain a commutator that reverses the connections to the brushes every half cycle. The commutator maintains a constant polarity of voltage to the load. AC generators use slip rings to connect the armature to the external circuit (load). The slip rings do not reverse the polarity of the output voltage produced by the generator. The result is an alternating sine wave output. **See Figure 10-27.**

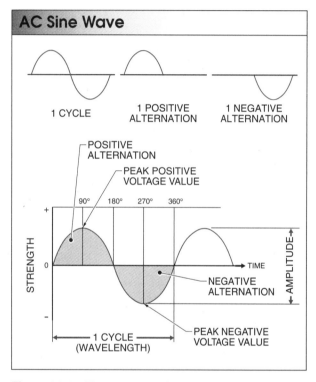

Figure 10-27. *The armature of a generator induces a varying voltage (AC) output that is positive then negative.*

As the armature is rotated, each half cuts across the magnetic lines of force at the same speed. The strength of the voltage induced in one side of the armature is always the same as the strength of the voltage induced in the other side of the armature. However, since the two halves of the coil are connected in a closed loop, the voltages add to each other. The result is that the total voltage of a full rotation of the armature is twice the voltage of each coil

half. The total voltage is obtained at the brushes connected to the slip rings, and is applied to an external circuit (grid).

SINGLE-PHASE AC GENERATORS

Each complete rotation of the armature in a single-wire (1ϕ) AC generator produces one complete alternating current cycle. **See Figure 10-28.** When the armature is in the vertical position (Position A), before the armature begins to rotate in a clockwise direction, there is no voltage and no current in the external load circuit because the armature is not cutting across any magnetic lines of force (0° of rotation).

As the armature rotates from position A to position B, each half of the armature cuts across magnetic lines of force, producing current and voltage in the armature and external circuit. The voltage increases from zero to its maximum value while current travels in the same direction. The changing value of voltage is represented by the first quarter (90° of rotation) of the sine wave.

As the armature rotates from position B to position C, current continues to travel in the same direction. The voltage decreases from the maximum value to zero. The changing value of voltage is represented by the second quarter (91°–180° of rotation) of the sine wave.

As the armature continues to rotate to position D, each half of the coil cuts across the magnetic lines of force in the opposite direction. Cutting across magnetic lines in the opposite direction changes the direction of current flow. During this time, voltage increases from zero to the maximum negative value. The constantly changing value of voltage is shown by the third quarter (181°–270° of rotation) of the sine wave.

As the armature continues to rotate to position E (position A), voltage decreases to zero. After 360° of armature rotation, one cycle of the AC sine wave is completed.

Single-Phase AC Generators

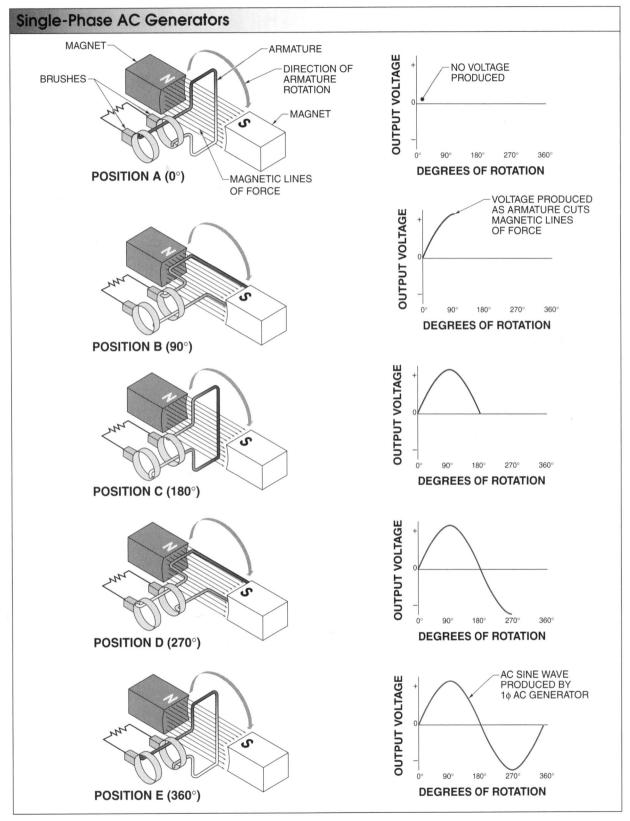

Figure 10-28. *In a 1φ AC generator, as the armature rotates through 360° of motion, the voltage generated is a continuously changing AC sine wave.*

HOME EMERGENCY STANDBY GENERATORS

Standby generators are installed during new construction or retrofitted into existing residences and businesses. Home generators are installed outside similarly to the condenser of a home air conditioning unit. Standby generators are typically placed on a solid surface as with air conditioning condensers. **See Figure 10-29.** Standby generators are powered by gasoline, natural gas, or LPG. Typical home emergency standby generators range in capacity from 6500 W to 40,000 W. The size of a generator is determined by the number of preselected lighting and appliance circuits that must be powered during a power outage.

Emergency Standby Generators

ELECTRIC START CONTROLLED BY AUTOMATIC TRANSFER SWITCH

Baldor Electric Co.

Figure 10-29. *Residential emergency standby generators typically range in capacity from 6500 W to 40,000 W.*

Because generators are chosen based on capacity in watts, it is important to understand the relationship between volts (V), amperage (A), and watts (W). The basic formula for calculating wattage when the voltage (V) and amperage (A) are known is watts equal volts times amps, or W = V × A. When an appliance is plugged into a 120 V outlet and draws 5 A, the watts are 600 W (600 W = 120 V × 5 A). In most cases an appliance has a nameplate stating the start and running wattages. **See Figure 10-30.**

Nameplate Information

CLOTHES DRYER

SUMP PUMP

MICROWAVE

GARBAGE DISPOSAL

Figure 10-30. *Ratings are typically found on the nameplates of electrical devices. When a nameplate cannot be easily located, refer to the operation or installation manual from the manufacturer for the information.*

When computing the total wattage required from a generator, the calculation must account for some appliances that require more power (watts) to start than to run. **See Figure 10-31.** It is also extremely important to understand which circuits (appliances) are considered critical circuits and must have power supplied during a power outage. For example, in winter it is critical that the furnace of a residence operate, but in summer it is more important to have air conditioning and a freezer operating. **See Figure 10-32.** All appliances, HVAC systems, lighting, and receptacles of residences have wattage ratings for determining the total load created.

Appliance Starting and Running Wattages

Appliance	Wattage (Starting)*	Wattage (Running)*
Refrigerator	2800	700
Freezer	2500	500
Well Pump-2 HP	6000	2000
Well Pump-3 HP	9000	3000
Gas Furnace Fan	500 to 2350	300 to 875

* in watts

Figure 10-31. *Appliances have typical wattage ratings. It is extremely important that each residence log the specific wattage ratings of appliances being used.*

READING AN ELECTRIC METER

An electric meter has four dials that look like clocks. Each dial has a hand. **See Figure 10-33.**

Note: Electric meters have two dials that read clockwise and two dials that read counterclockwise.

Always use the number that the hand has just passed (CW or CCW) on each of the dials. For example, the reading of the dials at the beginning of the month is 3456 kilowatt-hours (kWh). At the end of the month the readings of the dials is 3592 kWh. The difference is as follows:

End of month reading	3592
Beginning of month reading	-3456
Kilowatt-hours used in month	136

Typical Appliance Wattages

Appliance	Typical Wattage*
Lights	4500
Electric Water Heater	10,000
Electric Cooktop Top-8˝	2100
Washing Machine	1200
Electric Clothes Dryer	6000
Electric Fry Pan	1000
Electric Oven	6500
Cofeemaker	1100
Microwave	600 to 1200
Dishwasher	700
Fan	275
Toaster	200
Hair Dryer	1500
Computer	700 to 1000
Computer Monitor	200 to 800
Printer	400 to 800
Radio	40 to 225
Television	300 to 800

* in watts

Figure 10-32. *Some appliances draw more power when starting up than when running. Ensure startup wattages are known for use in circuit load calculations.*

Permanently connected appliances include furnaces (indoors), air conditioner condensers (outdoors), electric oven/ranges, garbage disposals, and electric baseboard heating units (indoors). Most home appliances that are plug-and-cord-connected are typically located in the kitchen. These appliances include the refrigerator, microwave oven, gas oven/range, and dishwasher. Other residential plug-and-cord-connected appliances are the clothes washer, clothes dryer, and sump pump.

Calculating Appliance Operating Costs

To calculate the cost to operate an appliance for a month, the nameplate on the appliance must be checked for amperage and wattage specifications. When amperage is provided, the power formula converts amperage and voltage into watts. The formula states that 1 A × 115 V = 115 W. Therefore, a 10 A iron consumes 1150 W (10 A × 115 V = 1150 W). When the wattage of an appliance is known, operating cost per hour can be determined. **See Figure 10-34.**

Reading Electrical Meters

METER READING – BEGINNING OF MONTH

CCW DIAL	CW DIAL	CCW DIAL	CW DIAL
3	5	9	2

METER READING – END OF MONTH

Figure 10-33. *Electric meters have two dials that read clockwise (CW) and two dials that read counter-clockwise (CCW).*

AUTOMATIC TRANSFER SWITCHES

An *automatic transfer switch* is an electrical device that transfers the load of a residence from public utility circuits to the output of a standby generator during a power failure. An automatic transfer switch (ATS) has electronic circuitry that can sense an interruption in power. **See Figure 10-35.** When a power failure is detected, an ATS turns on a standby generator. The transfer switch also disconnects all the dedicated circuits in the service panel from the public utility source and transfers the dedicated circuits to the output of the emergency generator. When power is transferred, an ATS prevents electricity from flowing into the public service lines and accidentally injuring electric company workers who are working on the system to restore power.

Automatic transfer switches come in various sizes depending upon the power rating required. An ATS is installed in close proximity to the electrical distribution panel and should be installed by a licensed electrician.

When reading an electric meter, read and record the numbers shown on the dials from right to left. When the pointer is directly on a number, view the dial to the right. If it has passed zero, use the next sequential number. If the pointer has not passed zero, use the lower number. Record the numbers shown on the value of the dial to the extreme right. Record the next numbers in sequence. Should the hand of a dial fall between two numbers, use the lesser of the two numbers.

Small Appliance Hourly Operating Costs

Wattage Consumed by Appliance	.03 kWh	.04 kWh	.05 kWh	.06 kWh
100	10 hr for 3¢	7.5 hr for 3¢	6 hr for 3¢	5 hr for 3¢
300	3 hr for 2.7¢	2,5 hr for 3¢	2 hr for 3¢	1.66 hr for 3¢
500	2 hr for 3¢	1 hr for 2¢	1.2 hr for 3¢	1 hr for 3¢
700	1.4 hr for 3¢	1.1 hr for 3¢	1 hr for 3.5¢	1 hr for 4.2¢
900	1.1 hr for 3¢	1 hr for 3.6¢	1 hr for 4.5¢	1 hr for 5.4¢
1000	1 hr for 3¢	1 hr for 4¢	1 hr for 5¢	1 hr for 6¢

Figure 10-34. *To calculate the cost of operating an appliance for a month, the nameplate on the appliance must be checked for amperage and wattage specifications.*

Automatic Transfer Switches

Figure 10-35. *Automatic transfer switches transfer the load of a residence from public utility circuits to the output of a standby generator during a power failure.*

A checklist to use when installing a home emergency generator is as follows:

- Generator should be Underwriters Laboratory listed (UL listed).
- Generator should be properly sized for the calculated load.
- Generator should be properly positioned so the noise generated is acceptable.
- Generator should be properly housed for outdoor environmental exposure, such as to temperature, snow, and rain.
- Generator should operate with the available fuel, whether gasoline, natural gas, or LPG.
- Follow any special considerations due to the type of fuel.
- Generator battery should be charged automatically.
- Generator should have automatic safety shut downs to protect engine and generator in event of low oil pressure, high temperature, or overspeed.
- Generator should have a seven-day exerciser programmed to run the system for several minutes each week to maintain top running condition.

Voltage Changes

AC generators are designed to produce a specific amount of output current at a rated voltage. In addition, all electrical and electronic equipment is rated for operation at a specific voltage. *Rated voltage* is a voltage range that is typically within ±10% of ideal voltage. Today, however, with many components derated to save energy and operating cost, the range is typically +5% to −10%. A voltage range is used because an overvoltage is more damaging than an undervoltage. Equipment manufacturers, utility companies, and regulating agencies must routinely compensate for changes in system voltage.

Back-up generators are used to compensate for voltage changes and are powered by diesel, gasoline, natural gas, or propane engines connected to the generator. When there is time between the loss of main utility power and when the generator starts providing power, the generator is classified as a standby (emergency) power supply. Voltage changes in an electrical system are categorized as momentary, temporary, or sustained. **See Figure 10-36.**

Voltage Changes

0 V FOR 0.5 CYCLES TO 3 SEC

0 V FOR > 3 SEC TO 1 MIN

0 V FOR > 1 MIN

TO LOAD

A N B

NORMAL TYPE {A N B}   {A N B} EMERGENCY SUPPLY

MOMENTARY POWER INTERRUPTION

TEMPORARY POWER INTERRUPTION

SUSTAINED INTERRUPTION

Figure 10-36. *Voltage changes in an electrical system can be categorized as momentary, temporary, or sustained.*

Momentary Power Interruptions. A *momentary power interruption* is a decrease to 0 V on one or more power lines lasting from 0.5 cycles up to 3 sec. All power distribution systems have momentary power interruptions during normal operation. Momentary power interruptions can be caused when lightning strikes nearby, by utility grid switching during a problem situation (a short on one line), or during open circuit transition switching. *Open circuit transition switching* is a process in which power is momentarily disconnected when switching a circuit from one voltage supply or level to another.

Temporary Power Interruptions. A *temporary power interruption* is a decrease to 0 V on one or more power lines lasting between 3 sec and 1 min. Automatic circuit breakers and other circuit protection equipment protect all power distribution systems. Circuit protection equipment is designed to remove faults and restore power. An automatic circuit breaker takes from 20 cycles to about 5 sec to close. When power is restored, the power interruption is only temporary. If power is not restored, a temporary power interruption becomes a sustained power interruption. A temporary power interruption can also be caused by a time gap between a power interruption and when a back-up power supply (generator) takes over, or if someone accidentally opens the circuit by switching the wrong circuit breaker switch.

Sustained Power Interruptions. A *sustained power interruption* is a decrease to 0 V on all power lines for a period of more than 1 min. All power distribution systems have a complete loss of power at some time. Sustained power interruptions (outages) are commonly the result of storms, tripped circuit breakers, blown fuses, and/or damaged equipment.

The effect of a power interruption on a load depends on the load and the application. When a power interruption causes equipment, production, and/or security problems that are not acceptable, an uninterruptible power system is used. An *uninterruptible power system (UPS)* is a power supply that provides constant on-line power when the primary power supply is interrupted. For long-term power interruption protection, a generator/UPS is used. For short-term power interruptions, a static UPS is used.

Transients

A *transient* is a temporary, unwanted voltage in an electrical circuit. Transient voltages are typically large erratic voltages, or spikes that have a short duration and a short rise time. Computers, electronic circuits, and specialized electrical equipment require protection against transient voltages. Protection methods commonly include proper wiring, grounding, shielding of the power lines, and use of surge suppressors. A *surge suppressor* is a receptacle that provides protection from high-level transients by limiting the level of voltage allowed downstream from the surge suppressor. Surge suppressors are installed at service entrance panels and at individual loads. **See Figure 10-37.**

Tech Tip: Transient Voltages

Surge Suppressors

Figure 10-37. *A surge suppressor is a receptacle that provides protection from high-level transients by limiting the level of voltage allowed downstream from the surge suppressor.*

Chapter 10

Test

Name_____ Date _____

Service Entrances

_____ **1.** A service ___ has conductors run overhead.

_____ **2.** A service ___ has conductors run underground.

T   F **3.** Service conductors should be as long as possible.

T   F **4.** A service panel should be close to the kitchen to avoid costly runs to major appliances.

T   F **5.** The preferred position for a meter socket is on an outside bedroom wall.

T   F **6.** A service entrance for a one-family dwelling ~~should~~ MUST have a minimum ampere rating of 100 A.

_____ **7.** Residential services have a standard voltage of ___ V, 1ϕ.

_____ **8.** The minimum size Cu conductor used for service entrances is #___.

_____ **9.** The minimum size Al conductor used for service entrances is #___.

_____ **10.** The minimum conduit size for service entrance conductors is ___".

_____ **11.** The minimum ground wire size for copper service entrances is #___.

_____ **12.** The minimum ground wire size for aluminum service entrances is #___.

_____ **13.** The minimum ground rod size for service entrances is ___" in diameter.

T   F **14.** The minimum requirements of conductor sizes for a mobile home are the same as for a one-family dwelling.

T   F **15.** Large knockouts should be removed after the panel is mounted.

T   F **16.** Sealing compound or caulking may be applied to make the sill plate watertight.

_____ 17. In a typical residential electrical service, ___ V is obtained between the red and black service wires.

       A. 115   **C.** 480

       B. 230   **D.** none of the above

_____ 18. Service entrance conductors that run ___ a window are considered out of reach.

_____ 19. The service drop is owned and maintained by the ___.

_____ 20. The minimum clearance for service drop conductors passing over a private drive is ___′.

_____ 21. The minimum clearance for service drop conductors passing over an alley or street is ___′.

T   F   22. Drip loops are required between the service drop conductors and the service head.

T   F   23. A service head may be located not over 12″ to one side of the point of attachment for the service drop conductors.

_____ 24. ___ or finishing the service requires the installation of internal service conductors, circuit breakers, and branch circuit wiring.

_____ 25. Direct ___ cable is used to make the hookup when the service originates from a transformer pad.

T   F   26. Rigid galvanized conduit may be buried directly in most soils.

T   F   27. The minimum clearance for service drop conductors passing over a residential sidewalk is 10′.

T   F   28. A service head should be at least 8′ above a platform.

_____ 29. Service drop conductors shall have not less than ___′ clearance from a window.

_____ 30. The white wire is the ___.

Service Entrance Components

_____ 1. Cable connector

_____ 2. Sill plate

_____ 3. Cap

_____ 4. Strap

(A)

(B)

(C)

(D)

Service Entrance Parts

_____ 1. Roof flashing   _____ 4. Insulator bracket

_____ 2. Bottom reducer   _____ 5. Conduit support

_____ 3. Service head   _____ 6. Pipe strap

(A)

(B)

(C)

(D)

(E)

(F)

Service Drop

_____ 1. 18′ minimum

_____ 2. 3′ minimum

_____ 3. Not over 300 V between conductors

_____ 4. 10′ minimum

_____ 5. 12′ minimum

115 V – 230 V Electrical Service

_____ 1. The voltage at A is ___ V.

_____ 2. The voltage at B is ___ V.

_____ 3. Service wires enter the ___ at C.

_____ 4. Service wires are routed through a(n) ___ at D.

_____ 5. A(n) ___ is shown at E.

_____ 6. The ___ is shown at F.

_____ 7. The voltage at G is ___ V.

_____ 8. The voltage at H is ___ V.

_____ 9. The voltage at I is ___ V.

_____ 10. The panel has two hot ___ at J.

_____ 11. The ___ breaker is shown at K.

_____ 12. The voltage at L is ___ V.

Service Drop Clearances

_____ **1.** Conductors considered out of reach.

_____ **2.** Conductors shall have 3′ minimum vertical clearance below windows.

_____ **3.** Conductors shall have 3′ minimum clearance from fire escape or porch.

_____ **4.** Conductors shall have 3′ minimum horizontal clearance from windows.

_____ **5.** Service drop shall have 10′ minimum clearance above platforms.

Service Lateral

_____ **1.** ¼″ air space

_____ **2.** Grade

_____ **3.** Concrete wall

_____ **4.** Rigid galvanized conduit

_____ **5.** Utility company pole

_____ **6.** Service head

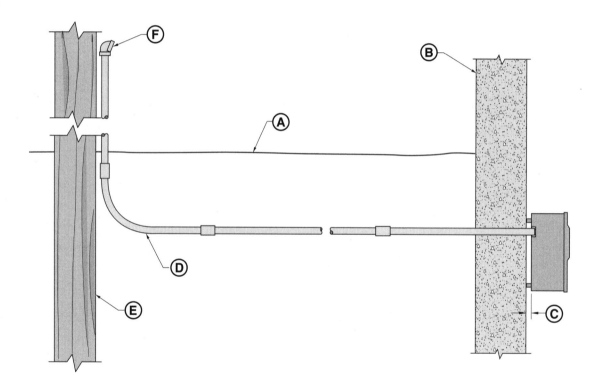

Chapter 11

Remodeling, Wiring, and Troubleshooting Electrical Systems

Chapter 11 provides an overview of how to test existing residential electrical circuits for defective parts and how to add devices and components to the system. Using fish tapes to route cables and wires through ceilings and walls to install boxes and raceways is also covered. Chapter 11 provides an overview of residential wood frame construction to aid in the process of pulling wires.

Construction drawings for dwellings are not as detailed as true electrical drawings. Typically, an electrician will only have a drawing of a basic floor plan to help aid in the design of an electrical system. Typical floor plans show only the room arrangement with some information on type of lighting and arrangement. True electrical drawings show receptacle and switching locations in addition to lighting types and locations.

RESIDENTIAL WOOD FRAME CONSTRUCTION

To route conduit or cables through an existing dry-walled or plaster home, an individual must understand how the home is constructed and where obstacles may exist that could prevent conduit or cables from being routed. Standard construction methods are used to construct the wood framing for one- and two-story residences. **See Figure 11-1.** Floor plans and associated detail drawings are used to construct the framing for one- and two-story homes. **See Figure 11-2.** Careful study of the prints for a home will indicate which areas are best for installing new conduit or cable.

Glue laminated timbers are typically used for beams in residential construction.

235

Residential Construction

Figure 11-1. *Platform framing is the typical construction method used for residential buildings.*

Framing from Prints

Figure 11-2. *Floor plans and associated detail drawings are used to construct the framing for residential structures.*

Residential prints include cutaway drawings that detail the construction used to attach the roof to the outside walls. **See Figure 11-3.** Routing wires through an outside wall to a ceiling fixture is one of the most difficult tasks to accomplish when remodeling.

Older homes are typically found with bridging between the studs in walls. **See Figure 11-4.** Bridging complicates the process of fishing wires through a wall. When bridging is encountered, the bridging must be notched or drilled to allow the routing of wires.

Roofing Prints and Framing

ROOF AND WALL CUTAWAY

ROOF AND WALL FRAMING

Figure 11-3. *Residential prints that include cutaway detail drawings of the construction used to attach the roof to outside wall are used to plan the routing of wires through an outside wall to a ceiling fixture.*

Figure 11-4. *Bridging encountered in walls, floors, and ceilings can be notched or drilled to allow the running of cables or conduit.*

INSTALLING RECEPTACLE BOXES

To install a receptacle box in an existing drywalled wall, the location for the box must first be determined. Then a hole must be cut in the plaster or drywall. The receptacle box is then mounted to a stud or to bracing attached to studs. Cable or wire must then be routed to the appropriate boxes for connection.

Determining Hole Location

When new receptacle boxes must be added to a room, holes will have to be cut in existing walls and ceilings. To avoid unnecessary holes and associated repairs, individuals must carefully select the proper location for a box before cutting any holes.

Wall studs and ceiling joists are laid out for residential construction on 16″ (sometimes 24″) centers. Once a stud or joist is located, other studs are found by measuring 16″ (or 24″) from the center of the located stud. Two methods are used to locate the first stud. The first method uses an electronic stud finder to zero in on any nails used to install the drywall. **See Figure 11-5.** The presence of a nail causes the arrow of the magnetic stud finder to point.

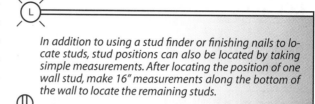

In addition to using a stud finder or finishing nails to locate studs, stud positions can also be located by taking simple measurements. After locating the position of one wall stud, make 16″ measurements along the bottom of the wall to locate the remaining studs.

Finding Wall Studs

FINISHED WALL
(DRYWALLED AND
PAINTED)

NAILS HIDDEN

STUDS HIDDEN

ELECTRONIC
STUD FINDER

Zircon Corporation

HIDDEN
STUD

HIDDEN NAIL

NAIL BEING
USED

HOLES 2″
APART

ELECTRONIC STUD FINDER

FINISHING NAIL

Figure 11-5. *To find a stud in a finished wall, stud finders are typically used. A finishing nail can also be used to find a stud.*

The second method used to locate a stud is to drive small finishing nails into a wall at 2″ intervals until a stud is located. The disadvantage of driving finishing nails every 2″ is that several small holes will require patching after a stud is located.

Individuals who are sure there is enough room between studs and supports must also check the area above and below the planned opening area to locate any unforeseen obstacles. **See Figure 11-6.** To check the area around a planned opening, a coat hanger with a bend larger than the planned opening is rotated 360° through a small hole. A hanger that rotates freely indicates a clear area, allowing the cutting of the hole for a box.

Figure 11-6. *To check the area around a planned box opening, a coat hanger with a bend is rotated 360° through a small hole to determine if the area is clear.*

Cutting Box Holes

Once an area is checked for box installation, electricians typically trace a pattern of the planned box opening on the wall. Drilling each corner of the pattern establishes a place to begin or end cutting and ensures that cutting does not overshoot the pattern. **See Figure 11-7.**

Figure 11-7. *Cutting the opening in finished walls for a new box requires defining the outer perimeter of the box in position, drilling the corners of the outer perimeter, and cutting or sawing the plaster walls or drywall.*

Modern wallboard or drywall is typically cut with a razor knife or small saw. When cutting into plaster walls, keyhole saws are the tools typically used. A faster method of cutting a box opening is to use a zip router.

When a large hole is required, the pattern is secured to the studs with thin strips of wood around the perimeter to avoid damaging the surrounding wallboard or drywall. **See Figure 11-8.**

Mounting Receptacle Boxes

Manufacturers are aware of the need of homeowners to update electrical systems in older homes. To aid homeowners, manufacturers produce products (boxes) that deal with the problems encountered when mounting boxes in existing ceilings and walls. Adding wooden braces for box mounting is not practical for most remodeling work.

A cut-in receptacle box (shallow box) is typically used for remodeling projects and attach to the face of the wall through drywall ears on the front of the box. Clamps hold the box to the back of the finished wall.

Cutting Large Access Holes

Figure 11-8. *When cutting large openings in drywall or plaster, wood strips that are secured in place protect the edges of the cut opening.*

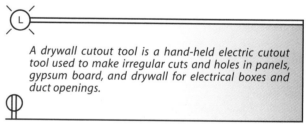

A drywall cutout tool is a hand-held electric cutout tool used to make irregular cuts and holes in panels, gypsum board, and drywall for electrical boxes and duct openings.

Tech Tip: Nail Spacing for Drywall

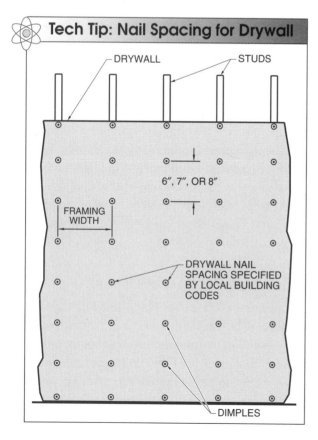

Box manufacturers use similar mounting systems to secure boxes to existing structures. **See Figure 11-9.** One common feature that box manufacturers use is a folding cleat on each side of the box that allows the box to be firmly secured from the inside of the wall opening. L clamps on the front of a rectangular retrofit box are used to keep the box from pulling through the drywall hole as the clamps are tightened. Rectangular retrofit boxes are useful for adding switches and receptacles to finished walls.

Installing Boxes in Existing Wall

L CLAMP

THREADED SCREWS

FOLDING SIDE CLEATS

RECTANGULAR BOX WITH FOLDING SIDE CLEATS

ADJUST L CLAMPS TO BE FLUSH WITH WALL

FOLD CLEATS TO INSERT BOX

OPEN CLEATS BEFORE TIGHTENING

NOTE: INSTALL BOX CONNECTORS BEFORE MOUNTING BOX

SECURE CLEATS BY TIGHTENING SCREWS

PULL WIRES THROUGH BOX

Figure 11-9. *Special mounting brackets are provided by box manufacturers to install boxes in existing walls and ceilings.*

Another method of securing rectangular boxes is the use of metal stampings. **See Figure 11-10.** Individual metal stampings are positioned in the wall and the tabs are bent over the box. The L clamps keep the box from pulling through the opening.

Mounting a box in a finished ceiling is a similar process to mounting a box in a finished wall. **See Figure 11-11.** Once a hole is cut, a strap with a threaded bolt is laid across the opening. Tightening the locknut through the box secures the box in place. Care must be taken to limit the size and weight of the fixture attached to a strapped box installation.

When it is necessary to have a fixture box mounted to the ceiling, bracing and toggle bolts can be used. **See Figure 11-12.** Holes are drilled that are large enough to accommodate large expandable toggle bolts. Tightening the toggle bolts pulls the box firmly into place. Fixture boxes are typically shallow and are totally covered by lighting fixtures.

Box Installation Accessories

Figure 11-10. *Metal stampings can be used to secure electrical boxes in existing walls.*

Installing Boxes in Existing Ceiling

CUT HOLE

INSERT SUPPORT BRACKET

PROCESS THE SAME FOR CONDUIT OR ARMORED CABLE

TIGHTEN FASTENING NUT

Figure 11-11. *Typically a three-part sequence is used to mount a box in an existing ceiling.*

Installing Fixture Box with Toggle Bolts

TOGGLE BOLT

TOGGLE BOLT

FIXTURE BOX

FIXTURE BOX

Figure 11-12. *Toggle bolts require that a larger than normal clearance hole be made in drywall to allow room for the wings of the toggle bolts.*

A circle cutter is a hand tool used to cut holes in drywall or thin wood sheets.

Routing Cables

Fish tapes are essential when routing cables through ceilings and walls. The proper use of fish tapes allows electricians to run wires that otherwise would be impossible to route.

Fish Tapes. Fish tapes require a five-part sequence to properly pull a wire or cable. **See Figure 11-13.** Fish tapes sometimes are required to be hooked together. Always take care when securing cable or wire to the ends of a fish tape. A little extra time taken to secure the wire to the fish tape ensures that the wire will not fall off halfway through a pull.

Back-to-back outlets can require two fish tapes to get the pull started for a cable. **See Figure 11-14.** Fish tapes are used to pull cable or wire through conduit along a wall from receptacle to receptacle. **See Figure 11-15.** A fish tape is also used to pull cable along the baseboard of a wall from Point A to Point B. **See Figure 11-16.**

Push a fish tape in to conduit until it stops. Move to the opposite end of the conduit and place another fish tape, or a piece of 10 AWG solid wire, though the end of the conduit and push it in until you feel it contact the first fish tape. Once it contacts the first fish tape, push additional 3' to 5'. Take the second fish tape or wire and twist it inside the conduit with a circular motion. Make at least 15 to 20 circular motions. Have enough slack in the first fish tape before pulling the second fish tape. Carefully pull the second fish tape until the hooked end is through the conduit.

Pulling Cables with Fish Tapes

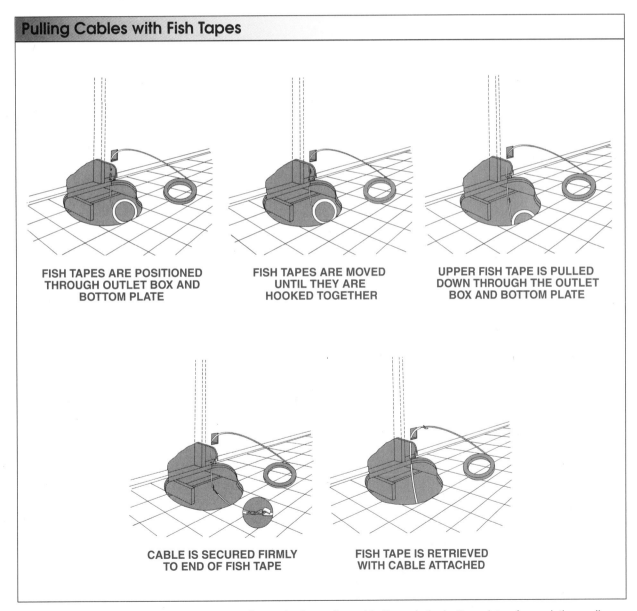

FISH TAPES ARE POSITIONED THROUGH OUTLET BOX AND BOTTOM PLATE

FISH TAPES ARE MOVED UNTIL THEY ARE HOOKED TOGETHER

UPPER FISH TAPE IS PULLED DOWN THROUGH THE OUTLET BOX AND BOTTOM PLATE

CABLE IS SECURED FIRMLY TO END OF FISH TAPE

FISH TAPE IS RETRIEVED WITH CABLE ATTACHED

Figure 11-13. *Typically a five-part sequence is required to pull a cable through the bottom plate of an existing wall.*

Pulling Wires or Cables through Back-to-Back Boxes

Figure 11-14. *Two fish tapes can be required to pull wires or cables through back-to-back boxes.*

Pulling Cable along Wall Baseboards

Figure 11-16. *Fish tapes are used to pull cables along wall baseboards to add additional outlet boxes.*

Pulling Wires or Cables from Box to Box

Figure 11-15. *Fish tapes are used to pull wires or cables from box to box along a wall.*

When doorways are encountered, the doorway trim can be removed and the cable routed around the opening. **See Figure 11-17.** After securing the cable, the doorway trim is reinstalled, hiding the cable.

When it is necessary to replace a ceiling box in an older two-story building, second-floor floorboards may have to be removed. **See Figure 11-18.** Each floorboard is carefully removed so that floor joists can be notched to accommodate the new cable or conduit. With the cable or conduit secured, the floorboards are carefully reinstalled.

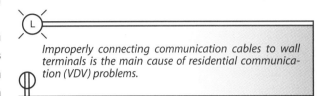

Improperly connecting communication cables to wall terminals is the main cause of residential communication (VDV) problems.

Routing Cables around Doorways

TRIM REMOVED

Figure 11-17. *Cables can be routed around doorways after the trim has been removed and the drywall grooved.*

Cables or conduit can be required to run from the attic through interior walls of a home. A drill bit is used to penetrate the top plate of a wall. Several drill extensions or an extended-length drill bit may be required to penetrate obstacles inside a wall. **See Figure 11-19.** Cables or conduit can also be required to run from the basement to a first-floor receptacle box. A drill bit is used to penetrate subflooring and the wall bottom plate. **See Figure 11-20.** By pushing a fish tape up from the basement and attaching the cable, the cable can easily be pulled from the receptacle box to the junction box in the basement.

Extended Length Drill Bits

TWIST DRILLS ARE MANUFACTURED IN 6″, 12″, 18″, AND 24″ LENGTHS

DRILL BITS CAN BE ORDERED WITH ANY LENGTH SHANK

Figure 11-19. *Drill bits can be purchased in various lengths or modified to be any length required.*

Replacing First-Floor Ceiling Box in Two-Story Dwelling

FLOORBOARDS

FLOOR JOIST

CEILING DRYWALL

CEILING BOX

WALL SWITCH BOX

ATTACHED JOISTS

Figure 11-18. *In two-story residences, it may be necessary to remove floorboards or plywood to install a ceiling box.*

Routing Cable from Basement to First-Floor Wall

DRYWALL

STUD

SUBFLOOR

JOIST NOT DRILLED

Figure 11-20. *Fish tapes aid dramatically when routing cables from the basement to first-floor walls.*

Surface Raceways

In some situations, such as with masonry walls, it is impossible to fish cables through the wall. When cables cannot be run through walls, cables must be run externally to walls. Cables being run externally to a wall must be run through surface raceways. **See Figure 11-21, Figure 11-22,** and **Figure 11-23.**

Surface Raceway – Feed

1 Bring Feed into 2000B Base.
Back-feed connection shown. See back of sheet for alternate methods of feeding.

2 Install 2000B Base on Surface.
Starting with feed section, mount entire run of 2000B Base with no. 8 flat head screws, through screw piercings and knockouts. Cut base to length at corners and end of run, as required.

A. Stub-in feed at beginning of run, ½ the distance or less from first receptacle. Cut off base so ½″ entrance knockout aligns with feed (also provides for cover to overlap base joints). Save base section cut off for opposite end of run.

B. Remove entrance knockout as shown.

C. Attach ½″ connector.

Snap in coupling where base sections but-up for grounding continuity.

Insert Internal Corner Coupling, and mount base on surface.

Slide next base section onto and mount.

AT END OF RUN
Insert Blank End Fitting, and mount base in place.

Figure 11-21. *Raceways use knockouts (sometimes piercings) to connect feed (power supply) cables to raceway.*

Surface Raceway – Snapicoil™

3 **Connect Snapicoil™ to Feed.**
Lay out Snapicoil™ along entire run of base so that receptacles are not located over feed or in corners. Connect to feed wires with pressure type wire connectors (for common connection of 2, 3, or 4 No. 12 or No. 14 solid conductors: NOT TO BE USED to connect equipment grounding conductors). Insert only conductors of same color in a connector.

Connecting 3-wire, two-circuit Snapicoil™

HOW TO USE WIRE CONNECTORS

A. Strip wire ends to width of strip gauge (½″).

B. Insert wire ends the full stripped distance.

Connecting 3-wire Snapicoil™ with insulated ground wire

SNAPICOIL™ INSTALLATION TIPS

To shorten ½″ connector inside base for feed wire clearance.

If receptacle falls at corner
Fold back wires to bring receptacle at least 6″ away from corner. Cut off cover to compensate for receptacle relocation before cutting it to length for corner.

Figure 11-22. *Raceway receptacles cannot be located over the raceway feed cable connection.*

⚛ Tech Tip: Surface Raceways NEC® Requirements

SURFACE METAL RACEWAYS PERMITTED IN DRY LOCATIONS
• 386.10(1)

INTERNAL CORNER

BLANK END FITTING

PLUG MOLD MULTIOUTLET SYSTEM

SIZE REDUCING CONNECTOR

COVER UP

TWO-GANG DEVICE BOX

ENTRANCE END FITTING

SINGLE-GANG DEVICE BOX

EXTERNAL CORNER

SURFACE RACEWAYS • ARTICLE 386, ARTICLE 388
STRUT-TYPE CHANNEL RACEWAY – ARTICLE 384
SURFACE METAL RACEWAYS – ARTICLE 386
SURFACE NONMETALLIC RACEWAYS – ARTICLE 388

Surface Raceway – Cover

④ Assemble Snapicoil™ and Cover in Base.
Cover sections should overlap base joints for rigidity and better ground continuity.

COVER

SNAP RECEPTACLES COMPLETELY INTO COVER

Starting at feed, snap receptacles completely into first cover section, so that white wire will be on bottom.

BASE

SNAP IN UPPER BEAD OF COVER

LOWER BEAD ENGAGED

Engage lower bead of cover in base and, starting at one end, snap in top bead. Be careful not to pinch wires. Continue snapping receptacles in covers, and covers into base, along entire run.

BASE

COVER

FIBER BUSHING

COVER

At inside corners
Cut cover at corner and snap wide end of fiber bushing into end of first cover section. Cut ¼″ from corner end of second cover section for wire slack, and snap covers into base, as shown.

BASE

COVER

COVER

At outside corners
Cut cover at corner even with base; cut ¼″ from corner end of second cover section and snap in both sections even with base. Snap External Elbow Cover over Covers.

TO SNAP COVER IN, WORK FROM ONE END TO THE OTHER, STRIKING SHARPLY WITH HEEL OF HAND

BASE JOINT

COVER JOINT

2000C COVER SECTIONS

Use Wire Clips (furnished) in cover to retain wires between receptacles (spaced 30″ or more apart) or in base to retain extra-circuit wiring bypassing receptacles as shown.

WIRE CLIPS

COVER

BASE

WIRE CLIP

WIRE CLIP

Figure 11-23. *Receptacles should be snapped into cover first with the white wire on the bottom.*

INSTALLING RECESSED LIGHTS

To install a recessed light in a ceiling, verify that there are no obstructions where the fixture is to be placed and that there is enough room to accommodate the entire fixture. Once an area is known to be clear, a hole can be cut using a hand saw or a hole saw and drill. **See Figure 11-24.** Hole saws are ideal for making holes in plaster or when creating several openings at one time. The opening created by a hole saw must provide a snug fit for the canister of the can light.

Creating Large Holes

Figure 11-24. *When an area is known to be clear, large holes can be cut using a handsaw, or with a drill and hole saw.*

Typically the most difficult problem when installing a recessed (can) light is running cable or conduit inside walls and ceilings from one room to another. Nonmetallic sheathed cable or armored cable is preferred for remodeling work because cable can be easily pulled and routed between ceilings, walls, and floors with a fish tape.

Fishing Wires

When cables must be routed around wall-ceiling corners of a finished home, the corner around which the cable must be routed is typically blocked by obstructions. **See Figure 11-25.** There are two methods by which corner obstructions can be bypassed. The first method uses a hole drilled at a diagonal from an opposite room, with a second hole drilled horizontally to meet the first hole. The two drilled holes provide an opening through the wall for cable. Some patchwork is required after the cable is routed.

Routing Cable from First-Floor Wall to First-Floor Ceiling

Figure 11-25. *Holes drilled from the first floor require patchwork while holes drilled from the second floor can typically be covered with the second-floor base molding.*

The second method of bypassing wall-ceiling corner obstructions is to remove the second-floor baseboard and drill a diagonal hole from one wall to the ceiling, forming the route for the cable. When the baseboard is replaced the drilled openings are not visible.

After drilling the necessary opening by either of the methods mentioned, cable is pulled through the opening using a fish tape. **See Figure 11-26.** To pull cable through the opening, push the hooked end of a fish tape through the drilled opening. Run another fish tape from the ceiling opening and hook the tape to the first fish tape. When the two hooked ends are joined, pull the first fish tape to the ceiling opening so that one fish tape is inside the wall and ceiling. Attach a continuous length of cable to the end of the fish tape and pull the cable into position.

When attic space is accessible, such as in one- or two-story houses with attics, floorboards, if present, can be lifted and a hole bored with an extended drill bit through any obstructions. **See Figure 11-27.**

Once a cable is fished, allow approximately 16″ of the cable to protrude out of the box for final wiring to a recessed light. **See Figure 11-28.**

½″ or ¾″ semi flexible plumbing tubing can be used in place of an electrician's fish tape when routing cable.

Remove Floorboards to Notch Ceiling Joists and Protect Cable

1/16″ STEEL PLATE IS ADDED OVER WOOD NOTCHES TO PROTECT AND SECURE CABLE

SECOND FLOOR ATTIC FLOORBOARDS REMOVED

Figure 11-27. *Removing second-floor or attic floorboards allows good accessibility to ceiling joists and fixture opening.*

Pulling Cable from First-Floor Wall to First-Floor Ceiling

HOOKED ENDS

FISH TAPE #2

EITHER OPPOSING ROOM OR 2ND FLOOR BASEBOARD DRILLING

FISH TAPE #1

INSTALLED RECESSED LIGHT

Figure 11-26. *Routing cable from a wall to a ceiling typically requires the use of two fish tapes.*

Extra Cable for Wiring Recessed Lights

Figure 11-28. *After a cable is fished into a ceiling box, allow approximately 16" of cable to protrude out of the box for final wiring to a recessed light.*

Wiring Recessed Lights

Recessed lights are manufactured with prewired junction boxes attached to the housing (can) of the light. Once the cover plate of the junction box is removed, the cable can be secured and connected to the box. The cable must be connected so that the cable cannot be pulled out of the junction box. Use standard wiring techniques to strip and connect the wires of the cable, white to white, red to red or black, and ground to ground. **See Figure 11-29.** In some cases the wire nuts should be taped for additional security to ensure the connections do not come undone when folded back into the junction box.

Wiring Recessed Lights

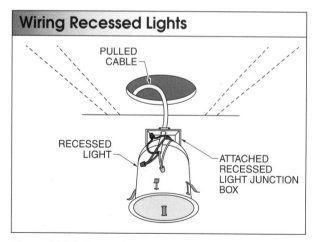

Figure 11-29. *Some circumstances require that wire nuts be taped for additional security to ensure that connections do not become undone when being folded back into the box.*

Securing Recessed Lights

Recessed lights designed for remodeling are equipped with mounting clips that clamp or secure the fixture to the ceiling. To secure the fixture, the mounting clips push down against the drywall. Once the recessed light fixture is pushed up into the hole, the clips are secured. The mounting clips provide an audible sound (short click) when pushed into clamping position. **See Figure 11-30.**

Securing Recessed Lights

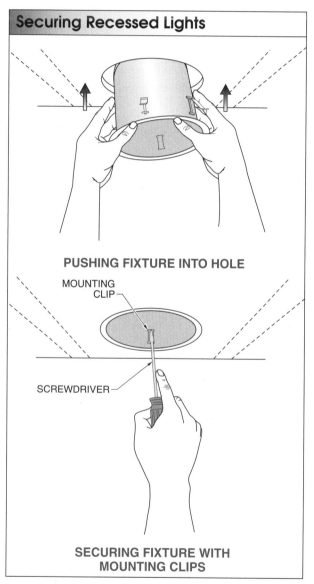

Figure 11-30. *Recessed lights designed for remodeling are equipped with mounting clips that clamp or secure the fixture to the ceiling drywall.*

Pressing a thumb against the clip on the inside of the fixture can help the process of securing a light fixture. Some fixtures require the aid of a screwdriver.

Recessed Light Trims

Some recessed light fixtures are manufactured with built-in pieces of trim. More commonly, the fixtures and trims are separate. **See Figure 11-31.** Ensure the trim is the same size and make as the recessed light fixture.

Recessed light trim is typically a ring that covers the gap between the ceiling material and the fixture. Trims with lenses are used for fixtures with standard light bulbs. When no lens is present, floodlight-type bulbs are typically used in the fixture.

An eyeball trim swivels so that the light emitted can be pointed in any direction to highlight a part of a room or a spot on a wall. Eyeball trim is typically used with spotlight bulbs, which produce a narrower beam of light than floodlight bulbs and can focus on an object such as a painting.

Choosing Recessed Lights

Recessed lights are manufactured in a variety of sizes and wattages for locations that are both wet and dry. Suppliers should be consulted to determine the correct recessed light for an application.

ADDING A CEILING FAN

When installing a ceiling fan in an existing home, the fan is typically replacing a light fixture in the center of the room. If the installation is a fan only, the circuit should be able to handle the load. If the installation includes a fan and light, a new circuit may be required.

Mounting Ceiling Fans

When mounting a ceiling fan, the weight of the fan is the number one consideration, but the force created by the blades rotating must also be considered. All ceiling fans are required to be mounted to a NEC® listed fan box that is properly mounted. Fans heavier than 35 lb must use the structural members of the house to support the fan. **See Figure 11-32.** Various manufacturers provide accessory kits to secure fans to the structural members of a house. A common feature of ceiling fan installations is the use of substantial screws such as lag screws.

The biggest challenge when mounting a ceiling fan arises when structural members are not directly available to secure the fan. To aid in mounting ceiling fans, manufacturers provide kits that reach out to the nearest structural member. **See Figure 11-33.** Typically electricians use bar hangers that fit between ceiling joists to provide support for heavy ceiling fans. To install a bar hanger, position the bar in place and

Recessed Light Trims

TRIM — —LENS

TRIM WITH LENS TO COVER A STANDARD LIGHT BULB

ADJUSTABLE EYEBALL TRIM

REFLECTOR CONE TO INTENSIFY LIGHT

Figure 11-31. *Trims with lenses are used for recessed fixtures with standard light bulbs, and fixtures with no lenses have floodlight-type bulbs.*

force the spikes at the end of the bar into the joists to hold the bar in place. Secure the bar flanges with screws. If access through the attic is not possible, there are fan brace kits that can be installed through the hole in the ceiling. **See Figure 11-34.**

Tech Tip: Lamp Fixture Mounting

STUD

HICKEY

THREADED ADAPTER

LOCKNUT

WIRE NUT

FIXTURE BASE

FIXTURE IS HELD BY STUD, HICKEY, AND THREADED ADAPTER. LOCKNUT HELPS HOLD BOTH FIXTURE AND BASE

OVER 20 LB

Attic Access Bar Hangers

JOIST

INSULATION

JOIST

CEILING BOX

SPIKES HOLD BAR IN PLACE UNTIL SECURED WITH SCREWS

BAR HANGER

CEILING DRYWALL

Figure 11-33. *Electricians use bar hangers that fit between ceiling joists to provide support for heavy ceiling fans.*

Ceiling Fan Mountings

LAG SCREW

RAFTER

NEC® LISTED FAN BOX

SLOPING CEILING

JOIST

LAG SCREWS

HORIZONTAL CEILING

LAG SCREW

LARGE WASHER

Figure 11-32. *All ceiling fans are required to be mounted to a NEC® listed fan box. Fans heavier than 35 lb must be supported by structural members of the house.*

Hole Access Bar Hangers

Figure 11-34. *To aid in mounting ceiling fans, manufacturers provide mounting kits that reach out to the nearest structural member.*

Never assume a circuit is OFF even after turning the breaker OFF or removing the fuse.

Electrical ceiling boxes are typically mounted to a joist for maximum support of light fixtures and ceiling fans.

Grounding Ceiling Fans

The two types of ceiling fans are flush mount and downrod mount. **See Figure 11-35.** *Flush mount* is a type of ceiling fan mounting used to allow maximum head clearance. *Downrod mount* is a type of ceiling fan mounting used to adjust head clearance or for angle mounting to vaulted ceilings. The wiring difference between the two mountings is the type of grounding used. In flush mount the ground goes directly to the metal junction box. In the downrod mount the ground is attached to the metal junction box and the downrod.

Wiring Ceiling Fans

When wiring a ceiling fan, two-wire or three-wire cable is used, depending on the application. A two-wire cable contains a black wire (hot), white wire (neutral), and a bare wire (ground). A three-wire, metallic or nonmetallic cable contains a black wire (hot), red wire (hot), white wire (neutral), and a bare wire (ground) in one outer cover. Two-wire cables are used when a fan will only be turned on and off. **See Figure 11-36.** Three-wire cables are used when it is necessary to control a fan and a light attached to the fan. When connecting a fan with light(s), the fan and light fixture wires are green, white, black, and blue.

Ceiling Fan Grounding

Figure 11-35. *A flush-mount ceiling fan has the ground going directly to a metal junction box. A downrod type of ceiling fan mounting has the ground attached to the metal box and the downrod.*

Wiring Ceiling Fans

Figure 11-36. *Three-wire cables are used when it is necessary to control a fan and a light attached to the fan.*

The green grounding wire of the fixture connects to the bare ground wire of the supply cable. The white and black wires connect to the white and black wires of the cable. The red cable wire connects to the blue wire of the fan so the light(s) can be switched separately. At the switch box of a fan and light combination, there are two switches with power going to the bottom of each. **See Figure 11-37.** One switch will connect to the black wire in the cable for controlling the fan. The red wire will connect to the other switch to control the lighting circuit.

Wall Fan and Light Controls

FAN CONTROLS

FAN AND LIGHT CONTROLS

Cooper Wiring Devices

Figure 11-38. *A fan can be started or reversed, its speed can be controlled, and the lights dimmed, all from one wall box.*

Ceiling Fan Switch Connections

Figure 11-37. *A ceiling fan with light has two switches. One switch controls the fan and the other switch controls the light(s).*

Ceiling Fan Controls

Fans with new technology provide many additional features. A fan can be started or reversed, its speed can be controlled, and the lights dimmed, all from a remote control. Typically, fans and fans with lights are controlled by wall controls. **See Figure 11-38.** However, fans can be controlled by handheld remote controls. **See Figure 11-39.**

Remote Fan and Light Controls

REMOTE CONTROL FAN SWITCH

REMOVABLE FACE REMOTE CONTROL

Cooper Wiring Devices

Figure 11-39. *A fan can be started or reversed, its speed can be controlled, and the lights dimmed, all from a handheld remote control.*

PROPERLY INSTALLING AND TESTING RECEPTACLES

To be properly installed, receptacles must be tested. Receptacles are tested for proper polarization, grounding, and GFCI operation.

Polarization

In the early stages of residential wiring, receptacles were considered properly installed if the receptacle was polarized. Polarized plugs and receptacles keep the external surfaces of appliances such as toasters on the "ground" side of any current flow. The white wire (neutral) is connected to the long slot of a receptacle and the black wire (hot) is connected to the shorter slot for proper polarization. **See Figure 11-40.**

Grounding

Grounding is recognized as being required to protect homeowners from residential electrical system problems. A properly grounded receptacle has a ground wire or metallic sheathing that is tightly connected at all points leading back to the ground bar of the service panel. **See Figure 11-41.**

A grounded receptacle provides an unbroken path to earth for current flow. Current flow will travel to earth ground and not through the body when proper grounding is in place. The third prong of a grounded plug fits into an arched hole in a grounded receptacle. The arched hole is connected through a wire or metal sheathing to the ground bar of the service panel. The ground bar is connected to earth ground through an electrode. **See Figure 11-42.**

DANGER

Many homeowners simply replace old, ungrounded receptacles with new three-hole grounded receptacles. The newly installed receptacles look grounded but are not, and are dangerous.

A receptacle with a common ground can act as a large antenna and conduct electrical noise that interferes with television, radio, computer, and home security systems. Installation of an isolated ground receptacle minimizes electrical noise by providing a separate grounding path for each plug.

Polarized Receptacles

Figure 11-40. *A polarized receptacle has a white wire (neutral) connected to the long slot of the receptacle and a black wire (hot) connected to the short slot of the receptacle.*

Properly Grounded Receptacles

Figure 11-41. *A grounded receptacle provides an unbroken path to earth for current flow.*

Plug Grounding Path to Earth

Figure 11-42. *The arched hole of a receptacle is connected through a wire or metal sheathing to the ground bar of the service panel and from there to a grounding electrode in the earth.*

GROUND FAULT CIRCUIT INTERRUPTERS

The latest device to provide protection from electrical shock in the home is the ground fault circuit interrupter (GFCI). **See Figure 11-43.** GFCIs can be permanent or plug-in. Check manufacturer specifications as to ratings and locations for proper GFCI installation instructions. A GFCI that is being retrofitted into a box of an older home typically requires a box extender. **See Figure 11-44.** A box extender allows all connections to be made without stuffing the GFCI device into a cramped, wire-filled area. The pressure on the wires can cause connections to come apart or to overheat during operation.

Ground Fault Circuit Interrupters

COMMERCIAL GRADE
GFCI – 15 A

SWITCHED GFCI
PROTECTED RECEPTACLE

Cooper Wiring Devices

Figure 11-43. *Ground fault circuit interrupters (GFCIs) can be of a permanently installed design or of a portable (plug-in) design.*

Box Extenders

BOX EXTENDER

GFCI TAKES UP LARGER VOLUME OF BOX THAN STANDARD RECEPTACLE

Figure 11-44. *GFCIs being retrofitted into a box of an older home typically require that a box extender be used.*

Plug-in GFCIs

Plug-in GFCIs are the most convenient ground fault circuit interrupter device to use. By simply plugging a GFCI module into any grounded receptacle, any tool plugged into the GFCI device and the operator are protected. Electricians typically keep a plug-in GFCI unit in a toolbox, and use the device whenever working with power tools outdoors, especially when conditions are wet. **See Figure 11-45.**

Plug-in GFCIs

SINGLE RECEPTACLE
GFCI ADAPTER

EXTENSION CORD
SIGNALING GFCI

Cooper Wiring Devices

Figure 11-45. *By simply plugging a GFCI module into any grounded receptacle, the tool plugged into the GFCI device and the operator are protected.*

TESTING ELECTRICAL CIRCUITS

Electrical circuits can be tested safely and inexpensively with a neon tester. Most hardware stores sell simple test instruments such as neon testers. A neon tester is designed to light up in the presence of 115 V and 230 V circuits. A soft glow indicates a 115 V circuit; a brighter glow indicates a 230 V circuit. Many residential electrical system problems can be diagnosed by determining the presence or absence of voltage.

Testing for Defective Receptacles

One of the most common tests made with a neon tester is determining whether a receptacle is providing power. **See Figure 11-46.** The test leads of a neon tester or other test instrument must be firmly pressed into the receptacle slots to form a good electrical connection.

When voltage is present, the neon bulb will glow softly. When the tester does not light, the receptacle cover should be removed so that a second voltage check can be made at the terminals of the receptacle. **See Figure 11-47.** When voltage is present at the terminals of a receptacle but not at the slots, the receptacle is defective and must be replaced.

When voltage is not present at either the slots or terminals of a receptacle, the problem lies in the overload protection (fuses and circuit breakers) or in the electrical circuit (wires) leading to the troubled receptacle.

When the problem is in the electrical circuit leading to the receptacle, check each splice or each terminal point along the entire circuit for a break or loose connection.

Tech Tip: GFCI Receptacle Tester

OPEN GROUND	○	●	○
OPEN NEUTRAL	○	●	○
OPEN HOT	○	○	●
HOT/GRD. REVERSE	●	○	●
HOT/NEU. REVERSE	●	●	○
CORRECT	○	●	●

INDICATOR LIGHT—CODE

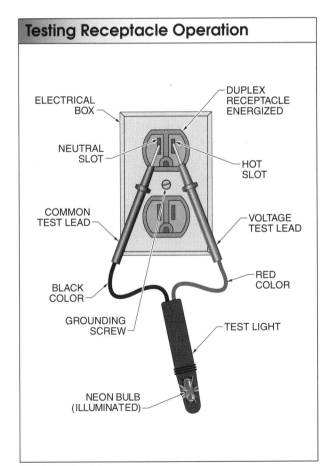

Testing Receptacle Operation

ELECTRICAL BOX

DUPLEX RECEPTACLE ENERGIZED

NEUTRAL SLOT

HOT SLOT

COMMON TEST LEAD

VOLTAGE TEST LEAD

BLACK COLOR

RED COLOR

GROUNDING SCREW

TEST LIGHT

NEON BULB (ILLUMINATED)

Figure 11-46. *The test leads of a test instrument must be firmly pressed into the slots of the receptacle to form a proper electrical connection.*

Testing Receptacle at Terminals

VOLTAGE TEST LEAD

COMMON TEST LEAD

Figure 11-47. *When voltage measurements are unsuccessful at the slots of a receptacle, the receptacle must be removed from the box and tested at the terminals.*

Testing for Defective Switches

Determining whether a switch is defective requires only a simple two-step procedure. The first step is to determine if voltage is reaching the switch. **See Figure 11-48.** The second step is to determine if voltage is passing through the switch. **See Figure 11-49.** A system that is properly grounded requires that the leads of the test instrument only touch the metal box and the terminals.

CAUTION

In older homes without a ground, it is necessary to remove the wire nut from the neutral wire and use the neutral as the ground test point.

If voltage is not present at either switch terminal, the problem lies in the overload protection (fuses and circuit breakers) or in the electrical circuit leading to the troubled switch.

Testing Voltage to Switch

Figure 11-48. *A switch is tested by first measuring for incoming voltage to the switch (bottom terminal).*

Testing Voltage from Switch

Figure 11-49. *When a switch has incoming voltage, the switch is turned ON and the switch is tested for voltage leaving the switch (top terminal).*

When the problem is in the electrical circuit leading to the switch, each splice or terminal point should be checked along the entire circuit for a break or loose connection.

DANGER

Before starting any voltage test procedure, ensure the power to the suspected switch has been turned off. Remove the faceplate from the switch and unscrew the switch from the box. Pull the switch safely away from the metal box and position the switch so that no bare wires touch the box. When the switch is in a safe position, power is restored and the test procedures started.

Testing for Hot Wires

When remodeling, it is necessary to identify which wire(s) bring power to a circuit and which wire(s) feed other circuits. A neon tester can simplify this procedure by individually identifying hot wires. Any hot wire measured to common wire or ground by a neon tester will cause the neon tester to glow.

Grounded systems are the easiest to test for a hot wire because only the potential hot wires must be disconnected, separated, and tested. **See Figure 11-50.** The wire that causes a neon tester to glow is the hot lead.

An ungrounded system can be checked like a grounded system except any solderless connectors must be removed from the neutral wires. The neutral wires are used as the reference for ground in an ungrounded system. **See Figure11-51.**

To determine if voltage is reaching a light fixture, turn the light fixture switch to the ON position. A properly installed circuit will cause the neon tester light to glow. **See Figure 11-52.**

Testing Receptacle Grounds

A simple test procedure is used to check the grounding of receptacles. **See Figure 11-53.** The test is used to ensure that each receptacle in a home is grounded.

Figure 11-50. *Grounded systems are the easiest to test for a hot wire.*

Figure 11-51. *The neutral wires are used as the reference for ground in ungrounded electrical systems.*

Testing for Voltage at Ceiling Fixture Box

CEILING FIXTURE BOX

COMMON TEST LEAD

VOLTAGE TEST LEAD

LIGHT OFF

CHECKING WHITE WIRE

COMMON TEST LEAD

VOLTAGE TEST LEAD

LIGHT ON

CHECKING RED WIRE

Figure 11-52. *The switch must be ON to a ceiling fixture box to test for voltage at the box.*

To test the grounding of receptacles, one lead (black) of the neon tester is held stationary on the ground terminal while the other lead is repositioned on each plug slot. If the receptacle is properly grounded, the neon light will only light when the test lead is placed in the hot slot. If the light does not glow with the test lead in either slot, the receptacle is not grounded.

Testing Circuit Breakers and Fuses

Circuit breakers can trip and fuses can blow, shutting off circuits in a residence. The ability to properly test circuit breakers and fuses is a must.

Circuit Breakers. A circuit breaker operates in much the same manner as a switch. A circuit breaker is either ON or OFF. To test a circuit breaker, the common test lead of a test instrument (voltage tester) is placed on the neutral bus bar and the positive test lead is placed on the screw terminal of the circuit breaker. **See Figure 11-54.** When the breaker is good, the voltage tester will indicate voltage when the breaker is in the ON position and will not indicate voltage when the breaker is in the "tripped" (OFF) position.

When a voltage tester indicates voltage in both circuit breaker positions, the breaker is shorted and must be replaced. When a voltage tester does not indicate voltage in either position, the circuit breaker is open and must be replaced.

Fuses. When a fuse is suspected of being defective, the fuse is checked with a multimeter set to measure resistance using the following procedure. **See Figure 11-55.**

1. First disconnect the power from the incoming lines to the fuses.
2. Remove the fuses from the fuse holder.
3. Measure the resistance of one of the removed fuses. The resistance of the fuse should be low (a few ohms).
4. Measure the resistance of the other removed fuse. The resistance of the fuse should be low (a few ohms) and within a measured ohm or two of the first measured fuse.
5. Reinstall tested fuses that are good or replace with new fuses.

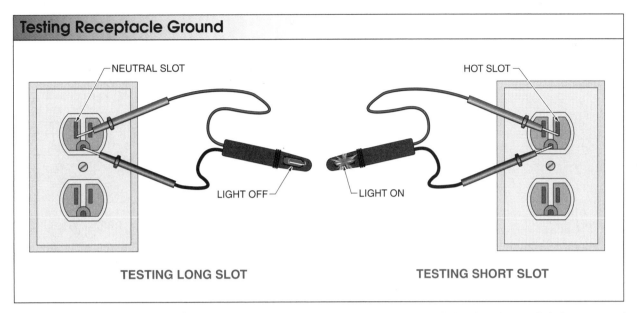

Figure 11-53. *A properly wired and grounded receptacle should only turn on a neon light when the test light is connected from ground (arched hole) to the hot (short) slot.*

ADDING A CIRCUIT PANEL (SUBPANEL)

Subpanels are added to existing service panels to obtain additional circuits. **See Figure 11-56.** The service panel must have breakers large enough to meet the demands of the subpanel—30 A, 50 A, or 60 A. The service panel circuit breakers protect the subpanel from overloading. Check with the specifications of the subpanel manufacturer to determine what size breakers to use in the service panel.

An AC/DC voltage tester is different than an AC voltage tester as it includes a beeper or other indicator (solenoid that vibrates) when the tester is connected to AC voltage.

⚠️ **CAUTION**

Do not replace fuses unless the fuses are de-energized and then only with the use of a fuse puller.

Testing Voltage at Circuit Breakers

Figure 11-54. *A voltage tester should indicate 115 V when connected between the neutral bus bar and energized circuit breaker.*

Checking Fuses

Figure 11-55. *The fuses used in a service panel have low resistance and the resistance should be the same from fuse to fuse.*

Adding a Subpanel

Figure 11-56. *Subpanels are added to residential electrical systems for garages and air conditioning condensers, or for additional circuit capacity.*

Name_____ Date _____

Remodeling, Wiring, and Troubleshooting Electrical Systems

_____ **1.** Studs and joists are typically laid out on ___" centers.

        A. 16   **C.** 32

        B. 24   **D.** both A and B

_____ **2.** A(n) ___ knife can be used to cut small openings in drywall walls and ceilings.

_____ **3.** Metal ___ can be used to mount electrical boxes in existing walls.

_____ **4.** A(n) ___ tape is used to route cables through ceilings and walls.

T   F **5.** A soft glow on a neon tester indicates 230 V.

T   F **6.** When a light switch is operating properly and is in the ON position, voltage is present at the top terminal screw of the switch.

T   F **7.** A subpanel can be added to an existing service panel provided enough current is available.

T   F **8.** The hot wire of a grounded circuit is easier to check than the hot wire of an ungrounded circuit.

_____ **9.** A(n) ___ stud finder can be used to locate studs in existing walls.

_____ **10.** Folding ___ on each side of a box are used to keep the box from pulling back into the holes as the clamps are tightened.

_____ **11.** When voltage is present at the terminals but not at the receptacle slots, the receptacle is ___.

_____ **12.** To determine if a switch is good, ___ must reach and pass through the switch.

T   F **13.** Splices and terminal points in a circuit should be checked for breaks or loose connections.

269

T	F	**14.** A neon tester can be used to identify a hot wire.
T	F	**15.** To determine if a fuse is operating correctly, a multimeter set to measure resistance is used.
T	F	**16.** Fish tapes can be used to pull wires through back-to-back boxes.
T	F	**17.** Sawcuts should go completely through surface raceways when installing raceways around an outside corner.

_____ **18.** Receptacles in surface raceways should be at least ___" from corners.

_____ **19.** A neon tester will illuminate when touched to a good circuit breaker and the ___ bar in the service panel.

_____ **20.** Horizontal ___ is used as a brace in stud walls.

_____ **21.** ___ boxes are typically very shallow.

T	F	**22.** Cables and wires can be routed around a door behind the trim.
T	F	**23.** Fish tape is easily used to fish wires through masonry walls.
T	F	**24.** A neon tester can be used to check splices for breaks or loose connections.

_____ **25.** When a switch is in the OFF position, voltage is present at the ___ terminal.

Exterior Wall Section

_____ **1.** Double top plate

_____ **2.** Backing

_____ **3.** Wall stud

_____ **4.** Gypsum board

_____ **5.** Frieze

_____ **6.** Rafter

_____ **7.** Sheathing

_____ **8.** Vent

_____ **9.** Plywood panel

_____ **10.** Roof joist

Testing Electrical Circuits

_____ 1. Voltage is reaching the switch.

_____ 2. The switch is good.

_____ 3. Testing for the hot wire in a grounded system.

_____ 4. Testing for the hot wire in an ungrounded system.

_____ 5. Voltage is not reaching the switch.

_____ 6. The switch is defective.

_____ 7. The receptacle is properly grounded.

_____ 8. The receptacle is not properly grounded.

Chapter 12

Structured Wiring

Chapter 12 provides an overview of low-voltage residential electrical systems and how the systems are installed and operated. Where appropriate, low voltage provides an economical and convenient way of signaling and controlling a variety of devices. Low voltage has become more popular because of the energy savings provided by low power consumption.

STRUCTURED WIRING ELECTRICAL SYSTEMS

Structured wiring electrical systems are commonly known as low-voltage systems. Low-voltage systems in homes operate at less than 30 V. Typically, the range is between 12 V and 24 V. Doorbells, intercoms, security systems, and remote control wiring are examples of structured wiring (low-voltage) systems.

Low voltage is used with structured wiring systems because low voltage is safer and more economical than 115 V or 230 V. Safety is increased because the lower voltage reduces the hazard of electrical shock. Installation costs are reduced because low-voltage systems use smaller wires that are less expensive. In addition, low-voltage systems

are easy to install and require no elaborate protective measures. For additional information on the installation of low-voltage equipment, refer to NEC® Article 720, *Circuits and Equipment Operating at Less than 50 Volts* and NEC® Article 411, *Lighting Systems Operating at 30 Volts or Less.*

ELECTROMECHANICAL SIGNALING SYSTEMS

Electromechanical signaling systems are used to notify the occupants of a visitor or of conditions existing in a specific room or area of a residence. Electromechanical systems include doorbell (bell/buzzer or chimes) systems and radio/audio/intercom systems.

Doorbell/Buzzer Systems

The simplest low-voltage system typically found in a residence is a doorbell/buzzer system. A simple doorbell/buzzer circuit consists of a step-down transformer, pushbutton switch, and a bell or buzzer. **See Figure 12-1.** A step-down transformer changes the 115 V to 12 V to safely power a doorbell/buzzer system.

Depressing a momentary contact pushbutton (PB) completes the circuit and allows current to flow through the doorbell/buzzer as long as the pushbutton is held closed. Releasing the pushbutton opens the circuit.

Door Bell/Buzzer System

Figure 12-1. *A simple bell/buzzer circuit consists of a step-down transformer, a pushbutton, and a bell or buzzer.*

Multiple Location Activation. When a doorbell/buzzer is to be activated from two or more locations, a circuit with several pushbuttons is wired in parallel so that depressing any one of the pushbuttons activates the doorbell/buzzer. **See Figure 12-2.**

Door Bell/Buzzer System — Multiple Activation Locations

Figure 12-2. *When the bell/buzzer is to be activated from two or more locations, a circuit with several pushbuttons is wired in parallel so that depressing any one of them would activate the bell/buzzer.*

Return Call Systems. Return call systems provide a circuit for return signals to be generated, similar to an intercom system. **See Figure 12-3.** Depressing pushbutton 1 (PB1) completes a circuit, allowing current to flow through bell A and return to the trans-former. Depressing pushbutton 2 (PB2) completes the opposite circuit, allowing current to flow through bell B and return to the transformer.

The return call system can be simplified by the use of double-contact pushbuttons. Double-contact pushbuttons are arranged in series, rather than in parallel as with a single-contact pushbutton system. **See Figure 12-4.**

An intercom can be used with a doorbell/buzzer system and be connected to the same circuit.

Figure 12-3. *Depressing pushbutton one (PB1) completes one circuit allowing current to flow through Bell A and return to the opposite side of the transformer. Depressing pushbutton two (PB2) completes the opposite circuit, allowing current to flow through Bell B and return to the opposite side of the transformer.*

Figure 12-4. *The return call system can be simplified by the use of double-contact pushbuttons.*

Chime Systems

Chimes, although more expensive, have replaced doorbell/buzzer systems in many homes. **See Figure 12-5.** Chimes are available with simple musical notes or with very complex melodies. The complexity of the sound and the outward physical appearance dictate the price. The introduction of digital chimes allows the homeowner to program a wide range of sounds or melodies.

Most magnetic chime systems have wiring similar to a doorbell circuit. **See Figure 12-6.** When pushbutton 1 (PB1) is depressed, chime A (front door) is activated. When pushbutton 2 (PB2) is depressed, chime B (back door) is activated. A common transformer is used to power both systems. Different tone sequences are used to differentiate between the front and back doors. For example, the front door chime may produce several tones while the back door chime produces only a single tone.

Chimes

Wilden Enterprises, Inc.

Figure 12-5. *Chimes, although more expensive, have replaced bell/buzzer systems in many homes.*

Magnetic Chime System

STEP-DOWN
TRANSFORMER

CENTRAL
CHIME

PB1

FRONT
DOOR
SWITCH

PB2

BACK
DOOR
SWITCH

CH
A

CH
B

115 V

12 V

FROM SERVICE PANEL

Figure 12-6. *With a magnetic chime system, when pushbutton one (PB1) is depressed, the front door chime is activated. When pushbutton two (PB2) is depressed, the back door chime is activated.*

To install a door chime, route a hot wire from each pushbutton (front and back door) and connect the hot wires to the chime. **See Figure 12-7.** Connect the chime common terminal to the transformer.

In multilevel homes, such as two-story homes or bi-levels, centrally located chimes can be impossible to hear. In multilevel homes, two chimes that are wired in parallel are typically used. **See Figure 12-8.** Both chime circuits are activated simultaneously, allowing the chimes to be heard anywhere in the house.

Radio/Audio/Intercom

A radio/audio/intercom combines the functions of chimes, intercoms, and audio systems into one master unit. The master unit is used to control the various systems. **See Figure 12-9.** With radio/audio/intercom systems, a piece of equipment can be used to serve more than one function. Each manufacturer has several models and types ranging from economy to deluxe, including one or several of the following features:

- Room-to-room intercom that allows for calling any or all stations at one time from any station
- Audio monitoring of specific stations such as a child's bedroom
- Remote station privacy settings to shut off specific rooms
- Hands-free answering of calls
- Music muting or intercom override
- FM-AM radio
- CD and audio inputs

Wiring diagrams vary according to the manufacturer and should be followed closely when setting up a system. A properly installed radio/CD intercom can provide many hours of convenience and pleasure. A fire/security system is typically part of most whole-house systems. Some individuals prefer stand-alone intercom and security systems because either the security or communication system still functions when the other has crashed.

Low-voltage wiring for doorbell cicuits must be separate from power and lighting circuits and not occupy the same conduit or outlet boxes as these circuits unless a divider is provided to separate the systems.

Figure 12-7. *To install a door chime, route two wires from each device and connect them at the chime.*

Figure 12-8. *In multilevel homes, two chimes wired in parallel are typically used. With this type of circuit both chimes are activated simultaneously, allowing them to be heard throughout the house.*

SECURITY/FIRE SYSTEMS

The need for protection from intruders and the devastating effects of house fires have increased the demand for security/fire systems. *Security/fire systems* are home protection systems composed of three elements: detectors, controls, and annunciators. **See Figure 12-10.** A *detector* is an electrical device used to detect noise, heat, gases, or movement. Detectors are used to identify problems when the problem first exists and respond by opening or closing circuits to controllers. A *control* is an electrical device that accepts signals from detectors and turns annunciators ON and OFF. The control determines which detector is responding and uses that signal to trigger an annunciator. An annunciator is an electrical load that acts as an alarm. Annunciators respond to control signals by ringing a bell, flashing a light, or sounding a siren to alert individuals of danger.

Tech Tip: Grounding Transformer For Secondary Circuit

Radio/Audio/Intercom System

Figure 12-9. *A radio/audio/intercom combines the functions of chimes, intercoms, and audio systems into one master unit. The master unit is used to control the different systems.*

Security/Fire Systems

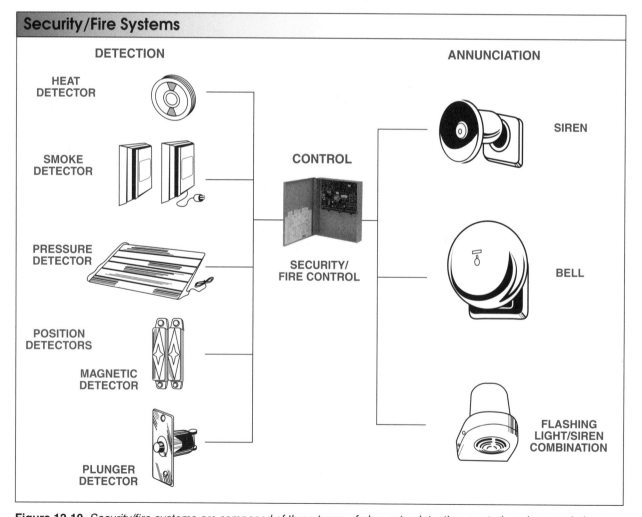

Figure 12-10. *Security/fire systems are composed of three types of elements: detection, control, and annunciation.*

Closed-Circuit Wiring (Security)

Security/fire systems operate with closed-circuit or open-circuit systems. Closed-circuit systems are typically used for the security portion of a security/fire system. A closed-circuit system is used for security because the system is a series circuit, which remains continuous unless a detector is activated, or a wire is cut. **See Figure 12-11.** The detectors are in series with the normally closed relay. As long as the detectors remain in a closed position, the current to the detector circuit relay R1 will hold contacts C1 open in the annunciator circuit. If a detector circuit wire is cut or a detector is activated, the current to relay R1 stops because the series circuit is broken. Because relay R1 is de-energized, contacts C1 close and the annunciator (bell) is activated. Although the circuit is quite simple, the circuit is difficult for an intruder to override.

Open-Circuit Wiring

Open-circuit wiring systems are typically used on the smoke (fire) detection portion of a security/fire system. An open-circuit system consists of several open contacts wired in parallel with a normally open relay. An open-circuit system can be used on fire systems because the circuit is tamperproof. The principle behind an open-circuit system is that, as long as the fire detectors remain in an open position, no current will reach the detector circuit relay R1 and the annunciator circuit will remain inoperative. **See Figure 12-12.** If any one detector or several detectors are activated, current passes through relay R1, and contacts C1 in the annunciator circuit close. With C1 closed, the bell, siren, or light turns on. The relay is used in this circuit so that the detectors can operate on low voltage while the annunciator operates on standard voltage.

Figure 12-11. *A closed circuit system is typically used with security systems because it is a series circuit, which remains continuous unless one of the detectors is activated, or the line is cut.*

Open Circuit Systems

Figure 12-12. *Open circuit wiring systems are typically used on the smoke (fire) detection portion of a security/fire system. An open circuit system consists of several open contacts wired in parallel with a normally open relay.*

Detector Types

Detectors are the sensing portion in both fire and security systems. A detector determines when a problem (smoke, fire, intruder) exists, and sends a signal to the controller indicating the problem. Detector types include plunger button, magnetic, infrared, wireless control, heat, and smoke/combustion gas detectors.

Plunger Button Detectors. A *plunger button detector* is an electrical sensing device used on windows and doors to determine if the window or door is open or closed. **See Figure 12-13.** A plunger button detector is typically used in closed-circuit systems where a door or window holds the contacts of the detector in the closed position. Opening a door or window activates the detector. Plunger button detectors are easier to install on new construction than during remodeling.

Plunger Button Detectors

Figure 12-13. *Plunger button detectors are typically used on windows and doors where they can be installed in a concealed location.*

Magnetic Detectors. A *two-piece magnetic detector* is an electrical sensing device used on windows to determine if the window is open or closed. A magnetic detector is composed of a permanent magnet in one section and a sensor (switch) in the other section. As long as the two sections are close to each other, the switch remains closed. Movement of the door or window removes the switch from the magnet and the circuit is opened, activating a closed-circuit system. **See Figure 12-14.** The switch is permanently mounted with the magnet as the movable section. On existing construction, two-piece magnetic detectors are easier to mount than plunger button detectors.

Low-voltage hardwiring for telephone and television service is typically roughed-in by the electrical contractor during the construction of a new dwelling. A doorbell/buzzer system is sometimes included in this process. Additional hardwiring for systems such as computer networks, intruder (burglar) alarms, intercoms, smoke detection, heat detection, CO (carbon monoxide) detection, audio/video security, and other types of systems is installed by a contractor that specializes in the installation of such systems.

Two-Piece Magnetic Detector

Figure 12-14. *Movement of the door or window removes the switch from the magnet, activating the sensor and the circuit is opened, activating a closed circuit system.*

Infrared Detectors. An *infrared detector* is an electrical sensing device used for security purposes to determine if movement exists in a room or area. Infrared detectors are a combination transmitter-receiver recessed into the wall. The transmitter projects an invisible pulsating beam at a specially designed bounce-back reflector on the opposite wall. An interruption of the beam signals the receiver to activate the system alarm. **See Figure 12-15.** Because infrared is virtually invisible, infrared detectors have become more readily accepted than photoelectric detectors operating on a visible light beam.

Heat Detectors. A *heat detector* is another electrical sensing device used to detect excess heat levels within a structure. Heat detectors are often used in conjunction with smoke detectors. **See Figure 12-16.** Heat detectors warn of fire when the temperature in the area near the detector reaches a certain level.

Heat detectors do not detect smoke. A heat detector is often used in areas such as kitchens and attics, where smoke detectors are not practical. Heat detectors are not recommended for use in bedrooms or sleeping areas. Heat detectors are typically classified as fixed temperature or rate of rise temperature detectors. A *fixed temperature detector* is a heat detector designed to respond when a room reaches a specific temperature. Once the specific temperature is reached, the contacts in the detector close and the alarm is activated.

Infrared Detectors

Figure 12-15. *An infrared detector transmitter projects an invisible pulsating beam at a specially designed bounce-back reflector on the opposite wall. An interruption of the beam signals the receiver to activate the system alarm.*

Heat Detectors

Nutone, Division of Scovill

Figure 12-16. *Heat detectors are used to detect excess heat levels within a structure and are often used in conjunction with smoke detectors.*

A *rate of rise detector* is a heat detector designed for flash fires or slow-burning fires. The elements of a rate of rise heat detector sense any rapid change in temperature, such as a 100°F temperature change in 30 seconds, to trigger an alarm. As added protection, most rate of rise units have fusible alloy elements which, when heated to a certain temperature, melt and cause the contacts of the detector to close.

Smoke Detectors. A *smoke detector* is an electrical device used to sense products of combustion (smoke) and activate an alarm when smoke is detected. Smoke detectors are required for home safety because smoke detectors provide an early warning to evacuate a home before a fire becomes out of control. **See Figure 12-17.**

Smoke detectors use smoke or products of combustion to trigger the generation of a signal. Some units rely on the density of smoke to trigger an annunciator, while others are triggered by the presence of certain products of combustion. In either case, contacts are closed as with all detectors, and an alarm is sounded. Smoke detectors are available that operate on 115 VAC with a battery-power backup, while others operate only on battery power. A smoke detector that is installed in the center of a room will protect a 400 sq ft area.

Smoke Detectors

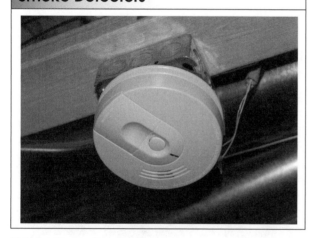

Figure 12-17. *Smoke detectors are essential to home safety because they provide the early warning necessary to help evacuate the home before the fire or amount of smoke is out of control.*

National Fire Protection Association (NFPA) Standard 72 indicates the number and placement of smoke/heat detectors. NFPA Standard 72 indicates that early-warning fire detection is best achieved by the installation of fire detection equipment in all rooms and areas of the house including the following:

- Outside each separate sleeping area
- On each additional story of the family living unit
- Basements
- Living rooms
- Dining rooms
- Kitchens
- Hallways
- Attics
- Furnace areas
- Utility/storage rooms
- Attached garages

Wireless Control Detectors. A *wireless control detector* is a device used for security purposes in existing construction to eliminate hard wiring. Because running wires for long distances is impractical in an existing building, wireless control detectors are used. Each detector is attached to a transmitter that is capable of sending a signal to a radio receiver. When a detector senses a forced entry, the transmitted signal triggers the wireless receiver control unit, which sounds an alarm.

In addition to regular detectors, some wireless units provide a portable transmitter that can be hand-carried or placed on a piece of furniture.

Security/Fire Alarm System Controls

The control section of a security/fire alarm system receives signals from the detectors (sensors) and causes the appropriate annunciator to be activated. A control box is composed of a series of relays which open and close in response to the opening and closing of sensors. Each manufacturer labels terminals differently, but all manufacturers supply a complete set of step-by-step installation instructions. The choice of which unit to install typically depends on specific needs and cost considerations.

Annunciators

An *annunciator* is a signaling device that notifies individuals that one or more detectors have been activated. Annunciators, controls, and detectors are integrated into a system to fit specific needs. A complete security-alarm/fire-detection system includes various types of signaling devices (detectors) controlled by a master panel. Depending on the application, the system can be as simple or as complex as required. Manufacturers of annunciators and related equipment try to design systems that fit the requirements of the user. **See Figure 12-18.**

REMOTE CONTROL WIRING

Remote control wiring is a method of controlling standard-voltage devices through the use of low-voltage relays and low-voltage switches. A basic remote control wiring system is used to control a light. A remote control system is composed of a transformer, switch, and magnetic relay. **See Figure 12-19.** Remote control wiring systems are popular because the transformer, switch, and magnetic relay are interconnected by low-voltage wire. The smaller the wire, the less the cost and the greater the ease of routing the wire.

Security — Alarm/Fire System

Figure 12-18. *Specific manufacturers of annunciators and related equipment can help design a system that fits the requirements of the user.*

Remote Control Systems

Figure 12-19. *A remote control system is composed of a transformer, switch, and magnetic relay.*

Remote Control Relay

Figure 12-20. *Remote control relays have an ON coil and an OFF coil with a common center plunger.*

Relay Operation

The main component of the remote control wiring system is the relay. A remote control relay differs from those used in security-alarm/fire-detection systems. Remote control relays have an ON coil and an OFF coil with a common center plunger. **See Figure 12-20.** The use of two coils allows the movable plunger to be moved positively in either direction without the use of springs.

When switch SW1 is pressed, current will pass through the ON coil and cause the movable plunger to shift into the ON position. **See Figure 12-21.** As the movable plunger moves to the ON position, contacts C1 close and the load circuit (light) goes on.

The relay will move to and maintain the ON position even when switch SW1 is closed only momentarily. Other types of relays spring back from the closed position once power is cut off. When pushbutton PB1 is released, current will pass through the OFF coil, causing the movable plunger to shift to the OFF position. As the plunger moves, contacts C1 are opened and power to the load (light) is turned off. The relay maintains the OFF position until the switch energizes the ON coil again.

Relays (mounted to junction box knockouts) for low-voltage systems are capable of controlling 20 A of tungsten, fluorescent, or inductive loads at 115 VAC or 277 VAC. Low-voltage relays are also available for ½ HP 115 VAC and 1½ HP 230 VAC operation.

Remote Control Relay Operation

Figure 12-21. *The use of two coils allows the movable plunger to be moved positively in either direction without the use of springs.*

Remote Control Switches

One of the advantages of remote control wiring is that one basic switch, the single-pole, double-throw, momentary contact, normally open switch, does the same job as the single-pole, double-pole, three-way, and four-way switches used in conventional wiring. When two or more switches are wired in parallel, each is capable of controlling the relay. In theory, this allows a device to be controlled from as many locations as there are switches. Control switches are available with or without pilot lights. Control switches are typically wired into a transmitter that sends signals to a remote control receiver to control lights, ceiling fixtures, and other electronic systems. **See Figure 12-22.**

Figure 12-22. *A transmitter sends signals to a remote control receiver to control lights, ceiling fixtures, and other electronic systems.*

STRUCTURED WIRING SYSTEMS

Structured wiring systems are used in homes and businesses for the routing of low-voltage electrical systems such as telephone, voice-data-video, and home security systems. Typical structured wiring applications use copper connectivity, but with recent technological advances, fiber optic connectivity is used more frequently to outfit a home or business. Fiber optic technology offers several advantages over copper systems such as a smaller space requirement, the ability to deliver more data, higher security, and lower attenuation rate.

Distribution System

Structured wiring is used to distribute a variety of audio, video, or data signals throughout a home or business. Examples are data lines, telephone lines, and audio/video information. **See Figure 12-23.** Structured wiring may also include security systems and computer networking. The challenge in creating an effective system is to create an infrastructure that meets current needs while establishing a system for the home or business of the future.

A distribution panel is the main part of a structured wiring system. Distribution panels are where the majority of cables are connected to distribute data and control signals to subsystem components throughout the home. A distribution panel is the common point of wire origination, distribution, and termination. Distribution panels contain a series of modules designed to distribute and control telephone, data, and entertainment signals originating from within the home or from outside the home. Distribution panels are designed to allow changes to be made to the configuration of the low-voltage wiring network either by rearranging the appropriate patch cables or by adding additional modules.

Structured Wiring Systems

NETWORK SYSTEMS

TELEPHONES

FAX MACHINES

DISTRIBUTION
PANEL

HOME ENTERTAINMENT
AUDIO/VIDEO SYSTEMS

SATELLITE
TV SYSTEMS

CLOSED CIRCUIT
TELEVISIONS

MODEM AND INTERNET
CONNECTIONS

Figure 12-23. *Structured wiring is used to distribute a variety of audio, video or data signals throughout a home or business.*

Cabling Systems

Integral to the distribution system is the transmission cabling installed in each room. Cabling is the pipeline that delivers the signals and data throughout a home to specific locations. Typical transmission cable types include wire, communication cable, cable, and cord. **See Figure 12-24.** Communication cable includes unshielded twisted pair (UTP), coaxial cable, shielded twisted pair (STP), screened twisted pair (ScTP), and fiber optic cable. UTP, STP, and ScTP type cables are also identified as "copper

cable." Copper cabling is more commonly used when routing a home network because of its low cost and ease of termination. Manufacturers provide a variety of cabling options based on the need to transfer power signals or data.

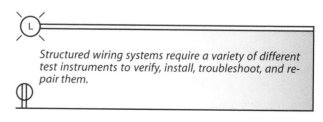

Structured wiring systems require a variety of different test instruments to verify, install, troubleshoot, and repair them.

Figure 12-24. *Typical transmission cable types include wire, communication cable, cable, and cord.*

Cabling can be very simple or very complex, depending on the application. To make installation easier, cabling can be purchased packaged in bundles to accommodate many of the common uses required in a specific location. **See Figure 12-25.** Manufactured bundling makes it easier to pull cables through walls when compared to routing six separate cables.

Cable Bundles

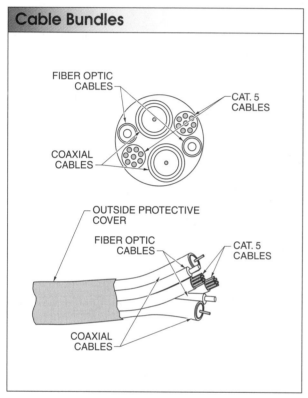

Figure 12-25. *To make installation easier, cabling can be purchased packaged in bundles to accommodate many of the common uses required in a specific location.*

Understanding the terminology associated with communication cables is required when installing the cables in a home. For example, copper communication cables are classified into categories designated Category 1 through Category 8. **See Figure 12-26.** A typical analog telephone line in an older existing structure uses Category 1 cabling. Category 5 and Category 5e cabling is recommended for all new construction.

Cable ratings are based on the final application and the transmission capacity of the cable. The greater a cable's transmission capacity, the greater the cost. **See Figure 12-27.**

Communication Cable Category Rating

* No longer in Standard ANSI EIA/TIA 568

Figure 12-26. *Copper communication cables are classified from Category 1 through Category 8.*

FIBER OPTIC CABLE

As the need for data transfer and streaming video has increased, use of fiber optic technology for telecommunications cabling systems has increased. Currently, most cable bundles include at least one fiber optic cable as part of the bundle. Fiber optic cables must be protected from physical damage and moisture. To protect the glass fibers, protective cladding and coatings are used along with strength members. **See Figure 12-28.** Cladding is a layer of glass or other transparent material surrounding the fiber core that causes light to be reflected back to the central core for the purpose of maintaining signal strength over long distances.

Fiber Optic Cable Applications

Cable Rating	Typical Applications
Category 1 (CAT 1)	Older construction, used with Plain Old Telephone Service (POTS) and with frequencies less than 1 MHz
Category 2 (CAT 2)	Indoor wire and cable, voice and data transmission of up to 4 MHz
Category 3 (CAT 3)	Indoor wire and cable, voice and data transmission of up to 16 MHz
Category 4 (CAT 4)	Indoor wire and cable, voice and data transmission of up to 20 MHz
Category 5 (CAT 5)	Indoor wire and cable, voice and data transmission of up to 100 MHz
Category 5e (CAT 5e)	Indoor wire and cable, voice and data transmission of up to 100 MHz. Used with longer cable runs because wire is packaged tighter.
Category 6 (CAT 6)	Indoor wire and cable, voice and data transmission of up to 250 MHz
Category 7 (CAT 7)	Indoor wire and cable, voice and data transmission of up to 600 MHz
Category 8 (CAT 8)	Indoor wire and cable, voice and data transmission of up to 1.2 GHz

Figure 12-27. *Cable ratings are based on the final applications and the cost of the cable. The greater the transmission capacity of the cable, the greater the cost of the cable.*

Fiber Optic Cable

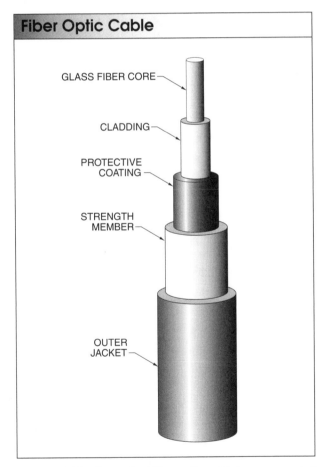

Figure 12-28. *A standard fiber optic cable is composed of a glass fiber core, cladding, protective coating, strength member, and an outer jacket.*

Fiber Optic Operating Principles

Fiber optic technology is typically used as a transmission link. As a transmission link, fiber optics connect two electronic circuits, a transmitter and a receiver. Fiber optics uses a thin flexible glass or plastic optical fiber to transmit light. **See Figure 12-29.**

Figure 12-29. *Fiber optics uses a thin flexible glass or plastic optical fiber to transmit light.*

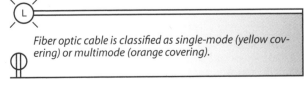

Fiber optic cable is classified as single-mode (yellow covering) or multimode (orange covering).

The central part of the transmitter is the light source. The source consists of a light emitting diode (LED), infrared emitting diode (IRED), or laser diode that changes electrical signals into light signals. A receiver typically contains a photodiode that converts light back into electrical signals. The output circuit of a receiver also amplifies the electric signal to produce the desired results, such as voice transmission or video signals. Advantages of fiber optic cables over copper cables include large bandwidth, low cost, low power consumption, low signal loss (attenuation), shielding from electromagnetic interference (EMI), small size, lightweight construction, and security (the inability to be tapped by unauthorized users).

Light Source

The light source feeding a fiber optic cable must be properly matched to the light-activated device for a fiber optic cable to operate effectively. A light source must also be of sufficient intensity to drive the light-activated device.

Laser Diodes. A *laser diode* is a fiber optic light source (similar to a light emitting diode) with an optical cavity that is used to produce laser light (coherent light). **See Figure 12-30.** An optical cavity is formed by coating opposite sides of a chip to create two highly reflective surfaces.

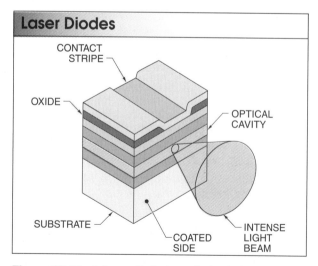

Figure 12-30. *A laser diode is a diode similar to a light emitting diode (LED) but with an optical cavity, which is required for laser (emitting coherent light) production.*

Fiber Connectors

The ideal interconnection of one fiber to another is an interconnection that has two fibers that are optically and physically identical. A *fiber connector* is a device that splices two fiber cables by squarely aligning the center axes of both cables and holding the two fiber cables together. The joining of the fibers is completed with an index-matching gel so that the interface between the cables has no influence on light propagation. A perfect connection is limited by variations in fibers and the need for high tolerances in the connector or splice.

Fiber-Connecting Hardware

Splices and fiber interconnections are often a negative factor due to alignment problems that can arise. Alignment problems can be eliminated through proper installation of fiber splices, connectors, and couplers. Recent advances in fiber optic technology allow for improved termination of connectors to cables through the use of crimp-style, prepolished connectors. Formerly, fiber connectors had to be factory polished, or hand polished in the field, resulting in lower quality connections. Poor connections result in signal loss. Common causes of signal loss with fiber optic cable include axial and angular misalignment, excessive end separation, and rough (unpolished) ends. **See Figure 12-31.**

Applications for Fiber Optic Cables

Because of the increased data transfer capabilities of fiber optic cable over other types of cabling, fiber optic cable is used extensively in high-speed computer networking, voice and data transmission, and security camera systems. As methods for installing fiber optic cable are improved and new devices are created, technologies such as digital satellite television, cable television, Internet, and telephone communications are improved by adding higher speed data transfer at a lower cost.

Wall Plates and Inserts

The type of wall plate and insert are chosen to suit the room of the house. The type of wall plate chosen must accommodate the type of service routed to a particular box. Wall plates are designed to accommodate different cable jacks (inserts) for single or multiple voice, data, and video connections. **See Figure 12-32.** Wall plates are decorated to lend particular designs to a room. The two types of wall-mounted service jack arrangements used to connect equipment in each room are interactive outlets and service outlets. An *interactive jack* is a connecting device such as a computer Ethernet connection that allows signals to be sent and received. A *service jack* (outlet) is a connecting device that provides connection to a service such as television reception through a coaxial cable.

Wallplates and Cable Jacks

Figure 12-32. *Wallplates are designed to accommodate different cable jacks (inserts) for single or multiple voice, data, and video connections.*

Causes of Signal Loss

Figure 12-31. *Common causes of signal loss with fiber optic cable include axial and angular misalignment, excessive end separation, and rough (unpolished) ends.*

STRUCTURED CABLING SYSTEM APPLICATIONS

Structured cabling system applications include computers and related networks, telephone systems, home entertainment systems, home security systems, and video monitoring systems. Systems can be routed so that moves, adds, or changes to the system can be performed with little or no difficulty.

Computer Network Systems

Personal computers (PCs), scanners, and printers are a sizable investment for a home. With a structured cabling system, multiple PCs can share a single Internet connection. Also, network system files that are located on any network PC's hard drive can be shared. Network systems allow for sharing devices such as printers and scanners from any location within the network. **See Figure 12-33.** With a network system, multiple users work on various projects simultaneously.

Computer Network Systems

Figure 12-33. *Network systems allow for sharing devices such as printers and scanners from any location within the network.*

Home Entertainment

As with computer systems, a home entertainment system is a sizable investment. A home that has a structured cabling system can transmit audio and video signals to multiple rooms and locations throughout the home. **See Figure 12-34.**

Telephone System

Telephone systems can be hardwired, wireless, or part of a structured cabling system. The main advantage of a hardwired system is that a hardwired system has a separate power source and continues to operate during a power failure without a backup generator. Wireless systems allow roaming throughout a home or within 200′ of the telephone base unit without being tied to a permanent location. Structured cabling offers the greatest ability to manage and change the distribution of telephone lines to wall plate outlet locations in various rooms throughout a house.

While a digital video disc (DVD) is the same diameter as a compact disc read-only memory (CD-ROM), a DVD disc has smaller physical pits beneath the disc surface, allowing it to store more information than an ordinary CD-ROM.

Home Entertainment System

Figure 12-34. *With a structured cabling system, a home entertainment system audio and video signals can be routed throughout the home into a variety of rooms and locations.*

A structured cabling system allows control of which telephone lines will be dedicated for voice and which will be dedicated for data, such as for a computer. By accessing the distribution panel, cables can be moved, added, or changed to redirect telephone lines.

SECURITY SYSTEMS

Along with home entertainment, home security has become a requirement in home construction and remodeling. The most common accessory added for home security through a structured cabling system is a video monitoring system.

Video Monitoring

Indoor and outdoor video monitoring allows complete visual monitoring anywhere in or near a house by the use of video cameras. **See Figure 12-35.** Video monitoring systems allow areas inside and outside of a home to be viewed from any television or monitor in the house. For example, to monitor a child's

bedroom, an indoor camera can be installed in the bedroom. Typical video monitoring camera types include wall mount, dome (ceiling) mount, and standard mount. **See Figure 12-36.** Through the use of a modulator, a preset channel can be selected with a remote control that will display live pictures from any room on any television or monitor in the home tuned to the preset channel. By adding a video sequencer to the distribution panel, any room can be watched by viewing pictures from each installed camera at regular intervals.

Video security is used to monitor commercial buildings, parking lots, and homes. Originally designed to monitor safety concerns, video security is continually evolving to serve many business and home uses. Businesses use video security systems to monitor employees, to trigger alerts in case of fire or motion, and to watch over entrances to buildings. Home uses include monitoring the outside of a home for unwanted visitors.

Figure 12-35. *Indoor and outdoor video monitoring allows complete visual monitoring anywhere in or near the house through installation of video cameras.*

Video Monitoring Camera Types

WALL MOUNT

DOME (CEILING)

STANDARD MOUNT

Figure 12-36. *Typical video monitoring camera types include wall mount, dome (ceiling) mount, and standard mount.*

STRUCTURED CABLING ROUGH-IN

When preparing a home for a structured cabling system, proper rough-in techniques must be used. The structured cabling system should be designed so as to locate the distribution panel in an accessible location so that cabling, patch cords, and other equipment can be easily installed or changed. The type of wall material (drywall or plaster) must be taken into consideration when roughing in a structured cabling system.

Locating the Distribution Panel

The rough-in process refers to work required to install a structured cabling system prior to drywall installation. Although the first step in the rough-in process is to mount the structured cabling distribution panel, the process can vary according to the equipment manufacturer. Refer to the specification manual for the equipment when installing any distribution panel. The location of the panel determines the installation procedures.

Running Cables

Cables and cable bundles are typically routed through rafters and stud walls. **See Figure 12-37.** The drilling of holes and the routing of cables and bundles are accomplished with typical remodeling methods. Routing structured cabling requires that care be taken to avoid damaging the cable and to minimize electrical interference. Steel nailing plates are required to cover areas where a cable has been routed through a notch or hole in a stud. **See Figure 12-38.** When hole openings are less than 1¼″ from the edge of the stud, the area must be protected by a steel plate to prevent damage from drywall fasteners. To avoid electrical noise, a structured cabling box should not be placed near a power box or share drilled stud and rafter holes with power feed conductors or other conductors. Power feed cables and structured wiring cables should only cross each other at 90° angles.

Securing Cables

Cables are secured in place by several different methods. Staple guns are a quick method of securing cables. Staples must be of sufficient size as to not pinch or penetrate the cable. The same precautions must be followed when hammering staples manually, as with a staple gun. For multiple cables and some cable bundles, J-hooks or similar devices are used to support the cables. Multiple low-voltage cables can be bundled together through the use of cable ties or a cable tie gun.

Routing Cables

Figure 12-37. *Cables and cable bundles are routed through rafters and stud walls.*

When a voice-data-video (VDV) cable such as a CAT 5E copper cable or single-mode fiber optic cable is installed and certified, continued cable testing must be part of a preventative maintenance program. As loads are added to a system and new cables installed, cables that appear to be working properly can be damaged to the point that the cable is unusable. Problems never occur at a time when lost data is not a problem. Routine testing of a VDV cable will indicate signal losses (attenuation) and other potential problems.

Cable Routing Requirements

Figure 12-38. *Routing structured cabling requires care to avoid damage to the cable and to minimize electrical interference.*

A *cable tie gun* is a handheld device that is used to hold and tighten cables together with plastic or steel ties. **See Figure 12-39.** Bundles of low-voltage cable can be quickly tied together in multiple locations by squeezing the trigger handle of the cable tie gun at different points along the wires to be bundled. Cable tie guns automatically tension and cut off the excess tie material. Cable tie guns are designed to reduce fatigue and increase the productivity of the individual. Cable ties should only be used on low-voltage telecommunications cable.

WARNING

Never bundle standard power conductors together as the heat from the current flow could damage insulation and possibly cause a fire or electric shock.

Cable Tie Guns

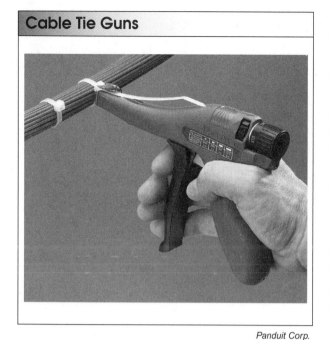

Panduit Corp.

Figure 12-39. *Multiple low-voltage cables may be quickly and efficiently bundled together through the use of cable ties and a cable tie gun.*

Over 50% of signal failure and transmission loss is caused by cable being installed incorrectly. Cable not properly installed changes the impedance or the ability of the cable to carry the signal at the required operating speed. Common installation problems include cables bent tighter than the minimum bend radius, cables overstretched through a cable support or overstretched throughout a run, staples driven too tightly, over tightened cable ties, and twists or knots in the cable. **See Figure 12-40.**

Plaster/Drywall Rings

Cables are typically terminated to single-gang plaster or drywall rings. Single-gang plaster or drywall rings are mounted either horizontally or vertically, depending on the location and application. Typically, at least 12″ of cable should extend beyond the ring for termination purposes. **See Figure 12-41.** Refer to individual manufacturer's guides as to the tools and techniques necessary for final terminations to outlet plates.

Causes of Cable Failure/Signal Reduction/Transmission Problems

Figure 12-40. *Over 50% of signal failure and transmission loss is caused by cable being installed incorrectly.*

Plaster/Drywall Rings

TO TRANSMISSION SOURCE

WALL STUD

PLASTER OR DRYWALL RING

ALLOW 12" OF CABLE TO EXTEND BEYOND RING

WIRE BUNDLE TO RECEPTACLE

Figure 12-41. *Cables are typically terminated to single-gang plaster or drywall rings and at least 12" of cable should extend past the plaster or drywall ring.*

X10 TECHNOLOGY

X10 technology is a communications protocol that allows AC control devices to "talk" on existing household electrical wiring. X10 technology communications uses a low-level signal intermixed with current flow to transmit instructions to turn appliances or lights ON or OFF as programmed.

For example, if two dimmer switches are plugged into different receptacles, X10 technology uses the wires that connect all of the house receptacles to the service panel as a circuit to communicate. X10 uses a language that allows compatible X10 devices to talk to each other using the existing wiring in the home. X10 transmitting devices send a coded low-voltage signal that is superimposed on the 115 VAC current. An X10 receiver device connected to the house electrical system receives the coded signals. The receiver may respond to 256 different address-

es that are programmed into the device. When more than one device must respond to the same signal (address), all affected devices are programmed with the same address.

This communication protocol originally was referred to as *power line carrier* (PLC) but is now commonly referred to as X10 communication. Many different companies manufacture X10-compatible switches, receptacles, and control devices.

X10 Programming

Typically, X10 programming consists of 16 unique house codes and 16 unique unit codes. The X10 house and unit codes are always used together (house codes are A–P and unit codes are 1–16) to send status or control instructions to various devices within a home such as A-1, A-15, and B-2. The instruction or status is encoded and transmitted on the power line in an order that is predefined. Because there are 16 house codes and 16 unit codes, up to 256 separate electrical devices can be connected to a network system to communicate within the home. Any instruction to be transmitted is first converted into a binary code at the transmitting device and then imposed on the power line in the form of a low-voltage signal. The binary coding is required because each X10 device receives every X10 command and the coded address lets the specific device respond accordingly.

X10 Applications

X10 applications include lamp/lighting control, dimmer switch control, control of 3-way switches, control of energy-saving devices, motion detectors for security purposes, and leak detectors to help quickly locate water leaks and prevent structural damage.

X10 Lamp Control. The most common X10 modules are lighting control devices. Lighting control devices simply plug into a standard 115 VAC receptacle, between the lamp and the receptacle. X10 lighting control devices are used to control incandescent bulbs used in typical table lamps unless wired into a home during construction. **See Figure 12-42.**

X10 Lamp Control

Figure 12-42. *X10 lighting control devices are used to control incandescent bulbs usually used in table lamps.*

X10-Compatible Dimmer Switch Control. An X10 transmitter controls X10 dimmer switches directly at the dimmer switch or remotely. An X10 dimmer switch can be programmed to turn lights ON to a level of brightness ranging from 3% to 100% of maximum output. Once the program is set, there is no need to readjust the program each time the program is used. The unit has full manual control to make changes as needed. Switches with dimmer functions must be used only with incandescent lights. Fluorescent lighting systems cannot use a dimmer switch.

X10 3-Way Switches. When a light must be controlled from two or more locations, a 3-way ready switch and additional multi-way companion switch are used for communication purposes. A 3-way switch can be manually or electronically switched. When a 3-way switch is manually activated, the X10 controller has no way of taking commands and will not operate properly. By using an X10 switch that communicates with the controller, the controller will always be able to read whether the switch is "ON" or "OFF."

Neutral Wire. Some switches require a connector that includes a neutral wire. When a neutral wire is not present in a switch box, a switch must be used that does not require a neutral. Another, more costly, option is to have an electrician install a neutral wire to the switch location.

X10 Energy-Saving Devices. As the cost of energy continues to climb, various energy cost-cutting methods are used. One of the most common methods of cutting energy costs is to install a programmable thermostat. By using a programmable thermostat, changes in the heating cycle of a dwelling can be made based on the time of day and the day of the week. Other methods for cutting energy costs include controlling natural gas usage, controlling appliances, and motorizing window coverings. X10 technology can control any X10 devices from any location with telephone or computer access. With the proper interface, programs can be accessed through the Internet to turn on or off appliances such as hot water heaters, air conditioners, or furnaces. Window coverings can be programmed to open or close, depending upon the angle of the sun or time of day.

Units are available for up to 7800 W and must be hardwired between the overcurrent protection (service panel) and the appliance. These types of units require a 230 VAC device rated for that appliance as well as special heavy-duty switches because they require a large amount of electrical current to operate.

X10 Motion-Activated Floodlights. Motion-activated floodlights not only turn ON when motion is detected but can also be used to turn lights ON inside a home. Because motion-activated floodlights can interact with other X10 controlled devices, motion-activated floodlights can be used to turn ON bedroom lights, kitchen lights, or activate an alarm. X10 motion sensor units are adjustable to activate from 6 sec to 30 min after the last motion was detected.

Water Damage Protection. Using a wireless leak detector that automatically shuts OFF the water source when a leak is detected from an appliance or plumbing fixture prevents water damage. By placing water sensors in an area where leaks can occur, any sign of moisture sends a wireless signal to the shut-off valve that immediately shuts OFF the main water line before any damage occurs. **See Figure 12-43.**

Motion Detectors. Motion detectors are used indoors and outdoors to monitor the possibility of an intruder. Indoor motion detectors are typically used in combination with other devices such as foils and magnetic switches to provide a more comprehensive security system.

The three types of motion detectors include passive infrared (PIR), microwave, and combination (PIR/microwave devices). When used outdoors, PIR devices detect large objects moving in the area by detecting the heat given off by the object. A PIR device is combined with a light source that is turned ON when motion is detected. This type of sensor is typically designed to eliminate triggering by small animals or wind.

Microwave devices can be installed either indoors or outdoors. Indoor motion sensors are typically mounted to the ceiling or angled down from the top of a wall to scan a particular area. Outdoor sensors are generally located near the doors and windows of a building. Combination devices use passive infrared and microwave technology to detect motion in a given area.

Figure 12-43. *By placing water sensors in an area where leaks may occur, any sign of moisture sends a wireless signal to the shut-off valve that immediately shuts OFF the main water line before any damage occurs.*

X10 Controlled Receptacles. X10 receptacles are installed to control lights and appliances from remote locations. **See Figure 12-44.** The X10 receptacle control unit fits into normal receptacle boxes and can replace an existing receptacle. X10 receptacles can be programmed to have one outlet controlled by an X10 controller, while keeping the other outlet constantly powered. Dual receptacles are also available that allow for two X10 controlled receptacles.

X10 Controllers. An X10 controller can be a simple wall-mount controller, a tabletop mini-controller, or a full-scale PC-based system. For remodeling projects, manufacturers recommend that mini-controllers be used. For new construction, a variety of controllers can be installed along with PC-based systems. As more complex controllers are used for a system, the number of devices controlled and the range of activities that can be controlled in the system also increase.

X10 Controlled Receptacles

Leviton Manufacturing Co.

Figure 12-44. *X10 receptacles are installed to control lights and appliances from remote locations.*

One of the major advantages of X10 technology is compatibility with other forms of remote control devices, such as hardwired systems found in structured cabling. X10 systems can link up with infrared, radio frequency, and Internet controls to allow control of systems from any remote location.

Low-Voltage Symbols

Symbols are used to provide information about low-voltage systems. Signaling, fire, communication, and X10 low-voltage systems all use symbols that are specific to the field. **See Figure 12-45.**

Figure 12-45. *Typical use of low voltage symbols on wiring layout.*

Chapter 12

Test

Name_____ Date _____

Low-Voltage Systems

    T   F   **1.** Residential low-voltage systems operate at less than 30 V.

_____   **2.** Low-voltage systems are safer than standard-voltage systems because the hazard of ____ is reduced.

_____   **3.** Low-voltage systems are more economical than standard-voltage systems because smaller ____ are used.

_____   **4.** The most simple low-voltage system is the ____ system.

_____   **5.** ____ open or close a circuit when a problem develops in a low-voltage system.

_____   **6.** The ____ of an X10 system can communicate with each other.

_____   **7.** Closed-circuit wiring is typically used for wiring ____ systems.

    T   F   **8.** Open-circuit wiring is typically used for fire detection systems.

_____   **9.** ____ allow detectors to operate on low voltage while the annunciators operate on standard voltage.

_____   **10.** Plunger button detectors are typically used in closed-circuit systems where a door or window holds the contacts in a(n) ____ position.

_____   **11.** In a two-piece magnetic detector system, the ____.
        A. switch is permanently mounted   **C.** both A and B
        B. magnet is allowed to move   **D.** none of the above

_____   **12.** A(n) ____ detector projects an invisible, pulsating beam at a bounce-back deflector.

    T   F   **13.** Annunciators, when triggered, ring a bell, flash a light, or sound an alarm.

_____   **14.** Closed-circuit wiring is wired as a(n) ____ circuit.

_____ 15. Open-circuit wiring is wired as a(n) ___ circuit.

T   F   16. Controls determine which detector is responding and uses that signal to trigger an annunciator.

_____ 17. A(n) ___ heat detector responds when a specific temperature is reached.

_____ 18. Heat detectors are typically used in conjunction with ___ detectors.

_____ 19. Relays for low-voltage systems are capable of controlling ___ A of tungsten, fluorescent, or inductive loads at 115 VAC and 277 VAC.

_____ 20. Transformers in a remote control system reduce 120 V line voltage to ___ V.

T   F   21. Typically, transformers are mounted in 2″ x 2″ x 4″ boxes.

T   F   22. Transformers are sized according to the environment in which they are installed.

T   F   23. Relays may be mounted in junction box knockouts.

_____ 24. A(n) ___ heat detector is designed for use with flash fires or slow-burning fires.

T   F   25. X10 technology operates on a separately run low-voltage wiring system.

_____ 26. Low-voltage wire is available as three-, four-, and ___ -conductor cables.

_____ 27. Smoke/gas detectors are available to operate on 120 V or on ___.

_____ 28. The three basic parts of a security-fire system are ___.
 A. wiring, detection, and control
 B. wiring, control, and annunciation
 C. wiring, detection, and annunciation
 D. none of the above

_____ 29. A(n) ___-controlled detector can be used when running wires for long distances is impractical.

_____ 30. When two or more switches are wired in ___, each is capable of controlling relays.

Low-Voltage Symbols

_____ **1.** Relay

_____ **2.** Motor

_____ **3.** Low-voltage transformer

_____ **4.** Lighting fixture

_____ **5.** Low-voltage wire

_____ **6.** Rectifier

_____ **7.** Low-voltage symbol

_____ **8.** Motor master controller

_____ **9.** Momentary contact switch

_____ **10.** Grounding outlet

Low-Voltage Circuits

_____ **1.** Bell ___ will sound when PB_1 is depressed.

_____ **2.** Bell D will sound when ___ is depressed.

_____ **3.** Bell C will sound when ___ is depressed.

_____ **4.** When PB_6 is depressed, ___.

   A. Chime F sounds   **B.** Chime G sounds
   C. both A and B   **D.** none of the above

_____ **5.** Bell B will sound when ___ is depressed.

_____ **6.** When PB_7 is depressed, ___.

   A. Chime F sounds   **B.** Chime G sounds
   C. both A and B   **D.** none of the above

_____ **7.** To sound Bell E, depress ___.

303

One-Family Dwelling

_____ **1.** The motor in Bedroom #1 operates motorized ___.

_____ **2.** Outside lighting at the rear of the house is controlled by a(n) ___ switch from the Living Room.

_____ **3.** The lighting fixture in Bath #1 may be controlled by a switch near the bathroom door and in Bedroom #___.

_____ **4.** Outside lighting on the Garage and front of the house may be controlled by switches located in the Garage and ___.

_____ **5.** ___ wire is used to connect all switches and relays.

_____ **6.** Grounding outlets are installed in the ___.

_____ **7.** The low-voltage transformer is located in the ___.

ONE-FAMILY DWELLING

Residential Wiring

Appendix

Power Formulas - 1φ, 3φ					
Phase	**To Find**	**Use Formula**	**Example**		
			Given	**Find**	**Solution**
1φ	I	$I = \dfrac{VA}{V}$	32,000 VA, 240 V	I	$I = \dfrac{VA}{V}$ $I = \dfrac{32,000 \text{ VA}}{240 \text{ V}}$ $I = \textbf{133 A}$
1φ	VA	$VA = I \times V$	100 A, 240 V	VA	$VA = I \times V$ $VA = 100 \text{ A} \times 240 \text{ V}$ $VA = \textbf{24,000 VA}$
1φ	V	$V = \dfrac{VA}{I}$	42,000 VA, 350 A	V	$V = \dfrac{VA}{I}$ $V = \dfrac{42,000 \text{ VA}}{350 \text{ A}}$ $V = \textbf{120 V}$
3φ	I	$I = \dfrac{VA}{V \times \sqrt{3}}$	72,000 VA, 208 V	I	$I = \dfrac{VA}{V \times \sqrt{3}}$ $I = \dfrac{72,000 \text{ VA}}{360 \text{ V}}$ $I = \textbf{200 A}$
3φ	VA	$VA = I \times V \times \sqrt{3}$	2 A, 240 V	VA	$VA = I \times V \times \sqrt{3}$ $VA = 2 \times 416$ $VA = \textbf{832 VA}$

Electrical Symbols . . .

Lighting Outlets	Convenience Outlets	Switch Outlets
OUTLET BOX AND INCANDESCENT LIGHTING FIXTURE — CEILING / WALL	SINGLE RECEPTACLE OUTLET	SINGLE-POLE SWITCH — S
INCANDESCENT TRACK LIGHTING	DUPLEX RECEPTACLE OUTLET– 120 V	DOUBLE-POLE SWITCH — S_2
BLANKED OUTLET — B	TRIPLEX RECEPTACLE OUTLET– 240 V	THREE-WAY SWITCH — S_3
DROP CORD — D	SPLIT-WIRED DUPLEX RECEPTACLE OUTLET	FOUR-WAY SWITCH — S_4
EXIT LIGHT AND OUTLET BOX, SHADED AREAS DENOTE FACES.	SPLIT-WIRED TRIPLEX RECEPTACLE OUTLET	AUTOMATIC DOOR SWITCH — S_D
OUTDOOR POLE-MOUNTED FIXTURES	SINGLE SPECIAL-PURPOSE RECEPTACLE OUTLET	KEY-OPERATED SWITCH — S_K
JUNCTION BOX — J	DUPLEX SPECIAL-PURPOSE RECEPTACLE OUTLET	CIRCUIT BREAKER — S_{CB}
LAMP HOLDER WITH PULL SWITCH — L_{PS}	RANGE OUTLET — R	WEATHERPROOF CIRCUIT BREAKER — S_{WCB}
MULTIPLE FLOODLIGHT ASSEMBLY	SPECIAL-PURPOSE CONNECTION — DW	DIMMER — S_{DM}
EMERGENCY BATTERY PACK WITH CHARGER	CLOSED-CIRCUIT TELEVISION CAMERA	REMOTE CONTROL SWITCH — S_{RC}
INDIVIDUAL FLUORESCENT FIXTURE	CLOCK HANGER RECEPTACLE — C	WEATHERPROOF SWITCH — S_{WP}
OUTLET BOX AND FLUORESCENT LIGHTING TRACK FIXTURE	FAN HANGER RECEPTACLE — F	FUSED SWITCH — S_F
CONTINUOUS FLUORESCENT FIXTURE	FLOOR SINGLE RECEPTACLE OUTLET	WEATHERPROOF FUSED SWITCH — S_{WF}
SURFACE-MOUNTED FLUORESCENT FIXTURE	FLOOR DUPLEX RECEPTACLE OUTLET	TIME SWITCH — S_T
	FLOOR SPECIAL- PURPOSE OUTLET	CEILING PULL SWITCH
Panel Boards	UNDERFLOOR DUCT AND JUNCTION BOX FOR TRIPLE, DOUBLE, OR SINGLE DUCT SYSTEM AS INDICATED BY NUMBER OF PARALLEL LINES	SWITCH AND SINGLE RECEPTACLE — S
FLUSH-MOUNTED PANELBOARD AND CABINET	**Busducts and Wireways**	SWITCH AND DOUBLE RECEPTACLE — S
SURFACE-MOUNTED PANELBOARD AND CABINET	SERVICE FEEDER, OR PLUG-IN BUSWAY — B B B	A STANDARD SYMBOL WITH AN ADDED LOWERCASE SUBSCRIPT LETTER IS USED TO DESIGNATE A VARIATION IN STANDARD EQUIPMENT — a.b
	CABLE THROUGH LADDER OR CHANNEL — C C C	
	WIREWAY — W W W	

... Electrical Symbols

Commercial and Industrial Systems		
PAGING SYSTEM DEVICE		
FIRE ALARM SYSTEM DEVICE		
COMPUTER DATA SYSTEM DEVICE		
PRIVATE TELEPHONE SYSTEM DEVICE		
SOUND SYSTEM		
FIRE ALARM CONTROL PANEL	FACP	

Signaling System Outlets for Residential Systems

PUSHBUTTON		
BUZZER		
BELL		
BELL AND BUZZER COMBINATION		
COMPUTER DATA OUTLET		
BELL RINGING TRANSFORMER	BT	
ELECTRIC DOOR OPENER	D	
CHIME	CH	
TELEVISION OUTLET	TV	
THERMOSTAT	T	

Underground Electrical Distribution or Electrical Lighting Systems

MANHOLE	M	
HANDHOLE	H	
TRANSFORMER- MANHOLE OR VAULT	TM	
TRANSFORMER PAD	TP	
UNDERGROUND DIRECT BURIAL CABLE		
UNDERGROUND DUCT LINE		
STREET LIGHT STANDARD FED FROM UNDERGROUND CIRCUIT		

Above-Ground Electrical Distribution or Lighting Systems

POLE		
STREET LIGHT AND BRACKET		
PRIMARY CIRCUIT		
SECONDARY CIRCUIT		
DOWN GUY		
HEAD GUY		
SIDEWALK GUY		
SERVICE WEATHERHEAD		

Panel Circuits and Miscellaneous

LIGHTING PANEL	
POWER PANEL	
WIRING – CONCEALED IN CEILING OR WALL	
WIRING – CONCEALED IN FLOOR	
WIRING EXPOSED	

HOME RUN TO PANELBOARD
Indicate number of circuits by number of arrows. Any circuit without such designation indicates a two-wire circuit. For a greater number of wires indicate as follows: ─///─ (3 wires) ─////─ (4 wires), etc.

FEEDERS
Use heavy lines and designate by number corresponding to listing in feeder schedule

WIRING TURNED UP	
WIRING TURNED DOWN	
GENERATOR	G
MOTOR	M
INSTRUMENT (SPECIFY)	I
TRANSFORMER	T
CONTROLLER	
EXTERNALLY-OPERATED DISCONNECT SWITCH	
PULL BOX	

Receptacle Connection Slot Configurations

Component Plan Schedules . . .

Area	Convenience Receptacles	Special-Purpose Outlets	General Lighting	Major Appliances	General Switching for All Areas
Bedrooms	No space along a wall should be more than 6´ from a receptacle outlet. Any wall space 2´ or larger should have a minimum of 1 receptacle. NEC ® 210.52 (A).	TV outlet, intercom, speakers (music), and telephone jack	Ceiling, wall or valence light, lamp switched at receptacle	Room air conditioner, electric baseboard heat	Switches are typically placed opposite the hinged side of door. When there are two or more entrances to a room, multiple switching should be used.
Living Room	No space along a wall should be more than 6´ from a receptacle outlet. Any wall space 2´ or larger should have a minimum of 1 receptacle. NEC ® 210.52 (A).	TV outlet, intercom, speakers (music)	Ceiling fixture, recessed lighting, valence light, lamp switched at receptacle, possible dimmer	Room air conditioner, built-in stereo system, electric baseboard heat	Door switch can be used for closet light so that the switch turns the light ON and OFF as the door opens and closes.
Family Room	No space along a wall should be more than 6´ from a receptacle outlet. Any wall space 2´ or larger should have a minimum of 1 receptacle. NEC ® 210.52 (A).	TV outlet, intercom, speakers (music), bar area (ice maker, blenders, small refrigerator, hot plate), telephone jack, thermostat	Ceiling fixture, recessed lighting, valence lights, studio spot lights, lamp switched at receptacle, fluorescent light, possible dimmer	Room air conditioner, built-in stereo system, electric baseboard heat	Switches with pilot lights should be used on lights, fans, and other electrical devices which are in locations not readily observable.
Dining Room	No space along a wall should be more than 6´ from a receptacle outlet. Any wall space 2´ or larger should have a minimum of 1 receptacle. NEC ® 210.52 (A).	Elevated receptacles (48˝) for buffet tables, speakers (music)	Ceiling chandelier, recessed lighting, valence lighting, lighting for china hutch	Room air conditioner, electric baseboard heat	Combination switch/ receptacle may be used where space is limited. Fused switch may be used as a shut off for service and fuse protection as on a furnace.
Kitchen	Receptacle for each 4´ of work space. Double duplex (Quad) receptacles in food preparation area. Requires two 20 A small appliance circuits. GFCIs to serve counter tops. NEC ® 210.8 (A), 210.52 (B)(3).	Clock outlet, TV outlet, intercom, speakers (music), exhaust fan, telephone jack	Light over sink, light over desk, recessed lights over work areas, illuminated ceiling, central room lighting, light under cabinets	Refrigerator, microwave oven, dishwasher, garbage disposal, oven, range top, trash compactor, electric baseboard heat	Dimmer switches should be used where accent lighting is appropriate.
Laundry		Exhaust fan, intercom, speakers (music), telephone jack	Central light, light over work area	Washer, dryer, hot water heater, water softener, electric baseboard heat	Timer switch may be installed to turn lights or appliances ON and OFF at specific times. Photoswitch may be used to control equipment by light changes.
Garage	Elevated receptacles (48˝) placed for convenience. GFCI receptacles. NEC ® 210.8 (A)(2), 210.52 (G).	Garage door openers, work bench outlets, freezer, intercom, speakers (music), telephone jack	Ceiling fixtures located in front of garage door when open. Outside wall mount light to illuminate drive. Light beside outside door	Shop tools, welder, electric fan, forced air heater	
Bathrooms	Duplex receptacles on GFCI near sink and mirror. NEC ® 210.8 (A)(1), 210.52 (D).	Ventilating fan, intercom, telephone jack,	Light on either side of mirror (wall-mount or hanging), overhead general light, night light, illuminated ceiling light in enclosed shower, heat/light on timer	Electric fan, forced air heater	Switches are usually placed opposite the hinge side of the door. When there are two or more entrances to a room, multiple switching should be used.

. . . Component Plan Schedules

Area	Convenience Receptacles	Special-Purpose Outlets	General Lighting	Major Appliances	General Switching for All Areas
Hallways	One receptacle every 10′ of hallway. NEC ® 210.52 (H).	Thermostat	Recessed ceiling lights, wall-mounted lights, ceiling mounted lights	Electric baseboard heat	Door switch may be used on closet so that it turns ON and OFF as the door opens and closes.
Stairways	One receptacle may be necessary for vacuuming.		Ceiling light at top and bottom of stairs. Wall mount light (must be accessable to change bulb).		Switches with pilot lights should be used on lights, fans, and other electrical devices which are in locations not readily observable.
Closets			Recessed light, fluorescent light, ceiling-mounted light		
Foyers or Entrances	Receptacles for convenience in cleaning. Weatherproof receptacles if outside.		Light inside entrance. Wall-mounted light outside entrance, recessed lights	Electric baseboard heat	Combination switch/ receptacle may be used where space is limited. Fused switch may be used as a shut off for service and fuse protection as on a furnace.
Attic	Receptacle for general use.	Extra circuits tied off for future expansion	Lights as necessary for area used	Attic fan, power exhaust vents	
Basement or Utility Area	(Unfinished) Receptacles for convenience. (Finished) Use guidelines for family room, living room, and bathroom. NEC ® 210.8 (A)(5) and (6), 210.52 (G).	TV outlet, intercom, telephone jack, speakers (music)	Workbench light, light near furnace, light at stairs. If finished for recreation refer to family room, living room, and bathroom.	Hot water heater, furnace, central air conditioning, soft water system, electronic air cleaner	Dimmer switches should be used where accent lighting is appropriate. Timer switch may be installed to turn lights or appliances ON and OFF at specific times. Photoswitch may be used to control equipment by light changes.
Outside House	Weatherproof GFCI receptacles. NEC ® 210.8 (A)(3), 210.52 (E).	Intercom/public address speakers (music), telephone jack	Lighting at entrance, spot lights, decorative low voltage lighting yard light	Hookup for central air conditioning	

Residential Wiring

Glossary

A

abbreviation: A letter or combination of letters that represents a word.

AC voltage: Voltage that varies in strength at regular intervals.

alternating current (AC): Current that reverses its direction of flow at regular intervals.

ambient temperature: The temperature of air around a piece of equipment.

ampacity: The current that a conductor can carry continuously, under the conditions of use.

ampere (A): The number of electrons passing a given point in one second.

annunciator: A signaling device that notifies individuals that one or more detectors have been activated.

anti-short bushing: A plastic or heavy fiber paper device used to protect the conductors of armored cable.

appliance: Any utilization equipment which performs one or more functions, such as clothes washing, air conditioning, cooking, etc.

appliance branch circuit: A branch circuit that supplies energy to one or more outlets to which appliances are to be connected.

armature: The movable coil of wire in a generator that rotates through the magnetic field.

armored cable (AC): A factory assembly that contains the conductors within a jacket made of a spiral wrap of steel.

automatic transfer switch: An electrical device that transfers the load of a residence from public utility circuits to the output of a standby generator during a power failure.

audio system: An arrangement of electronic components that is designed to reproduce sound.

B

bare conductor: A conductor with no insulation or covering of any type.

bathroom: An area with a basin and one or more of a toilet, tub, or shower.

battery: A DC voltage source that converts chemical energy to electrical energy.

bend: Any change in direction of a cable, conduit, or raceway.

blade cartridge fuse: Snap-in type electrical safety device that operates on the heating effect of an element.

bonding: Joining metal parts to form a continuous path to conduct any current safely that is commonly imposed.

bonding wire: An uninsulated conductor in armored cable that is used for grounding.

box: A metallic or nonmetallic electrical enclosure used for equipment, devices, and pulling or terminating conductors.

branch circuit: The portion of the electrical circuit between the last overcurrent device (fuse or CB) and the outlets (appliances, TVs, and lamps).

branch-circuit conductor: The circuit conductor(s) between the final overcurrent device protecting the circuit and the outlet(s).

branch-circuit rating: The ampere rating or setting of the overcurrent device (fuse or circuit breaker) protecting the conductors.

brush: The sliding contact that rides against the slip rings and is used to connect the armature to the external circuit (power grid).

bushing: A fitting placed on the end of a conduit to protect the conductor's insulation from abrasion.

C

cable: A factory assembly with two or more conductors and an overall covering.

cable assembly: A flexible assembly containing multiconductors with a protective outer sheath.

cable tie gun: A handheld device that is used to hold and tighten cables together with plastic or steel ties.

Canadian Standard Association (CSA) label: A marking that indicates that extensive tests have been conducted on a device by the Canadian Standards Association.

cartridge fuse: A snap-in type electrical safety device that operates on the same basic heating principle as a plug fuse.

circuit: A complete path (when ON) for current to take that includes electrical control devices, conductors, and load(s).

circuit breaker: A fixed electrical safety device designed to protect electrical devices and electricians from overcurrents.

circuit breaker fuse: A screw-in type electrical safety device that has the operating characteristics of a circuit breaker.

circular mil: A measurement used to determine the cross-sectional area of a conductor.

clip grounding: A type of grounding where a grounding clip is merely slipped over the grounding wire from the electrical device.

cold solder joint: A soldered joint with poor electrical and mechanical properties.

color coding: A technique used to identify switch terminal screws through the use of various colors.

continuity tester: is a test instrument that is used to test a circuit for a complete path for current to flow.

communication cable: Cable (usually copper or fiber optic) used to transmit data from one location (or device) within a system to another location.

compact disc (CD) player: An electric device that plays music stored on a compact disc (CD) by means of reflecting light from a laser beam.

complete path: A grouping of electrical devices and wires that create a path for current to take from the power source (service panel), through controls (switches), to the load (light fixtures and receptacles), and back to the power source.

component grounding: A type of grounding when the ground wire is attached directly to an electrical component such as a receptacle.

component list: A list of electrical equipment indicating manufacturer, specifications, and how many of each electrical component are required for a room or area.

component plan: A group of schedules that state the required locations for receptacles, lights, and switches according to the NEC® and local codes.

compression connector: A type of box fitting that firmly secures conduit to a box by utilizing a nut that compresses a tapered metal ring (ferrule) into the conduit.

conductor: A slender rod or wire that is used to transmit the flow of electrons in an electrical circuit.

Conductor symbol: An electrical symbol that represents copper and aluminum respectively.

conduit: A rugged protective tube (typically metal) through which wires are pulled.

conduit coupling: A type of fitting used to join one length of conduit to another length of conduit and still maintain a smooth inner surface.

conduit seal: A fitting which is inserted into runs of conduit to isolate certain electrical apparatus from atmospheric hazards.

contacts: The conducting part of a switch that operates with another conducting part to make or break a circuit.

control: An electrical device that accepts signals from detectors and turns annunciators ON and OFF.

control switch: A switch that controls the flow of current in a circuit.

converter: An electronic device that changes AC voltage into DC voltage.

cord: Two or more flexible conductors grouped together and used to deliver power to a load by means of a plug.

covered conductor: A conductor not encased in a material recognized by the NEC®.

crimp-type solderless connector: An electrical device that is used to join wires together or to serve as terminal ends for screw connections.

current-limiting fuses: Fuses that open a circuit in less than ½ of a cycle to protect circuit components from damage caused by short-circuit currents.

D

damp location: A partially protected area subject to some moisture.

DC voltage: Voltage that flows in one direction at a constant strength.

dead front: A cover required for the operation of a plug or connector.

decibel (dB): The unit used to measure the intensity (volume) of sound.

detector: An electrical device (sensor) used to detect noise, heat, gases, or movement.

device box: A box which houses an electrical device.

digital display: An electronic device that displays readings as numerical values.

digital multimeter: is an electrical test instrument that can measure two or more electrical properties and display the measured properties as numerical values.

dimmer switch: A switch that changes the lamp brightness by changing the voltage supplied to a lamp.

disconnecting means: A device, or group of devices, by which circuit conductors are disconnected from their power source.

double-pole switch: A control device that is two switches in one for controlling two separate loads.

double offset (saddle): A common complex bend made in conduit to bypass obstructions.

downrod mount: A type of ceiling fan mounting used to adjust head clearance or for angle mounting to vaulted ceilings.

dry location: A location which is not normally damp or wet.

duplex receptacle: A receptacle that has two spaces for connecting two different plugs.

dwelling: A structure that contains eating, living, and sleeping space, and permanent provisions for cooking and sanitation.

E

Edison-base fuse: A plug fuse that incorporates a screw configuration which is interchangeable with fuses of other ampere ratings.

effectively grounded: Grounded with sufficient low impedance and current-carrying capacity to prevent hazardous voltage buildups.

electrical circuit: A assembly of conductors (wires and busbars), electrical devices (switches and receptacles), and components (lights and motors) through which current flows.

Electrical metallic tubing (EMT): A light-gauge electrical pipe often referred to as thin-wall conduit.

electrical noise: Any unwanted disturbance that interferes with an electrical signal.

electrical plan: A drawing and list that indicates what devices are to be used, where the electrical devices are to be placed, and how the devices are to be wired.

electrical tool pouch: A small, open tool container (pouch) for storing a few commonly used electrical tools.

electric-discharge lighting fixture: A lighting fixture that utilizes a ballast for the operation of the lamp.

Electrical shock: The condition that occurs when an individual comes in contact with two conductors of a circuit or when the body of an individual becomes part of an electrical circuit.

electricity: A form of energy where electrons jump from atom to atom through a conducting material.

electrode: A long metal bar used to make contact with the earth for grounding purposes.

electromagnetism: The magnetic field produced when electricity passes through a conductor.

enclosure: The case or housing of equipment or other apparatus which provides protection from live or energized parts.

energy: The capacity to do work.

equipment: Any device, fixture, apparatus, appliance, etc. used in conjunction with electrical installations.

equipment bonding jumper (EBJ): A conductor that connects two or more parts of the EGC.

equipment ground: A circuit designed to protect individual components connected to an electrical system.

equipment grounding conductor (EGC): An electrical conductor that provides a low-impedance path between electrical equipment and enclosures and the system grounded conductor.

exposed: As applied to wiring methods, is on a surface or behind panels with open access.

F

feeder: All circuit conductors between the branch-circuit overcurrent device or the source of a separately derived system and the final load (appliance or lighting).

fiber connector: A device that splices two fiber cables by squarely aligning the center axes of both cables and holding the two fiber cables together.

fishing: The term used for the process of pulling wires through conduit.

fish tape: A device used to pull wires through conduit.

fitting: An electrical system accessory that performs a mechanical function of connection.

fixed temperature detector: A heat detector designed to respond when a room reaches a specific temperature.

flat conductor cable (FCC): A cable with three or more flat copper conductors edge-to-edge and separated and enclosed by an insulating material.

flat-cord plug: An ungrounded plug that includes a core that snaps into a housing after the wires are connected.

flexible cable: An assembly of one or more insulated braided conductors contained within an overall outer covering and used for the connection of equipment to a power source.

flexible cord: An assembly of two or more insulated braided conductors contained within an overall outer covering and used for the connection of equipment to a power source.

flexible metallic conduit: A metal conduit (greenfield), with no wires, that can be bent by hand.

floodlight: A lamp that casts general light over a large area.

fluorescent lamp: A low-pressure discharge lamp in which ionization of mercury vapor transforms ultraviolet energy generated by the discharge into light.

flush mount: A type of ceiling fan mounting used to allow maximum head clearance.

footcandle (fc): The amount of light produced by a lamp (lumens) divided by the area that is illuminated.

four-way switch: A control device that is used in combination with two three-way switches to allow control of a load from three locations.

full-range speaker: A speaker designed to adequately reproduce most of the audio spectrum.

fuse: An electrical device used to limit the rate of current flow in a circuit.

G

general-purpose branch circuit: A branch circuit that supplies a number of outlets for lighting and appliances.

generated electricity: The alternating current (AC) created by power plant generators.

generator: An electromechanical device that converts mechanical energy into electrical energy by means of electromagnetic induction.

grade: The level or elevation of the earth on a job site.

ground: A conducting connection between electrical circuits or equipment and the earth.

grounded conductor: A conductor that has been intentionally grounded.

ground fault: Any current above the level that is required for a dangerous shock.

ground fault circuit interrupter (GFCI): A fast-acting electrical device that detects low levels of leakage current to ground and opens the circuit in response to the ground fault.

ground fault circuit interrupter (GFCI)-receptacle: A fast-acting receptacle that detects low levels of leakage current to ground and opens the circuit in response to the leakage (ground fault).

grounding electrode conductor (GEC): The conductor that connects the grounding electrode(s) to the grounded conductor and/or the EGC.

grounding receptacles: Receptacles which include a grounding terminal connected to a grounding slot in the receptacle configuration.

H

hard-wiring: The physical connection between electrical components.

heat detector: Another electrical sensing device used to detect excess heat levels within a structure.

heating element: A conductor that offers enough resistance to produce heat when connected to an electrical power supply.

heating system: A complete system of components such as heating elements, fasteners, nonheating circuit wiring, leads, temperature controllers, safety signs, junction boxes, raceways, and fittings.

horsepower (HP): A unit of power equal to 746 W or 33,000 lb-ft per minute (550 lb-ft per second).

hydromassage bathtub: A permanently installed bathtub with a recirculating pump designed to accept, circulate, and discharge water for each use.

I

illumination: The effect that occurs when light falls on a surface.

immersion detection circuit interrupter (IDCI): Circuit interrupter designed to provide protection against shock when appliances fall into a sink or bathtub.

incandescent lamp: An electric lamp that produces light by the flow of current through a tungsten filament inside a gas-filled, sealed glass bulb.

indenter connector: A type of box fitting that secures conduit to a box with the use of a special indenting tool.

individual branch circuit: A branch circuit that supplies only one box or receptacle.

infrared detector: An electrical sensing device used for security purposes to determine if movement exist in a room or area.

instantaneous-trip CBs (ITBs): CBs with no delay between the fault or overload sensing element and the tripping action of the device.

insulated conductor: A conductor covered with a material classified as electrical insulation.

interactive jack: A connecting device such as a computer Ethernet connection that allows signals to be sent and received.

inverse-time CBs (ITCBs): CBs with an intentional delay between the time when the fault or overload is sensed and the time when the CB operates.

inverter: Equipment used to change voltage level or waveform, or both, of electrical energy.

isolated-ground receptacle: A special receptacle that minimizes electrical noise by providing a separate grounding path for each connected device.

isolating switch: A switch designed to isolate an electric circuit from the power source. It has no interrupting rating and is operated only after the circuit has been opened by other means.

J

junction box: A box in which splices, taps, or terminations are made.

K

kick: A single bend in a raceway.

knockout: A round indentation punched into the metal of a box and held in place by unpunched narrow strips of metal.

L

lamp: An output device (load) that converts electrical energy into light.

lampholders: Devices designed to accommodate a lamp for the purpose of illumination.

laser diode: A fiber optic light source (similar to a light emitting diode) with an optical cavity that is used to produce laser light (coherent light).

lateral service: An electrical service in which service-entrance conductors are run underground from the utility service to the dwelling.

lateral service entrance (cabinet): A cabinet that encloses the service wires, meter socket, and meter.

lateral service entrance (conduit): A service entrance where all service wires are buried underground, creating a condition where the wires are subjected to less damage from the environment (weather) and allowing unsightly poles and service wires to be removed from streets and alleys.

light: That portion of the electromagnetic spectrum which produces radiant energy.

lighting box: A box intended for the direct connection of a lampholder, a lighting fixture, or pendant cord terminating in a lampholder.

lighting track: An assembly consisting of an energized track and lighting fixture heads which can be positioned in any location along the track.

liquidtight flexible nonmetallic conduit (LFNC): A raceway of circular cross-section with an outer jacket which is resistant to oil, water, sunlight, corrosion, etc. The inner core varies based on intended use.

lockout: The process of removing the source of electrical power and installing a lock which prevents the power from being turned ON.

lubricant: A wet or dry compound that is applied to the exterior of wires to allow wires to slide better.

lumen (lm): The unit used to measure the total amount of light produced by a light source.

Luminaire: A complete lighting fixture consisting of the lamp or lamps, reflector or other parts to distribute the light, lamp guards, and lamp power supply.

luminaire temperature: The temperature at which a lamp delivers its peak light output.

M

magnet: A device that attracts iron and steel because of the molecular alignment of its material.

magnetic circuit breaker: An electrical safety device that operates with miniature electromagnets.

magnetic detector: An electrical sensing device used on windows to determine if the window is open or closed.

magnetism: A force that interacts with other magnets and ferromagnetic materials.

main bonding jumper (MBJ): The connection at the service equipment that ties together the EGC, the grounded conductor, and the GEC.

manually controlled circuit: Any circuit that requires a person to initiate an action for the circuit to operate.

mean lumen: The average light produced after a lamp has operated for approximately 40% of its rated life.

mercury-vapor lamp: An HID lamp that produces light by an electrical discharge through mercury vapor.

metal-clad cable (MC): A factory assembly of one or more conductors with or without fiber-optic members, enclosed in a metallic armor.

metallic-sheathed cable: A type of cable that consists of two or more individually insulated wires protected by a flexible metal outer jacket.

mobile home: A transportable factory-assembled structure or structures constructed on a permanent chassis for use as a dwelling. A mobile home is not constructed on a permanent foundation but is connected to the required utilities. The term "mobile home" includes manufactured homes.

momentary power interruption: A decrease to 0 V on one or more power lines lasting from 0.5 cycles up to 3 sec.

motion sensor: An infrared sensing device that detects the movement of a temperature variance and automatically switches when the movement is detected.

motor: A machine that develops torque (rotating mechanical force) on a shaft which is used to produce work.

motor efficiency: The measure of the effectiveness with which a motor converts electrical energy to mechanical energy.

motor torque: The force that produces, or tends to produce rotation in a motor.

N

National Electrical Code® (NEC®): A book of electrical standards that indicate how electrical systems must be installed and how work must be performed.

National Fire Protection Association (NFPA): A national organization that provides guidance on safety and assessing the hazards of the products of combustion.

network: A system of computers, terminals, and databases connected by communication lines.

nipple: A short piece of conduit or tubing that does not exceed 24" in length.

nonadjustable-trip CBs (NATCBs): Fixed CBs designed without provisions for adjusting either the ampere trip setpoint or the time-trip setpoint.

nongrounding receptacles: Receptacles with two wiring slots for branch-circuit wiring systems that do not provide an equipment grounding conductor.

nonmetallic extensions: Assemblies of two insulated conductors in a nonmetallic jacket or an extruded thermoplastic covering. Nonmetallic extensions are surface extensions intended for mounting directly on the surface of walls or ceilings.

nonmetallic-sheathed cable: An electrical conductor (cable) that has a set of insulated electrical conductors held together and protected by a strong plastic jacket.

nonmetallic wireway: A flame-retardant nonmetallic trough with a removable cover that houses and protects wires and cables laid in place after the wireway has been installed.

non-time delay fuses (NTDFs): Fuses that may detect an overcurrent and open the circuit almost instantly.

O

offset: A compound bend in conduit used to bypass many types of obstructions.

Ohm's law: The relationship between voltage, current, and resistance properties in an electrical circuit.

one-family dwelling: A dwelling with one housing unit.

open circuit transition switching: A process in which power is momentarily disconnected when switching a circuit from one voltage supply or level to another.

outlet box: An electrical device designed to house electrical components and protect wiring connections.

output: A device that is used to produce work, light, heat, sound, or display information.

overcurrent: Any current in excess of that for which the conductor or equipment is rated.

overcurrent protection device (OCPD): A disconnect switch with a circuit breaker (CB) or fuse added to provide overcurrent protection of the switched circuit.

overlamping: Installing a lamp of a higher wattage than for which a fixture is designed.

overload: A small-magnitude overcurrent, that over a period of time, leads to an overcurrent which may operate the overcurrent protection device (fuse or CB).

overhead riser service entrance: A type of service entrance that has wires running from a utility pole to a service head, where the meter socket and riser are firmly secured to the exterior of a dwelling, while the service panel is placed inside.

oxide: A thin, but highly resistive coating that forms on metal when exposed to air.

P

pads: Small round conductors to which component leads are soldered.

panel: A collection of modules, secured together, wired, and designed to provide a field-installable unit.

panelboard: A single panel or group of assembled panels with buses and overcurrent devices, which may have switches to control light, heat, or power circuits.

parallel conductors: Two or more conductors that are electrically connected at both ends to form a single conductor.

patch cord: A cable that consists of two wires: a thin center conductor that carries the signal and a woven shield wire that encircles it.

Pegboard: A thin constructed board typically available in 4' x 8' sheets that is perforated with equally spaced holes for accepting hooks.

pendants: Hanging light fixtures that use flexible cords to support a lampholder.

permanently-connected appliance: A hard-wired appliance that is not cord-and-plug connected.

permanently installed swimming pool: A pool constructed in ground or partially above ground and designed to hold over 42" of water, and all indoor pools regardless of depth.

Personal protective equipment (PPE): Clothing and/or equipment worn by individuals to reduce the possibility of injury in the work area.

pictorial drawing: A drawing that shows the length, height, and depth of an object in one view (isometric or oblique).

pigtail grounding: A type of grounding where two grounding wires are used to connect an electrical device to a grounding screw in a box and then to system ground.

pigtail splice: A splice that consists of twisting two or more wires together.

plug: The device at the end of a cord that connects the device to the electrical power supply by means of a receptacle.

plug fuse: A fuse that uses a metallic strip which melts when a predetermined amount of current flows through it.

plunger button detector: An electrical sensing device used on windows and doors to determine if the window or door is open or closed.

polarized receptacle: A receptacle where the size of the connection slots determines the plug connection.

pole: The number of completely isolated circuits that a relay can switch.

polyethylene fish tape: A more flexible type of wire-pulling device typically used to pull wire within conduit systems.

power line carrier: Now commonly referred to as X10 communication.

power source: The service panel in a residence.

pull box: A box used as a point to pull or feed electrical conductors into conduit or raceway systems.

pulling grip: A device that is attached to a fish tape to allow more leverage.

Q

quick connector: A mechanical connection method used to secure wires to the backs of switches and receptacles.

R

raceway: An exposed metal or nonmetallic enclosed channel for conductors.

rated voltage: A voltage range that is typically within ±10% of ideal voltage.

rate of rise detector: A heat detector designed for flash fires or slow-burning fires.

rigid fish tape: A wire-pulling device used for pulling wires through conduit, and pulling wires through walls and ceilings during remodeling.

receptacle: A contact device installed for the connection of plugs and flexible cords to supply current to portable electrical equipment.

receptacle tester: A test instrument that is plugged into a standard receptacle to determine if the receptacle is properly wired and energized.

redundant grounding: Grounding with two separate grounding paths.

remote control wiring: A method of controlling standard-voltage devices through the use of low-voltage relays and low-voltage switches.

resistance (R): 1. The opposition to the flow of electrons. **2.** Any force that tends to hinder the movement of an object

resistivity: The resistance of a conductor having a specific length and cross-sectional area.

resistor: A device that limits the current flowing in an electronic circuit (security).

rigid metal conduit (RMC): A heavy-duty pipe that is threaded on the ends much like standard plumbing pipe.

ripcord: a cord included in a cable that aids in removing the outer jacket.

roughing-in: A phrase that refers to the placement of electrical boxes and wires before wall coverings and ceilings are installed.

S

safety glasses: An eye protection device with special impact-resistant glass or plastic lenses, reinforced frames, and side shields.

schematic diagram: A drawing that indicates the electrical connections and functions of a specific circuit arrangement using graphic symbols.

security/fire systems: Home protection systems composed of three elements: detectors, controls, and annunciators.

selector switch: A switch with an operator that is rotated (instead of pushed) to activate a specified electrical contact.

self-grounding receptacles: Grounding type receptacles which utilize a pressure clip around the mounting screw to ensure good electrical contact between the receptacle yoke and the outlet box.

service: The electrical supply, in the form of conductors and equipment, that provides electrical power to a building or structure.

service conductors: The conductors from the service point or other source of power to the service panel.

service drop: A method of electrical service that runs wires from a utility pole to a service head on or above a residence.

service entrance: The connecting link between a residence and the power company.

service-entrance cable (SE): A multiconductor assembly with or without an overall covering.

service-entrance conductors — overhead systems: Conductors that connect the service equipment for a building or structure with the electrical utility supply conductors.

service-entrance conductors — underground systems: Conductors that connect the service equipment with a service lateral.

service equipment: All of the necessary equipment to control the supply of electrical power to a building or a structure.

service jack: A connecting device that provides connection to a service such as television reception through a coaxial cable.

service lateral: Any service to a residence that is achieved by burying the wires underground.

service mast: An assembly consisting of a service raceway, guy wires or braces, service head, and any fittings necessary for the support of service-drop conductors.

service panel: An electrical device containing fuses or circuit breakers for protecting the individual circuits of a residence and is a means of disconnecting the entire residence from the distribution system.

service point: The point of connection between the local electrical utility company and the premises wiring of the building or structure.

set screw connector: A type of box fitting that relies on the pressure of a screw against conduit to hold the conduit in place.

short circuit: The unintentional connection of two ungrounded conductors that have a potential difference between them. The condition that occurs when two ungrounded conductors (hot wires), or an ungrounded and a grounded conductor of a 1φ circuit, come in contact with each other.

shunt: A permanent conductor placed across a water meter to provide a continuous flow path for ground current.

signal level: The amplitude or strength of an electronic (audio) signal.

single-pole switch: An electrical control device used to turn lights or appliances ON and OFF from a single location.

single receptacle: A single contact device with no other contact device on the same yoke.

slip rings: Metallic rings connected to the ends of an armature and are used to connect the induced voltage of a generator to the electrical distribution system.

smoke detector: An electrical device used to sense products of combustion (smoke) and activate an alarm when smoke is detected.

solder: An alloy of tin (Sn) and lead (Pb) used to make permanent electrical connections.

Soldering: The process of joining metals by using filler metal and heat to make a strong electrical and mechanical connection.

soldered connection: A connection that joins conductors by heat to make a strong electrical and mechanical connection.

solderless connector: A device used to join wires firmly without the help of solder.

spa (hot tub): An indoor or outdoor hydromassage pool or tub that is not designed to have the water discharged after each use.

speaker: An electric device that converts electrical signals into sound waves.

splice: The joining of two or more electrical conductors by mechanically twisting the conductors together or by using a special splicing device.

split-bolt connector: A type of solderless mechanical connection used for joining large cables such as in service entrances.

split-wired receptacle: A standard receptacle that has had the tab between the two brass-colored (hot) terminal screws removed.

standard plug fuse: A screw-in type electrical safety device that contains a metal conducting element designed to melt when the current through the fuse exceeds the rated value.

static electricity: An electrical charge at rest.

stereo system: An audio system that uses two independent channels that are routed to a pair of speakers situated to the right and to the left of the listener.

storable swimming pool: A pool constructed on or above ground and designed to hold less than 42" of water, or a pool with nonmetallic, molded polymeric walls or inflatable fabric walls regardless of size.

strip gauge: A short groove that indicates how much insulation must be removed from a wire so the wire can be properly inserted into a switch.

surface raceway: An enclosed channel for conductors which is attached to a surface.

surge suppressor: A receptacle that provides protection from high-level transients by limiting the level of voltage allowed downstream from the surge suppressor.

surround sound: An effect that provides a feeling of left/right and front/back sound movement as well as reverberated and reflected sound similar to a concert hall.

switch: An electrical device used to control loads in a residential electrical circuit.

switchboard: A single panel or group of assembled panels with buses, overcurrent devices, and instruments.

symbol: A graphic element that represents a component, device, or quantity.

system ground: A special circuit designed to protect the entire distribution system of a residence.

T

tap splice: A splice that connects two wires together when one wire is to remain unbroken.

temperature: The measurement of the intensity of heat.

temperature rise: The amount of heat that an electrical component produces above the ambient temperature.

temperature switch: A switch that responds to temperature changes.

temporary power interruption: A decrease to 0 V on one or more power lines lasting between 3 sec and 1 min.

test light (neon tester): A test instrument that is designed to illuminate in the presence of 115 V and 230 V circuits.

thermal circuit breaker: An electrical safety device that operates with a bimetallic strip that warps when overheated.

thermally protected: Designed with an internal thermal protective device which senses excessive operating temperatures and opens the supply circuit to the fixtures.

thermal-magnetic circuit breaker: An electrical safety device that combines the heating effect of a bimetallic strip with the pulling strength of a magnet to move a trip bar.

three-way switch: An electrical control device used in pairs to control a light or load from two locations.

throw: The number of closed contact positions per switch pole.

time delay fuses (TDFs): Fuses that may detect and remove a short circuit almost instantly, but allow small overloads to exist for a short period of time.

timer: A control device that uses a preset time period as part of a control function.

tinning: The process of applying solder to a clean soldering iron tip to prevent corrosion on the tip.

torque: The force that causes an object to rotate.

transformer: An electric device that uses electromagnetism to change (step-up or step-down) voltage from one level to another.

transient: A temporary, unwanted voltage in an electrical circuit.

transistor: A three-terminal device that controls current through the device depending on the amount of voltage applied to the base.

T rating: Special switch information that indicates a switch is capable of handling the severe overloading created by a tungsten load as the switch is closed.

travel trailer: A vehicle that is mounted on wheels, has a trailer area less than 320 sq ft (excluding wardrobes, closets, cabinets, kitchen units, fixtures, etc.), is of such size and weight that a special highway use permit is not required, and is designed as temporary living quarters while camping or traveling.

tuner: An electric device designed to receive radio broadcast signals and convert them into electrical signals that can be amplified.

tweeter: A small speaker that is designed to reproduce high frequencies between 4 kHz to 22 kHz.

twisted conductors: Conductors that are intertwined at a constant rate.

2-way switch: A single-pole, single-throw (SPST) switch.

type NM cable: A nonmetallic-sheathed cable that has the conductors enclosed within a nonmetallic jacket.

type NMC cable: A nonmetallic-sheathed cable that has the conductors enclosed within a corrosion-resistant, nonmetallic jacket.

type S plug fuse: A screw-in type electrical safety device that has all the operating characteristics of a time-delay plug fuse plus the added advantage of being non-tamperable.

U

UL label: A stamped or printed icon that indicates that a device or material has been approved for consumer use by Underwriters Laboratories Inc.®

ungrounded conductor: A current-carrying conductor that is connected to loads through fuses, circuit breakers, and switches.

unfinished basement: The portion of area of a basement which is not intended as a habitable room, but is limited to storage areas, work areas, etc.

underground (service lateral): A method of electrical service that buries the wires to a residence in the ground.

Underwriters Laboratories Inc.®(UL): An independent organization that tests equipment and products to see if they conform to national codes and standards.

uninterruptible power system (UPS): A power supply that provides constant on-line power when the primary power supply is interrupted.

utilization equipment: Any electrical equipment which uses electrical energy for electronic, electromechanical, chemical, heating, lighting, etc. purposes.

V

visible light: The portion of the electromagnetic spectrum to which the human eye responds.

voltage (E): The amount of electrical strength in a circuit.

voltage dip: A momentary low voltage.

voltage indicator: A test instrument that indicates the presence of voltage when the test tip touches, or is near, an energized hot conductor or energized metal part.

voltage spike: An increase in voltage (normally several thousand volts) that lasts for a very short time (microseconds to milliseconds).

voltage stabilizer (regulator): A device that provides precise voltage regulation to protect equipment from voltage dips and voltage surges.

voltage surge: A higher-than-normal voltage that temporarily exists on one or more power line.

voltage tester: An electrical test instrument that indicates the approximate amount of voltage and the type of voltage (AC or DC) in a circuit by the movement of a pointer (and vibration, on some models).

voltage-to-ground: The difference of potential between a given conductor and ground.

voltage variance: The difference in voltage between a voltage surge and a voltage dip.

W

water pipe ground: A continuous underground metallic pipe that supplies a residence with water and is typically the best electrical ground for a residential electrical system.

watt (W): A unit of measure equal to the power produced by a current of 1 A across a potential difference of 1 V.

wattage: The number of watts a device uses to operate.

Western Union splice: A type of splice that is used when the connection must be strong enough to support long lengths of heavy wire.

wet location: Any location in which a conductor is subjected to excessive moisture or saturation from any type of liquids or water.

wire: Any individual conductor.

wireless control detector: A device used for security purposes in existing construction to eliminate hard wiring.

wire marker: A preprinted peel-off sticker designed to adhere to insulation when wrapped around a conductor.

wire nut: An electrical device that holds wires together and provides insulative protection.

wire stripper: A tool that is designed to properly remove insulation from small gauge (normally AWG sizes 10–22) wires.

wireway: A metallic or nonmetallic trough with a hinged or removable cover designed to house and protect conductors and cables.

wiring diagram: A drawing that indicates the connections of all devices and components in a residential electrical system.

wiring layout: A schematic that indicates how the component parts of a circuit will be connected to one another and where the wires will be run.

wiring plan: A floor plan drawing that indicates the placement of all electrical devices and the wiring required to connect all the devices into circuits.

woofer: A large speaker that is designed to reproduce low-frequency sounds.

X

X10 technology: A communications protocol that allows AC control devices to "talk" on existing household electrical wiring.

Y

Z

Residential Wiring

Index